The SLP Entrepreneur

*The Speech-Language Pathologist's
Guide to Private Practice and
Other Business Ventures*

The SLP Entrepreneur

*The Speech-Language Pathologist's
Guide to Private Practice and
Other Business Ventures*

Sonia Sethi Kohli, MS, CCC-SLP
Adrienne Wallace, MBA, MS, CCC-SLP

PLURAL
PUBLISHING
INC.

5521 Ruffin Road
San Diego, CA 92123

e-mail: information@pluralpublishing.com
Website: https://www.pluralpublishing.com

Typeset in 10.5/13 Palatino by Flanagan's Publishing Services, Inc.
Printed in the United States of America by McNaughton & Gunn, Inc.

Library of Congress Cataloging-in-Publication Data:

Names: Sethi Kohli, Sonia, author. | Wallace, Adrienne, author.
Title: The SLP entrepreneur : the speech-language pathologist's guide to
  private practice and other business ventures / Sonia Sethi Kohli,
  Adrienne Wallace.
Other titles: Speech-language pathologist entrepreneur
Description: San Diego, CA : Plural Publishing, Inc., [2023] | Includes
  bibliographical references and index.
Identifiers: LCCN 2022020551 (print) | LCCN 2022020552 (ebook) | ISBN
  9781635503852 (paperback) | ISBN 9781635503869 (ebook)
Subjects: MESH: Speech-Language Pathology--organization & administration |
  Entrepreneurship | Professional Practice | United States
Classification: LCC RC428.5 (print) | LCC RC428.5 (ebook) | NLM WL 21 |
  DDC 616.85/50068--dc23/eng/20220613
LC record available at https://lccn.loc.gov/2022020551
LC ebook record available at https://lccn.loc.gov/2022020552

Contents

Acknowledgments

Thank you to all of our SLP Entrepreneur teachers, trendsetters, and trailblazers. Thank you for so thoughtfully sharing your stories that inspire us and guide us, and help deepen our unique community.

A special thank you to our expert contributors who generously took their time to thoughtfully share their expertise and insights with our readers.

Thank you to the Plural Publishing team for your support and guidance throughout this process. Thank you to our (blind) Peer Reviewers for your insightful comments and feedback in helping us make this resource as meaningful as possible for our readers.

A special acknowledgment to CORSPAN for being the catalyst for us to meet and embark on our journey together, and to Bob McKinney for introducing us to Plural.

Lastly, we appreciate being able to share in this creative venture together, as our journey continues to unfold.

Reviewers

Chelsea Bell, MA, CCC-SLP
Chelsea Bell SLP, LLC

Dalit Burgess, MS, CCC-SLP
SLP/Owner and Founder
Clear Expression Coaching

**Theresa Harp, MA, CCC-SLP, LSLS
Cert. AVT**
SLP/Private Practice Owner

Jill Hendricks, MS, CCC-SLP
Riverview Medical Center

Alexis Malis, MA, CCC-SLP
Corporate SLP

Tara Roehl, MS, CCC-SLP
Speechy Keen SLP
The Telepractice Course

Judith O. Roman, SLPD, CCC-SLP
Clinical Faculty
Northwestern University

Jennifer Wilson
Center for Speech and Language
   Pathology

Michelle Zeglin
Simply Communication, President
AAPPSPA, Vice President

Adrienne Wallace Dedication

In Memory of Curtis Alexander 1926–2021

I dedicate this book to my Grandfather, who taught me the importance of faith and family and to cherish every single day. May your legacy of light and love live on through me.

Mom and Dad—thank you for your unconditional love and support. You've taught me to always pursue my dreams and that there is nothing beyond my reach.

To all of my family—thank you for always lifting me up and never letting me down.

And last but not least, Andre and Alexandria, you inspire me to be better each and every day.

Sonia Sethi Kohli Dedication

To All of My Family and Friends—thank you for always believing in me, supporting me, and understanding when I'm "running behind on life" and phone calls.

To Narinder and Surinder Sethi—Mom and Papa, thank you for your unconditional love, your unwavering support, and for being sources of immense inspiration throughout my life.

To Preeti, Navdeep Veerji, Simran, and Tejdeep—thank you for being such positive pillars of support, advice, and never-ending cheerleading.

To my Sonepal— thank you for your friendship, mentorship, and life-love partnership.

To my Ekas and Ajooni—thank you for being my "Sunshines" and the guiding light behind everything I think, feel, and do.

Introduction

ADRIENNE'S STORY

I started out my entrepreneurship journey by selling chocolate chip cookies when I was 15 years old. My aunt was a baker, and she sold her cakes and pies at the local farmer's market. As a young child, I loved going to my aunt's house to help her bake and learning how to perfect my own recipes. My first business lesson came from her, as she explained to me how to set my prices by calculating the cost of my expenses and multiplying it by three. She explained that by doing that, I would have enough money to cover my overhead costs, pay myself, and still have some profit left over. Over 20 years later, I still remember my aunt's delicious baked goods and her tips as an entrepreneur.

Upon entering college, my original intention was to earn a degree in business, and I actually started by majoring in accounting. However, while the image of dressing in a nice suit, carrying a briefcase, and going to an office in a high-rise building appealed to me at the time, I very quickly realized that my heart was not in it. Therefore, after my first year as an accounting major, I did something that would alter the course of my life. I took an Introduction to Communication Disorders class. Taking this class set me on a path to becoming a speech-language pathologist. After getting my degree in Speech-Language Pathology and working with kids in preschool-12th grade via telepractice for over 10 years, in preparation to climb the corporate ladder, I went *back* to school to earn my Masters of Business Administration. I was already a senior manager of a large department of telepractice SLPs and was no longer providing direct therapy. By the time I was halfway through my MBA program, I had my first child, left my stable full-time job, and started my own business, Online Speech Services. While this was one of the scariest things I had ever done in my professional life, I was more motivated than ever to become my own boss and take control of my future.

About a year after starting my online telepractice business, I saw an online ad for Teachable, which is an online course creation platform. Seeing that ad prompted me to start doing some research to find out, *How do I create my own online courses? Where do I sell them? Will people buy them?* And of course, *Can I make money from this?* All of these were questions racing through my mind when I ultimately decided, "You know what, I can do it! What's the worst that could happen?" At that time, there was zero financial commitment (with a free starter plan), so I had nothing to lose and everything to gain. After attending several free webinars to learn how to create online courses, I launched my first online mini-course about telepractice rules and regulations. Then, I continued to launch several more courses for two years before I started partnering with other SLPs to help them launch their own courses too. Over 1,000 course sign-ups later, I surveyed my email list and realized that people were looking for more high-quality telepractice materials. So what did I do? Naturally, I taught myself how to make Boom Card decks and sell them on Teachers Pay Teachers. Soon after that, I started the blog http://www.Telepractice Tools.com and opened my own online store to sell telepractice materials. Soon after that, at the end of 2020, I was approached by a colleague to acquire The Interaction Coach, a website for parents and SLPs who work with young children with speech and language delays. That acquisition quickly connected me with three branches of my business: direct client services through Online Speech Services, training and materials for SLPs through Telepractice Tools, and resources for parents and SLPs through The Interaction Coach.

Much of my business growth occurred during the COVID-19 pandemic, while I was also teaching business courses at a University as an adjunct instructor and learning how to homeschool my preschooler. This path has not been easy, and I could not have done any of this without a supportive family. Over time, I've learned how to juggle being a wife, mom, and entrepreneur. So, that means a lot of late nights, a lot of early mornings, and little sleep. I learned the term "sweat equity" very early on in my entrepreneurial journey. As a beginning solo entrepreneur, YOU are it. So that means every sales call, every marketing material, product, and service all start and end with you. I would not trade this path for anything else, and I do not intend to turn back. If you are doing something that you are passionate about, then it doesn't feel like work. While it may be challenging, *you can do anything you set your mind to*. This is something that I teach my business students. You just need to have the drive and decide that you are going to give it your all to make it happen no matter what. I didn't *need* to go back to school to get an MBA ten years after becoming an SLP, nor did I *need* to raise an infant while I was going to school full-time. However, I *decided* that I could not put off my dreams any longer.

If you have a business idea, all it takes is that first step, the desire to achieve, and the commitment to keep going no matter what. Sure, life may throw a wrench at you—maybe you don't get the sales that you want or the number of followers that someone else has, but you make your business uniquely fit you: your life, your dreams, your goals, and your aspirations.

SONIA'S STORY

Growing up, I always was on the fence about whether I should pursue a career in medicine or in education. I was introduced to the field of medical speech-language pathology during the summer before my senior year in high school when my paternal grandmother, who was visiting us, suffered a stroke, resulting in aphasia.

Although she could understand and speak a limited amount of English prior to her stroke, after her stroke, it was most appropriate for her speech and language deficits to be treated in Hindi and/or Punjabi, her native and more preferred languages. Despite a thorough search across various parts of the United States, there were no board-certified speech-language pathologists who were able to evaluate or treat her in Hindi and/or Punjabi at that time, and as such, my family and I ended up serving as "translators" between the SLP and my grandmother. Without the science and knowledge behind what the SLP was looking for in my grandmother's responses, and what she was trying to re-train, it was less than ideal, but we made the best out of the situation with the circumstances given to us.

It was at that time that I decided I would pursue a career in speech-language pathology. Having this new introduction into medical speech-language pathology, knowing that there were possibilities of also serving in educational settings, and being a lover of the intricacies of language, communication, and culture, this was a perfect choice for me. With the additional proficiency in Spanish (which I would later minor in during my undergraduate studies while living and studying in Madrid, Spain), Hindi, Punjabi, and Urdu, in addition to English, my goal was to be able to help a wider variety of people with speech-language/cognitive-communicative/ feeding-swallowing/voice challenges as I pursued this path. As I worked through the years of graduate school and beyond, I have had the fortunate opportunity to work in a variety of settings ranging from infants in the neonatal ICU, early child-hood, and school-age children, all the way through more senior adults in the neuro/ medical/surgical ICU, acute rehabilitation, outpatient/day rehab, long-term, and, sometimes, end of life care. I have always been someone that has appreciated variety and balance. Working in Chicago and its surroundings for the entirety of my career thus far, I have been blessed with patients, clients, and colleagues from culturally and linguistically diverse backgrounds, which has allowed me to utilize my multi-lingual background to serve a wider population, as well as connect with and learn more about various cultures and communities.

When I first left my first job and transitioned into my next role, I recognized the more "business" value that my daily interactions as a clinical SLP might hold. I tran-sitioned from a full-time, salaried position in a hospital to a well-established contract company where I was now being paid hourly and had to account for mileage to travel to various facilities, as well as extra time spent for meetings and trainings. During this time, my eyes were also opened to the vast potential of opportunities for SLPs beyond the traditional clinical employee as part of the hospital/medical facility or educational setting. It was during this phase of my career that I also served as a consultant and creator of therapeutic products for a speech-language pathology publishing company, while also working as adjunct faculty within a local SLP-Assistant program. I also started serving as an independent consultant for school districts to complete bilingual speech-language evaluations, and inde-pendently pursued further professional development to start offering services in the area of accent modification. When the opportunity arose to return to where I did my graduate training as an employee, working in a large academic medical center and serving as a clinical faculty member in the graduate program, I seized that opportunity. The years that I spent there allowed me to serve in the capacity of a clinician for a wide array of culturally and linguistically diverse patients; an educator for graduate SLP clinicians, other medical/health care professional students, resident physicians, other health care colleagues through interprofessional training, and the general public through outreach efforts; a researcher when contributing to departmental or larger hospital-wide initiatives; and a collaborator when working on process improvement and change management strategies for various aspects of the department and organization.

Through these experiences, the variety of manners in which I was using my SLP expertise was exhilarating, inspiring me to expand my thoughts of all of the possibilities that could lie ahead, and helping guide and propel my decision to pursue my entrepreneurial path. As I started down this path, I intentionally transitioned to serving as PRN/Registry for various hospitals/health care facilities that allowed me the time and resources I needed to establish my private practice. I established my business with the clear distinction that I would have two separate divisions of my practice, a clinical division, and a corporate division. This has allowed me to still practice within my clinical scope of expertise while also expanding my corporate practices beyond accent modification and presentation skills training.

For me, my business continues to grant me the ability to pursue my career passions with variety and balance. On the corporate side of my business, I have expanded my service offerings to include training individuals and organizations through leadership communication, executive presence coaching, and cultural and linguistic diversity consultation. On the clinical side, I am still able to serve a wide variety of patients/clients in-person, online, and on-site, and appreciate being able to tailor my service delivery in a manner that is most conducive to my clients. My time with the Corporate Speech Pathology Network (CORSPAN) on the Executive Board, as well as during my presidency, has allowed me the experience of managing a large organization and putting in the time and effort to plan and strategize for all aspects of a larger business. I find great reward in serving as an advisor to various organizations and as a mentor to SLPs and related professionals who are growing their private practices or other related businesses. What I appreciate most is that my business has allowed me to still pursue my creative outlets, my personal passions of helping others, and my distinct connection to people, languages, and cultural diversity, while allowing me the flexibility and balance I need for my family/friends and personal obligations.

I truly feel that the speech-language pathologist of today is well equipped to serve in a variety of roles, not only as a clinician, but also to help our communities and global society in non-traditional ways, and I look forward to continuing to support and promote our unique SLP Entrepreneur community. I have made many mistakes throughout my career, and I have no doubt that I will make more mistakes as I continue to pursue my passions and grow my business. However, I know that

I will continue to grow and sustain that outlook of perseverance and positivity to reach my desired outcomes. When I need that support and a reminder to reframe my thinking, I turn to my community, my network of professional colleagues on the clinical, corporate, and entrepreneurial side, and I turn to my family and friends for respite and reminders of why I am doing what I am doing.

HOW ADRIENNE AND SONIA MET

We met through a professional organization, The Corporate Speech Pathology Network (CORSPAN). Sonia was serving as president of the organization at the time, and Adrienne, although new to the organization, quickly became an active member. Adrienne had agreed to present to the group on telepractice basics and how one might incorporate that into their corporate speech pathology practice for CORSPAN's professional development lecture series. Sonia reached out and set up a call with Adrienne to prepare and coordinate scheduling for this presentation. The meeting started with the intended topic of talking about the telepractice presentation, but then led Adrienne and Sonia down a path that resulted in our collaborative partnership.

From that video conference call, we took our first steps into creating *The Communication Collective*, online classes for children and teens, focusing on public speaking, presentation skills, leadership communication, diversity training, and social-emotional learning. We quickly established our short-term plan, as well as our long-term vision, and welcomed our first cohort of students in a matter of months. As *The Communication Collective* blossomed, so did our business partnership, our familiarity with each other's personality, working style, and independent business pursuits, as well as our friendship, comradery, and support system of our collective business and each other's independent pursuits. As such, it was a natural fit for us to embark on the journey of our next collaborative project—this book, together.

WHY WE WROTE *THE SLP ENTREPRENEUR*

Through our various business endeavors, we have learned that there are so many opportunities for speech-language pathologists to not only build a private practice, but also to become entrepreneurs who are content creators, change-makers, visionaries, and the future of our profession. The skills required to build successful businesses are not currently taught in speech-language pathology graduate programs, yet the trajectory of SLPs wishing to pursue private practice or other related endeavors is continually growing. These vital skills are entrepreneurial elements that we learned through our own education, research, experience, and desire for more.

We wrote this book because we see the trajectory of our field changing, and we are living it as we speak. We cannot ignore the fact that during a worldwide pandemic in 2020, many SLPs realized that their "stable" jobs were not as stable as we all once believed. Yes, the future is still bright, but we have to take more control over it. The only way to do that is to carve out your own path, with multiple streams of income, which is sustainable for the long term. This book will inform you of steps you need to take, inspire you through success stories, and guide your transformation into a confident, skilled, and successful entrepreneur.

We decided to write this book as a guide for anything that you want to do, realizing that you are not limited. There is no "SLP box" that you have to fit into, and there is no ceiling to how high you can go! We know many SLPs who desire to get out of the daily grind of working for someone else. You've spent all of this money to go to school, get a degree, and work until retirement while pouring into other people's lives. Most SLPs do not go to school to get a degree in business, so even if we want to start our own practice or another type of business, we usually don't know where to begin. That's how the SLP Entrepreneur was born. If you dream it, you can achieve it! This book will show you how to do just that.

HOW TO USE THIS BOOK

This book is not your traditional how-to manual. While we will include the steps for starting a traditional private practice, these same principles can be applied to other types of related business ventures. We will guide you through developing a business plan, which includes elements such as writing your mission and vision, identifying your target market, and making financial projections. To help you plan and transform your ideas and ambitions into reality, we have included tangible, functional resources and exercises that will enable you to work through creating the path that you would like your business to take, and see your vision come to life. Each chapter begins with an overview of what to expect in that chapter. Templates and worksheets are embedded throughout the chapters for you to write in as you read along. At the end of each chapter, there is a checklist of action items that you can complete related to the chapter. Finally, at the end of the book, we include a comprehensive list of resources that are relevant to the topics discussed throughout the book, as well as a glossary of key terms for you to refer back to for easy reference. Here is a Master Checklist that you can print or copy and complete as you read this book. This is a composed list of the end-of-chapter checklists in one easy reference. Let the journey begin!

MASTER CHECKLIST

- Create an Aspirational Canvas (Figure 1–1)
- Write SMART(ER) goals for your business
- Schedule an email to your future self
- Decide when, how, and what to start
- Write your mission, vision, and value proposition (Figure 2–2)
- Identify your primary and secondary target audiences (Figure 2–3)
- Determine your products and services
- Decide how you will deliver your products and services to your target audience
- Brainstorm some marketing strategies for your business
- Determine the costs of your business
- Identify your potential revenue sources
- Complete your Business Expenses Worksheet (Table 2–2)
- Complete your Revenue Goal Worksheet (Table 2–5)
- Identify potential referral sources in your network
- Complete your Regulatory-Administrative Considerations Checklist (Figure 2–5)
- Create your SLP Entrepreneur Business Model (Figure 2–7)
- Complete Speaking to Your Specific Audience Worksheet (Figure 3–1)
- Set self-care goals (Figure 3–7)
- Complete the Gratitude Challenge (Figure 3–8)
- Set priorities for your business this week (Figure 3–4)
- Determine what customers you will serve (Figure 4–2)
- Decide on your service delivery options
- Determine which payment sources you will accept
- Set your rates
- Write a letter to potential referral sources (e.g., physicians, schools)
- Determine your expenses
- Create your practice forms

- Complete your business model (Figure 4–11)
- Decide on revenue sources for your business
- Select a platform to sell your products or services
- Set SMARTER goals for your business
- Create your content
- Choose your business name
- Define your brand elements
- Complete the SWOT Analysis Template (Figure 6–2B)
- Determine your marketing expenses (Table 6–2)
- Create a marketing action plan
- Set your marketing objectives
- Choose your marketing channels
- Create your website (Figure 6–5)
- Create your social media profiles
- Select your email program
- Sign up to attend networking events (in person or online)
- Create your elevator pitch (may need different ones for different contexts/events) (Figure 6–9)
- Complete your Profit and Loss Statement (Figure 7–1)
- Identify ways to establish systems in your business
- Determine what can be automated
- Decide whether you need to hire employees/contractors or outsource tasks
- Identify your leadership style (Figure 7–7)
- Update policies and contracts
- Contact us to share your success story

CHAPTER 1

Embarking on the Journey of Entrepreneurship

Getting Ready to Take the First Step

In This Chapter

This chapter will help you make the decision about starting your own business. It will include the importance of having core foundational elements prior to embarking on this journey, such as strong clinical expertise and experience being a part of an organization.

Topics include:

- Setting Life Goals and Creating an Aspirational Canvas

- Setting Professional/Business Goals and Maintaining Measurable Expectations

- Factors to Consider When Embarking on the Journey of Entrepreneurship

Congratulations on taking the first step toward transforming into an entrepreneur! You are not an ordinary entrepreneur; instead, you are embarking on your journey as a specially trained, skilled *SLP Entrepreneur*. We have put this resource guide together for you based on our own personal and professional experiences, as well as expert insight and perspectives from not only fellow SLP Entrepreneurs but also other related industry professionals. We hope that while you read and work through this resource, you will gain the basic foundational tools to establish and grow a business, whether that is a more conventional private practice, or another related business endeavor utilizing your SLP expertise. If you are already an established SLP Entrepreneur and you are reading this book, we hope that you find benefit in gaining resources and tools to revisit some of these foundational pieces of your already established business and find ways to help strengthen, expand, or enhance your current business processes and outcomes.

We thoughtfully labeled these chapters because we know that this chosen path of entrepreneurship is a continuous and very interconnected journey. Within this journey, you will find yourself: embarking on new perspectives, thoughts, and ideas; establishing new systems utilizing a foundational framework; and thinking as not just an SLP, but rather an SLP Entrepreneur. From that embarking, establishing, and thinking, with continued planning and strategizing, you will be building and venturing into new avenues of your professional skillset and expertise. With your new skillset and expertise, including marketing, networking, and branding, you will be transforming into an established and experienced entrepreneur, continuously looking and learning from others in your own network, as well as from a broader, less familiar community. As you look ahead at your future as an SLP Entrepreneur, you will soon recognize that this cycle is continuous and always interconnected. Embracing each facet of this journey with positivity, mindfulness, drive, tenacity, and balance will allow you continued growth and success in your personal and professional pursuits.

SETTING LIFE GOALS AND ASPIRATIONS

Many life coaches, psychotherapists, and spiritual leaders guide individuals to engage in visualization practice via the creation of a Vision Board, or as we like to refer to it, an "Aspirational Canvas." Taking some time to reflect, review, and then revise your visions, goals, and desires for your life as a whole will help to keep you focused on the mission and vision of your business. Your Aspirational Canvas should be used as a reminder of what you are working toward, especially in moments when you are feeling overwhelmed. However, it should not only be a visual and tangible reminder of your ultimate goals but also a guide to executing some action steps to attain those goals. It can be reviewed and updated as time goes on. It can be made out of photos, quotes, or crafting materials, written as a journal, or written down on a board to visually represent your goals.

Initial evidence indicates that the components of the process of making a vision board/aspirational canvas can result in individuals more easily obtaining their success and goals, as it is a mechanism that allows an individual to self-reflect and become more aware of what they want and how they plan to go about getting it (Davis, 2021). Studies indicate that those who engage in some form of visualization of goals are more confident that they will attain those goals; however, there is a caveat. If you utilize a Vision Board or Aspirational Canvas and simply put images, quotes, and ideas of what you want without visual representations of certain tangible, productive steps to get those things, your board could potentially do more harm than good. It is essential that you not only put visual representations of your long-term goals and aspirations, but also be diligent about visually representing relevant activities that will help you eventually reach that aspirational level (Morin, 2021). Keep in mind that while creating an Aspirational Canvas can aid in overall well-being and success, it also needs to be realistic. It is vital to include tangible activities that you need to engage in to reach your goals. For example, if you simply put visual representations of luxurious travel destinations that you would like to visit, you also need to put a visual representation of the career path you will engage in to financially support those aspirational travel journeys. You may even extend to putting visualizations of you registering your business or acing that interview that will guide you closer to that career path and the subsequent financial gain, which finally gets you closer to your desired travel destinations. Your Aspirational Canvas should be seen as a tool to simply help you picture what you would like to manifest and how you envision *you making* that happen.

> **I desired upward mobility and more from my career than any institution could provide.**
>
> *Cara Bryan*
> *South Tampa Voice Therapy*

Look at the Aspirational Canvas template that we have provided for you in Figure 1–1. Take a bit of time, in an environment free from distractions, to self-reflect on what motivates you, what your values are, and what priorities you have in order to put visual representations in each category. Revisit this Aspirational Canvas from time to time and make note of priorities and goals that have been achieved and those that may have changed. Allow yourself to reflect and gain some self-awareness and

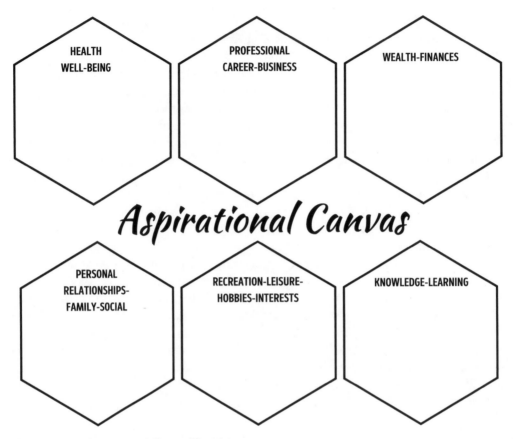

Figure 1–1. *Aspirational Canvas Template.*

ideas for revision as you revisit your board. Are your aspirations the same as they were when you first created your board? Did the steps you engaged in to reach your goals work, or did you navigate a different path to reach your ultimate goal? Remember to continue to revisit, reflect, and revise your board on a regular basis.

SETTING PROFESSIONAL BUSINESS GOALS AND MAINTAINING MEASURABLE EXPECTATIONS

Now that you have had time to reflect on some of your overarching life goals and aspirations, let's talk a bit about creating some shorter-term goals or aspirations in the same way that we do as clinicians creating a plan for the individuals we serve. You are a pro at establishing goals and knowing how to measure and modify goals with your clients every day in your clinical practice. We know that when establishing goals, we want to target a specific objective, in a specific context, with a specific amount of scaffolding or support if needed, and we want to make it measurable, either by time or by percentage achieved. In the same way that we create *SMART* [**S**pecific **M**easurable **A**ttainable **R**elevant **T**imely] goals or *SMART(ER)* [**E**valuated and **R**evised] goals for our clients, we want you to set some goals for yourself and your business endeavors. Whether these are short-term goals specific to one area of your business framework, which is discussed in Chapter 2, or more specifically related to private practice in Chapter 4, these can be benchmarks for any length of time and for any area of your business/professional development that you determine. You can choose any number of skills, tasks, or performance goals that will make you a better entrepreneur, a better clinician, a better advocate, a better keynote speaker, a better content creator, a better marketer, a better networker, a better work-life balanced small business owner . . . you get the idea.

> **❝**
> **Set goals, strategies, and know your capabilities. Keep asking the tough questions about where you want to go and whether the path that you are following will take you there.**
>
> *Allison Geller*
> *Connected Speech Pathology* **❞**

Create your goals so they are specific, measurable, attainable or actionable, relevant to whatever it is you are trying to achieve, and timely. Then you want to make sure that you're not just creating SMART goals, but you're creating SMARTER goals indicating you're going back and evaluating your goals and then based on that evaluation, you are revisiting and revising those goals (Harris, n.d.). Take a look at the following sample SMART(ER) goals that we have highlighted for some of the various areas related to SLP Entrepreneurship.

We will talk a little bit more about your growth mindset in Chapter 3, but as you go through this journey of entrepreneurship, you should recognize that there will definitely be a learning curve. The large majority of us did not go to school for this area of business expertise, and even people that may have complementary degrees in business, in addition to their speech-language pathology expertise, still learn something new about the ever-changing landscape of engaging in business pursuits every day. You will grow as an individual, you will grow as a professional, and yes, you will grow as an entrepreneur. With the right framework, planning, intention, skill-building, confidence, executive presence, and execution, you will succeed, although you are also guaranteed to have moments of "failure." It is important to know that you will experience "failures" or "setbacks" at some, often many, points along your journey. Knowing that beforehand is essential to maintaining

Sample SMART(ER) Goals

Specific **M**easurable **A**ttainable **R**elevant **T**imely (**E**valuated and **R**evised)

- Marketing—By (specific date/month) I will host a 1-hour complimentary virtual webinar for parents on bilingual Spanish–English speech and language development to increase my exposure for my target market in my local community, including a feedback form and special offer for my language enrichment summer camp.

- Social Media—On the first Saturday of every month, I will curate or create social media posts for a month's worth of weekly posts and schedule when to post to my Facebook and Instagram pages.

- Network—I will attend a virtual monthly local Women's Networking group sponsored by my local SCORE and connect with at least one new contact outside of the networking session each month.

- Client Volume/Service—We will add a 6-session/ 50-minute weekly summer reading enrichment group to our regular schedule that will offer 2 scheduling options for enrollment of 16 to 20 students (8 to 10 each session) with at least $2,500 in revenue after subtracting all costs.

- Skill Development—Within one calendar year after connecting with other SLP colleagues working as corporate SLPs, and completing continuing education related to accent modification and presentation skills training, I will add at least two corporate speech pathology clients each quarter.

appropriate expectations. Knowing that, yes, "failures" are inevitable, however, each "failure" is truly not a failure in itself, as it can be used as a tool and an impetus to reimagine, renovate, or repurpose your vision, strategy, or execution. Know that this will not be a smooth ride all the way through and that you will hit bumps, face obstacles, miss hurdles, and be challenged. However, you will learn from all of these experiences and get back up if you fall, reach eventual success, and persevere through this journey. Setting some goals not only will help to keep you on track, but will also help determine what your priorities are in terms of your business plan and business framework, and what you ultimately wish to achieve, as reflected in your Aspirational Canvas.

> 66
>
> **Don't be afraid to fail. Mistakes make you better. Fear is boring.**
>
> *Jennie Bjorem*
> *Bjorem Speech Publications*
> *Children's Therapy Services*
>
> 99

The next exercise that we would like you to try is to schedule an email to yourself that is written from the perspective of you either in your business, or at the initiation of your business, or (if you are already an established business owner) at the peak of your growth and scaling, or whatever it is that you hope to achieve (Westfall, 2018). We want you to write the email as though you are in that time period, and use this as somewhat of a SMARTER goal. Try to combine your knowledge of SMARTER goals, and a little of prospective visionary visualization and mindfulness, to set yourself up with a positive email that you will receive in the future. For example, if you want to envision having the confidence to execute a plan to host a webinar related to your area of expertise (one that you would use as a marketing method to get interested potential leads to know that you exist and that you offer expertise that is of value to these interested parties), you might write an email congratulating yourself on completing your marketing webinar. You had 30 attendees each of the three times you offered the webinar, your website is up and running, with your offering for the follow-up group session listed, and your group sessions are generating at least $3,000 per group.

Being able to envision this, schedule the email to be sent after the target date for attaining that goal. Revisiting whether you accomplished what you set out to do when you receive the email will help you strive toward your project goal, continue to give you the confidence to propel forward if you achieved what you set out to do, and revise when you are reminded that you did not complete what you aspired to accomplish. Consider the examples in Figure 1–2 as a guide. Doing this exercise allows you to not only visualize your goals into existence, but also reflect on and revisit those goals that you initially set to see if they still stand with relevance, or if they need to be adjusted due to circumstance. Examine whether you've learned a lesson in terms of something not working because you tried it, "failed," and now you're learning from it (the "ER" piece of SMARTER goals). Remember that as an SLP Entrepreneur, YOU get to decide what YOUR vision, YOUR plan, YOUR ideal

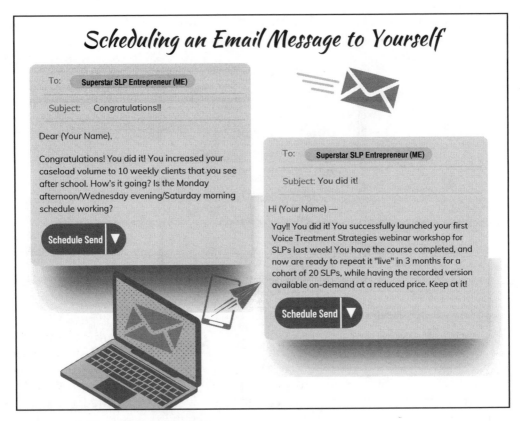

Figure 1–2. *Visionary Email to Self.*

scenario, YOUR next step, and YOUR next venture look like. Be as creative and driven as you would like when imagining how your future self and future business will look.

FACTORS TO CONSIDER WHEN EMBARKING ON THE JOURNEY OF ENTREPRENEURSHIP

When you are embarking on this journey, you need to consider several factors. Among the most important are *when* to start, *how* to start, and *what* to start.

When to Start

There are several considerations that you want to reflect upon before embarking on this journey. The first consideration is knowing when the right time is to embark on this journey of entrepreneurship. Although you can start doing the foundational work to start your business at any point in your SLP career, our recommendation is that you wait at least until you have *a minimum of three to five years* of strong clinical experiences prior to embarking on your own entrepreneurial venture. If your goal is to own and operate a private practice, you will need to have a strong understanding of your clinical skillset and your stylistic ways of practicing. You will also benefit from having the experience of seeing clients with initial support in your early career years, staying on top of documentation and other administrative tasks, being the most evidence-based clinician that you can be, knowing how to be part of a larger organization, and being someone else's employee.

You may further benefit from perhaps moving into some leadership roles within the organization, granting you the opportunity to gain more responsibility and leadership experience. This experience will help develop the necessary skills to serve as a leader in your own business if you decide to hire employees or contractors in the future. In the first few years of your clinical practice, you are still trying to navigate the transition from being a student in school to being a working professional. You are building your clinical skills as a clinical fellow (here in the U.S.) and only have limited supervision. You are learning to be an employee of an organization, which is important for you to understand and have first-hand experience prior to growing and scaling and potentially having employees or contractors as a part of your own business. It should be noted that the timing of starting a business does not have to be limited to early-to-mid-career SLPs. In fact, many successful SLP Entrepreneurs (a few of whom we have highlighted in this book) start planting the seeds for their business as they near retirement from their primary place of employment, and then are able to engage in opportunities to help flourish their own business after retirement.

> **66**
> **Take time to learn about what private practices are already serving your area and what niche they are serving. What are you bringing to the table?**
>
> *Gretchen McGinty*
> *New Leaf Voice* **99**

Knowing whether you are ready to start your own business can be explored by answering three questions: *Do I have the time? Do I have the money? Do I have the expertise?* Reflecting on these three aspects will help guide you when deciding what the right time might be to start laying down the foundation of your business pursuits.

Do I Have the Time?

If you're going to be your own boss, you must consider how much time it takes to run a business. Unless you have help (and many people don't when they are just getting started), you will be involved in everything from the marketing to the billing to the bookkeeping. Do you have the time that it takes to wear all those hats? Many speech-language pathologists want to start their practice slowly, on the side, while working in another job, and that is perfectly okay. This means after you get home from work, after your kids are asleep, or on the weekends when your friends might want to spend the day lounging, you are taking the time to fill out paperwork to register your business, design your logo, build your website, create marketing materials, and all of the other tasks that come along with starting and running a business. While you may feel as though you don't have any extra time, keep in mind that it is a choice you are making—a well-thought-out priority shift—in order to turn the vision of your business into a reality.

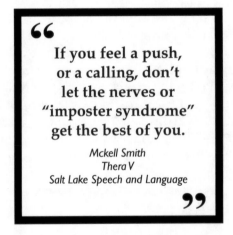

> **"**
> **If you feel a push,**
> **or a calling, don't**
> **let the nerves or**
> **"imposter syndrome"**
> **get the best of you.**
>
> *Mckell Smith*
> *Thera V*
> *Salt Lake Speech and Language*
> **"**

Do I Have the Money?

Depending on what type of business venture you decide to embark upon, the cost of starting your business will vary. We will talk more specifically about the related costs of different SLP-related business ventures in future chapters. In general terms, however, in the context of whether you have the money to start a business, one must consider (a) the stability of your current income to support your regular personal life expenses, and (b) the costs of starting a business.

ANTHONY PAUL

Financial Advisor
Author, Blocks of 10: A Financial Road Map for the
10 Year Blocks of Your Life

"I like 'smart debt.' Think about **what is it for**, will it **give incremental growth** in the business, and what is the **plan for paying it back?**"

Important Considerations for Entrepreneurs

Sit down and create a personal business plan—take stock and answer these 3 questions: Do I have a significant other who can handle expenses? Are there possibilities for strategic partnerships or something brand new? How long will it take to replace my current salary?

Pitfalls to Avoid

Small business owners tend to put all of their money into the business. Don't invest in your business for the sake of not investing in your future. If you bring in $1.00, $.25 goes to the business, $.50 to retirement, and $.25 to paying your bills.

Advice for Entrepreneurs

Whatever business you create, you need to put together a team. Don't feel like you have to do it all on your own.

Your Team = Accountant + Attorney + Real estate agent + Financial advisor + Banker

Your Current Income. When considering your current income, you should ensure that you have sufficient funds to continue to pay for your day-to-day expenses. If you are currently the primary earner for your household or your current income is relied on heavily to cover your household expenses, consider whether you could budget to allow for startup business costs. If you are currently not employed but are at home taking care of children or other loved ones, you need to consider the cost of childcare, should you start your business, and have children that are not yet in school. Another major contributing factor to consider is the cost of personal health insurance. Are you currently listed as a dependent on someone else's plan? Are you the primary insurance subscriber for your family? Taking account of these factors and planning on how your current finances may change when you start your business will help you consider when the right time is to start your business.

Startup Costs. Depending on what type of business you intend to start, your startup costs will vary. Look at Chapter 2 and Chapter 4 to take a deeper dive into costs and revenue for your SLP-related business. There are some expenses that every SLP Entrepreneur will incur, regardless of whether you are establishing a private practice or other SLP-related venture. For example, general administrative expenses will include a business license and liability insurance (either professional liability/

malpractice and/or general liability, depending on the business type), which will typically renew annually. Ongoing expenses would include things such as communication (e.g., phone, fax, email, internet, mailing address) and some level of digital media presence (e.g., website, website hosting, and/or social media pages). Finally, you need to consider the costs involved with having the necessary materials to provide your service (e.g., toys, intervention materials, and assessments for private practice), or the costs involved in producing your product if you are a product-based business. Please keep in mind that this list does not include the costs of hiring a lawyer or accountant, whose services you may use during the initial startup and on an ongoing basis. This also doesn't include variable costs such as taxes and payment processing fees. You should definitely consult professionals if you have questions about additional expenses and what they will do to your bottom line. If you are interested in seeking a grant or a business loan to help fund your business, visit the U.S. Small Business Administration website or your local SCORE chapter for more information. If your business is located outside of the United States, contact your local community business and/or banking centers to inquire about loans and/or financial grants available for your small business.

Do I Have the Expertise?

As mentioned earlier, our recommendation is that you wait until you have at least three to five years of strong clinical experience to allow you to gain confidence and demonstrate ease with your clinical decision-making. You also gain the experience of being an employee, part of a larger team, and perhaps gain some leadership experience within your roles, which will help when running your own business.

In terms of business expertise, unless you have a formal business degree or experience with running a business in the past, you most likely will experience a significant learning curve when trying to navigate this "new world." You will have to do a good amount of self-study through the plentiful amount of resources that are available online, as well as resources that are available (typically free of cost) through your local (U.S.) Small Business Administration office (SBA.gov). You can also consider hiring a business coach or consultant if you have the resources to do so. Some local programs, like SCORE, also offer free or low-cost business mentorship.

We hope that this book helps you in gaining a foundational level of business basics to help your business flourish. Although it can feel overwhelming at times, having a strong knowledge of the basics, and the confidence and drive to keep learning, will help set you up for long-term success. We also hope that reading the profiles of our inspirational SLP Entrepreneur colleagues in Chapter 8 will give you hope that *you can*, and *you will* learn things about running and growing a business that you never would have thought you would know.

> **❝**
> **A new business is a
> lot like a new baby—
> it requires constant
> attention and you
> have no idea if you're
> doing it right.**
>
> *Megan Sutton*
> *Tactus Therapy Solutions*
> **❞**

How to Start

If you are currently employed as a speech-language pathologist in either a school setting or health care facility, it is not necessary that you abruptly stop your employment at that job and then start your own business. Most likely, if that were to happen abruptly without planning or strategizing your business plan, you would have fewer chances of success. Starting off small, while picking up additional clients if a private practice or private consulting is what you want to do, not only can be lucrative but also allows you to start getting pieces in place in order to have a private practice of your own. If there are other ventures that you wish to embark upon, the same holds true. Start small and build up. Use the time when your caseload or other opportunities are lower in volume to plan and strategize how you will grow and eventually get to "cruising altitude." You might find initially that if you are starting at a smaller volume, it might help to navigate some of the procedures, policies, and products/services that you need to consider organizing and establishing for when your business is larger and encompassing a higher volume of clients or customers. By starting small, you have the flexibility to take on what you can at that moment, and also continue to have a stable income with your current position. You are also allowed the opportunity to get a "taste" of what some potential business opportunities might lie ahead for you, and whether this is the right fit for you.

Regardless of whether you choose to start small or take a giant leap into your business endeavors, know that you can also choose to start small as it relates to some of the tasks that you will inherently need to do as a small business owner. For example, you will need to have some sort of digital media presence, given that this is one of the primary ways that people become aware of products and services in today's digital age. Start small, and do not let it overwhelm you. Do not feel that you need to create social media posts right away because this can sometimes be a daunting task, and leave you feeling overwhelmed and uninspired with more potential to give up and not continue. Start by looking for articles and posts that relate to your scope of practice, your scope of service, or the scope of your product. Think about things that would resonate with your target audience and simply add a comment or two when resharing an article or post. This is referred to as curating content (gathering and resharing others' posts or articles that relate to your business), which is a small, but powerful step in getting some attention and engagement on your social media pages. This small step helps with your overall marketing strategy and helps you get started until you are more comfortable and experienced with creating your own content for your social media pages.

DAN PETERSON

Founder, FlipSwitch Social Media Group
www.FlipSwitchConsulting.com

"Start today."

5 Social Media To-Do's

1. Determine **which metrics matter**.

2. Use reports to analyze **what is working** and **what isn't**.

3. **Own your personality.**

4. Focus on **social customer service**.

5. **Be consistent and build** a strong **community**.

Once you start to notice that there is a market for what you are doing, and there is interest in how you are doing it, then you might start to consider whether you can gradually build up so that you can make a full-blown business venture out of it. There are still some people that choose to keep their employment at a different organization for stability and then create their practice or side business as just that—as a side business and continue that way for the duration, with no intention of scaling or moving their business to a full-time venture. Things to consider are the stability of income and revenue, the stability of having medical and health benefits, and the stability of paid continuing education, which you will not necessarily have if you venture into business on your own. These are just some of the considerations to make, but it is definitely possible to start small with a few clients or projects on the side, and then slowly start to build volume and start to pull away from your full-time position.

In addition to using good business sense, follow your heart!

Monica Lowy
Bodylink Speech Therapy

What to Start

When we were first approached to write this book, the intent behind it was to write a textbook about private practice for speech-language pathologists. While we have aimed to give you our solid understanding of foundational steps to establish and grow a conventional private practice, from our own experiences, we know that there is a wealth of other possibilities. These opportunities are not limited to conventional private practice and can be personally satisfying and financially lucrative, while also allowing speech-language pathologists to use their clinical expertise to add value and create change. That is why we felt strongly that we wanted to add information about the basics of business, not only private practice for SLPs. This was very intentional because we want to encourage you to think outside the box. There is great value within conventional or traditional private practices. We know that. There is also value in venturing out into other potential opportunities or business ventures using our skills and expertise that could benefit the mainstream population, and these can be done either separately, or in conjunction with owning and operating a private practice.

There are avenues to offer different products and services to the mainstream public utilizing our knowledge base. By utilizing our knowledge base and experiences as SLPs, we can become an advocate, community educator, or advisor, or create content, courses, and applications to train other speech-language pathologists. Our field has become extremely vast in terms of potential areas of practice. Having a strong knowledge base in all of the areas is really quite rare and will be a challenge as we start to specialize even further. This is a great opportunity for those experienced in certain areas to offer their services to help train others wanting to pursue potential career changes into a different area or niche market of our field or incorporate some of those elements into their own private practice. Also, given the landscape of our society as a whole, as well as our own field's changing landscape, building technological applications or platforms to provide teletherapy services and learning how to most effectively provide teletherapy services is also a great need and potential opportunity for SLPs.

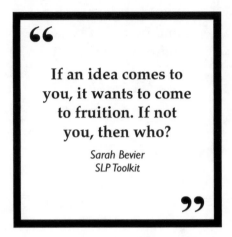

> **66**
>
> **If an idea comes to you, it wants to come to fruition. If not you, then who?**
>
> *Sarah Bevier*
> *SLP Toolkit*
>
> **99**

In the next chapter, we share more tips as we take a deep dive into creating your business from the ground up. Now that you've written goals and answered some important questions in preparation for starting your business, you are ready to create your business plan.

CHAPTER CHECKLIST

☐ Create an Aspirational Canvas (see Figure 1–1)

☐ Write SMART(ER) goals for your business

☐ Schedule an email to your future self

☐ Decide when, how, and what to start

REFERENCES

Davis, T. (2021 March 1). What is a Vision Board and why make one? *Psychology Today*. Retrieved August 1, 2021, from https://www.psychologytoday.com/us/blog/click-here-happiness/202103/what-is-vision-board-and-why-make-one

Harris, D., PhD. (n.d.). *How to make your SMART goals even SMARTER*. Quantum Workplace. Retrieved June 24, 2021, from https://www.quantumworkplace.com/podcast/how-to-make-your-smart-goals-even-smarter

Hoyt, A. (2020, December 17). *Can a Vision Board really affect your future?* HowStuffWorks. Retrieved July 1, 2021, from https://science.howstuffworks.com/life/inside-the-mind/human-brain/vision-board.htm

Mind Tools Content Team (2020, February 4). *SMART Goals: How to make your goals achievable*. Mind Tools. Retrieved August 21, 2021, from https://www.mindtools.com/pages/article/smart-goals.htm

Morin, A. (2021, January 5). Why Vision Boards don't work (And what you should do instead). *Inc.Com Magazine*. Retrieved July 1, 2021, from https://www.inc.com/amy-morin/science-says-your-vision-board-actually-decreases chances-of-living-your-dreams-heres-what-to-do-instead.html

Westfall, C. (2018). *Leadership language: Using authentic communication to drive results*. Wiley.

Zimmerman, E. (2016, January 28). Survey shows visualizing success works. *Forbes*. Retrieved August 1, 2021, from https://www.forbes.com/sites/eilenezimmerman/2016/01/27/survey-shows-visualizing-success-works/?sh=6badb4cf760b

CHAPTER 2

Establishing a Framework for Your Business
Creating Your Mission, Vision, and Business Plan

In This Chapter

This chapter will help you make big decisions that are an important process for every entrepreneur. Questions that we will help you answer include: What are my mission and vision? How do I write a business plan?

Topics include:

- The SLP Entrepreneur Business Model
- Mission/Vision/Value Proposition
- Customers
- Products and Services
- Service Delivery
- Marketing
- Costs and Revenue
- Network
- Regulatory Considerations

Now that you have reflected on some of your life goals, let's start to think more specifically about establishing a framework for your business. In Figure 2–1, we offer you *The SLP Entrepreneur Business Model* as a framework to utilize throughout this book. This foundational structure will help you organize the necessary elements to establish and/or expand your business. This framework can be used in the context of establishing or expanding a private practice and/or any SLP-related business venture. In Chapter 4, we talk more specifically about elements related to a "conventional" private practice in relation to The SLP Entrepreneur Business Model, but, initially, in this chapter, we will utilize this model to introduce and illustrate elements that could be applied to any business, specifically any SLP-related business venture.

We use the terms business model and business plan interchangeably throughout this chapter when referring to our SLP Entrepreneur Business Model. While there are a number of templates that you can choose from when creating your business plan, we have created a model that focuses on the major considerations that we think

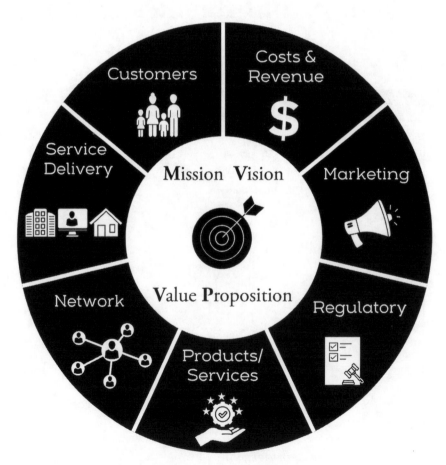

Figure 2–1. The SLP Entrepreneur Business Model.

are the most important: Mission/Vision/Value Proposition, Customers, Marketing, Network, Costs & Revenue, Regulatory, Products/Services, and Service Delivery. These foundational business matters are vital to consider and execute action toward establishing any business. As you initially read through Figure 2–1 and familiarize yourself with all of the listed elements, try to create a mental picture in your mind of what would fit *your* proposed business venture in each of these categories. It is important to note that we purposely have listed these elements in the form of a circle, as they are all interrelated and connected in some form. No element is more important than the other, and no element can stand on its own without impact from or influence on the others. We did however intentionally place the Mission, Vision, and Value Proposition at the center of the model, as that will be the factor that guides the other components of your business plan.

MISSION/VISION/VALUE PROPOSITION

At the center of your business plan are your Mission, Vision, and Value Proposition (what we will refer to as your "MVVP"). Developing your MVVP is a crucial foundational step as you venture into business, and it is a very personal piece of your business plan. *Your* goals, *your* passions, *your* vision, *your* skillset, *your* expertise, and *your* circumstance will dictate a large portion of the development of your Mission/Vision/Value Proposition. As such, take time to brainstorm, soul-search, and reflect on what it is that *you* wish to accomplish with your business prior to engaging with family/friends/colleagues and/or business coaches/advisors/mentors in discussions for their insight, advice, or guidance. As you embark on this journey of entrepreneurship, you must always keep in mind what your goal is as a business, while continuing to align with your own personal aspirations. Who are you servicing? Why? Who is your target market for your product and what value will you be bringing to them? When starting off, you will inevitably be "smaller" than when you are more established and/or when you scale and expand to a larger business. As you continue to grow, you MUST keep in mind your mission, vision, and value proposition. While opportunities might come along your way that seem to be aligned with your mission and vision, you need to fully evaluate your capacity to engage in that opportunity and if it will serve your mission at that phase of your business. You also need to consider whether you will be able to deliver the value that you intend to, given your available resources and return on investment. The core of any business is the MVVP. Many organizations choose to list their Mission/Vision/Values statements on their organization's website or other informational/marketing materials, as it allows potential customers to gain insight into what a business has to offer them, as well as speaks to the culture/vision of an organization for not only potential customers but also potential future employees or business partners. In upcoming sections, we will discuss having alternative or additional streams of revenue and/or multiple businesses. In the case of additional, unrelated business ventures, you would have a separate MVVP for that business. In the case of related business ventures (a related, but alternate revenue stream), that venture's MVVP should still align with your main business' overall plan and Mission/Vision/Value Proposition statement.

An important factor to keep in mind when establishing your MVVP is that it needs to be based on what will fulfill you/your drive/your passion/your exper-tise—it must have an intentional purpose. Having said that, you wouldn't write an MVVP statement based solely on the purpose of making money—that purpose does not serve your target client (They want your product/service. They do not care if you make money). On the other hand, if your MVVP is geared with a targeted purpose in mind that helps the local and/or global community and is very specifi-cally written for targeted audiences, you are on the right track. However, unless you are setting up a non-profit organization (which still needs money/revenue to thrive and serve the intended audience), you need to consider how you, as a business, need to earn sufficient revenue to support all of your incurred costs, and make a profit to help support the goals that you identified in your Aspirational Canvas (in Chapter 1). While your perspective as an SLP is coming from that as a service provider and caregiver, as an SLP Entrepreneur, you will still hold those roles, but also understand that the service you are providing and the care that you give is being packaged, marketed, and "sold" to your target audience. You know that you can add value to people's lives. As an entrepreneur, you need to do more work to make your targeted audiences aware of that too.

Defining Mission, Vision, Value Proposition

- **Mission (M):** *what* you want to accomplish

- **Vision (V):** *how* you wish to accomplish it

- **Value Proposition (VP):** what is it that you can *offer to your stakeholders* that will *positively impact* them while executing your Mission and Vision

JAY GRAVES MBA & Veteran
Founder & CEO, Pathfinder Business Consultants
www.PathBCS.com

"Is it going to **fulfill you?** Is it **just for money?** Are **people** willing to **buy it?**"

Important Considerations for Entrepreneurs

Take the time to build a business plan. Think about why and what you want to do . . . and who you want to impact. Following a business planning process will help entrepreneurs uncover potential barriers and help mitigate obstacles early in their venture.

Pitfalls to Avoid

I am a volunteer with SCORE, where I help underrepresented individuals who aspire to start businesses. The most common pitfall I encounter is a new business owner who launches their business based on a concept but lacking in details. Most fail because they don't have a good plan and when they start to meet challenges, they don't adapt and/or lose momentum.

Advice for Entrepreneurs

Never be too proud to ask for help! When I started my company, I had years of leadership, strategic corporate experience, and had just completed my MBA. While I had a wealth of knowledge, I still connected with individuals and mentors to help guide me through the business-building process. I would also advise them to stay humble, hungry, and inquisitive . . . and most of all, pay it forward!

You also need to consider how the mission/vision of your business/practice fits into the larger vision of what your *life* goals are. Remember that Aspirational Canvas you created in Chapter 1? Your Mission/Vision/Value Proposition (MVVP) should be aligned with propelling you in the direction of attaining those aspirations. We will work on how you communicate your Value Proposition to potential customers with confidence and clarity in Chapter 6, where we discuss messaging for marketing, networking, and branding. For now, take some time to think about what it is you want to do, how you wish to do it, and what benefit it could bring to your potential customers/clients. Create your MVVP in the next template in Figure 2–2. It does not have to be very detailed, as the other remaining elements of The SLP Entrepreneur Business Model will capture your specifics. As you initially establish and later expand your business, continue to revisit your MVVP and ensure that your business plan, with all of the interrelated elements, is aligned with your core MVVP goals. If not, you need to evaluate, reflect, and possibly revise your underlying MVVP or one or more of your surrounding business elements.

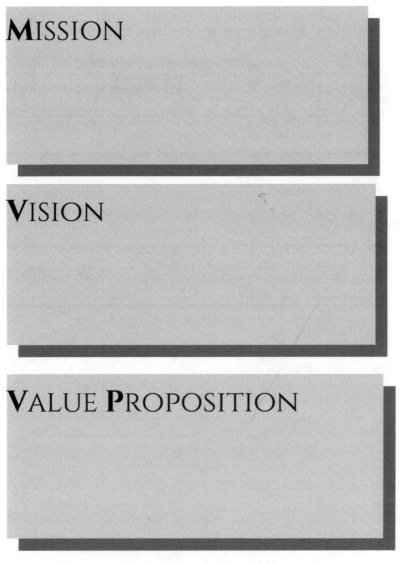

Figure 2–2. Mission Vision Value Proposition (MVVP) Template.

CUSTOMERS

Your Mission/Vision/Value Proposition (MVVP) will largely determine who your customers are. For example, if you are establishing a "traditional" brick and mortar private practice, where you are serving a pediatric population, your main customers are your pediatric clients and their parents/families. Alternatively, if you are wanting to venture into a business utilizing your expertise in language and literacy, you may target local school districts for paid speaking engagements/professional development workshops/online courses you create. Defining your target audience will in turn define your major target customer. However, as a business owner, you need to consider not just your customer/client, but all *stakeholders*. Stakeholders can be classified as anyone who is somehow involved in your service delivery or anyone that has a vested interest in your daily operations. In the earlier example, your stakeholders include not only the pediatric patient and their parents, but also the insurance company that you are in-network with, the pediatrician and/or school teacher/SLP, any employees or contractors you may have, and *your* family that is reliant on you to provide financially, as well as your time/availability to be at home with them.

In terms of marketing to customers, which is discussed in depth in Chapter 6, think about your customers as your target audience divided up into your primary audiences and then your secondary audiences. This is going to determine how you create and navigate your marketing/networking efforts to reach your targeted audiences. Take some time to think about who your primary customers/target audiences would be, and who your secondary audiences might include, as they relate to your overall MVVP. For example, consider if you were to run a marketing campaign to increase your client volume. If your primary clinical area of expertise is pediatric feeding/swallowing, your primary target audience to get referrals for that specific niche clientele would be those pediatric clients with known feeding/swallowing difficulties/their parents/caregivers, pediatric gastroenterology physicians/clinics, pediatric nutritionists/registered dietitians, and other related professionals. Your secondary customer group/target audiences may include referral sources to help you acquire a varied *type* of client or an *expansion* of your target base to increase the volume of potential leads. To illustrate this:

- Secondary Audience (Different **Type** of Client): If your primary audience is pediatric feeding/swallowing, you may add preschool-aged children with speech and/or language delays as your secondary audience. Your marketing efforts may now include more pediatricians (not just pediatric gastroenterologists), preschools, general parenting groups, etc.

- Secondary Audience (**Expansion** of Customer Base): Refer to the earlier example of utilizing language/literacy expertise for speaking engagements/workshops in schools, in which your primary audience/customer base is local/regional school districts. You might now expand your secondary audience/customer groups to include national/international schools via in-person and/or online engagements.

Take some time to reflect on who your primary and secondary audiences may be. Fill out Figure 2–3 as best as you can, and don't be afraid to stretch your mind a bit, to add some more creative customer groups that could potentially be a good source of referrals for your business.

Of note, it is important to keep your family/friends/significant others in mind as some of the (albeit more "indirect") stakeholders in your business—in terms of your business success, challenges, costs, revenue, and overall outcomes, which will relate to your self-care practices, mindset, and balance of priorities that we talk about more in Chapter 3. Taking stock of all of your potential customers and stakeholders, as well as the strengths/value you can deliver to them from the perspective of how *they* benefit, will guide you in terms of marketing/branding/networking approaches to generate more leads and a healthy volume of clientele. Doing this will also help you have more intentional communication to set boundaries and maintain a healthy work-life balance with your interpersonal/social relationships. In Chapter 3, we will work on an exercise to help you decipher how you communicate and demonstrate your value to varied customer groups/audiences/stakeholders, based on how your strengths impact and benefit the customer.

~MARKETING~
CUSTOMER GROUPS/TARGET AUDIENCES

PRIMARY	SECONDARY
• Niche Target Customer Group	• Broader Audience that includes niche Customer • Secondary Customer Group based off expansion of product line/service offerings

Figure 2–3. *Primary/Secondary Customers/Target Audiences.*

ETHNE SWARTZ PhD
Professor of Management, Montclair State University
Author, Business Continuity Management: A Crisis Management Approach

Important Considerations for Entrepreneurs

Developing their self-efficacy, their values, and then creating a clear business plan. There are tons of tools available and free resources that entrepreneurs should use to make this planning easier.

Pitfalls to Avoid

Customers—without customers there is no business. This is the most important constituency, and in the early phases of a company's life, the entrepreneur MUST understand what the customer wants and continue that dialogue so the customer remains loyal.

Advice for Entrepreneurs

Find free or affordable courses online and use local Small Business Development Center resources to get started. Talk to others about how they began and then be sure to have sufficient funds to keep the business funded for the period while you are growing a customer base.

PRODUCTS AND SERVICES

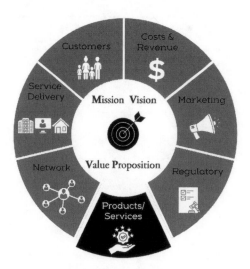

In our examples, we are going to be talking about a "traditional" private practice, in addition to other business types. By traditional, we mean that your customers are individuals who have communication/feeding/swallowing/voice disorders, and you are providing services in person, whether it's in a clinic or in the client's home. We'll get into the specifics of service delivery next. For now, let's take a look at the type of products and services that you will provide. In a traditional private practice, speech/language assessments and intervention are typical services. However, you may also decide to offer group therapy sessions, parent support groups, or other related services. If you are opening a multidisciplinary practice and will also provide occupational therapy, for example, then that will be added to your list of services. Some practices may also choose to sell products, such as intervention materials or other related merchandise, but as a speech-language pathologist, you are primarily a "service" provider. When we begin to look at alternative business endeavors in Chapter 5, you may only be selling products or a combination of both. For example, as a content creator, your products may include apps, digital downloads, or physical materials that you ship to your customers. Regardless of what your business is, you will need to decide what you are going to offer your customer to satisfy their needs, and that will be your products and services. Below are some examples of both products and services.

Examples of Services:
- Assessments of childhood speech sound disorders
- Assessments of fluency disorders
- Assessments of cognitive impairment
- Assessment of voice disorders
- Individual articulation therapy
- Intensive fluency group therapy
- Individual language therapy for adults with aphasia
- Early language development group for parents
- Accent modification [corporate speech pathology service]

Examples of Products:
- Articulation app
- Language workbooks for cognitive-communication
- Online vocal wellness course for professionals
- e-books for SLPs

After you've decided what your products and services will be, you will have to set your prices and fees for your services. Setting fees is one of the most challenging parts of setting up your business. If your fees are too high for your target market, you will likely have a hard time getting any clients. If your fees are too low, not only will you not be able to cover your expenses, but you may also devalue your services. People may think that they are getting less because they are paying less. Another unintended consequence of setting fees that are too low is that this may lower the fees for all providers in the area over time. If you are in-network with insurance companies, your fees should at least be higher than their reimbursement rates—otherwise, they will start to reimburse less for certain services. Consumers who tend to "shop around" will also demand lower prices, and other practices will have to lower their prices to stay competitive. Next, let's take a look at how you will deliver these products and services to your customers.

> **❝**
> **We trusted our instincts and put the time in to develop our brand in a way that represented our mission. We continue to lean into what feels right for us.**
>
> *Serena Murison*
> *Play Spark*   **❞**

SERVICE DELIVERY

Service delivery refers to the method through which you are providing your services to your customers. We discuss options for private practice in Chapter 4. For now, let's talk about content creators. Whether you are selling products or services, you will have a few options for how to distribute these to your customers. The method through which products and services are delivered is also called "distribution channels." Four types of distribution channels are retail, direct sales, e-commerce, and wholesale. Let's look at each of these in more detail.

1. **Retail:** This is the sale of goods or services directly to the end-user. Retail sales can occur through numerous distribution channels, including brick-and-mortar or online stores (Scott, 2019).

2. **Direct sales:** This is selling products directly to consumers in a non-retail environment. Instead, sales occur at home, work, online, or other non-store locations (Lilyquist, 2020).

3. **E-commerce:** This is when you sell products or services online. Buyers may be able to access your online store through your website or mobile app.

4. **Wholesale:** This is when you sell to other businesses or outlets that are not the end-user. Wholesalers sell products in large quantities, which lowers the per-item price (Scott, 2019).

Whether you are a product-based or service-based business, as your organization continues to grow in terms of the volume of clientele, hiring employees/contractors, and/or having collaborative business partnerships and vendor relationships, you will want to ensure that your contracts, policies, and agreements continue to be aligned with the needs of your growing organization. Refer to the *Contracts, Policies, and Procedures* section in Chapter 7 that takes a deeper dive into this topic.

MARKETING

Marketing is one of the areas that does not come naturally to speech-language pathologists. While we are great communicators, it can be difficult to be self-promoting. How do you sell yourself, your products, and your services without sounding "salesy"? Marketing is not just about being a salesperson. I repeat, marketing is not only about sales. Let that sink in for a moment before we look at what marketing actually is. Marketing is defined by the American Marketing Association as the "processes for creating, communicating, delivering, and exchanging offerings that have value for customers, clients, partners, and society at large" (American Marketing Association, n.d.). Let's break this definition down into the key words:

- **Creating:** Before you even think about "marketing" your products and services, you must first create something of value. If you are going to start a private speech and language clinic, you need to think about which services are going to create value for your clients and set you apart from your competitors (remember our discussion about products and services earlier in the chapter). If you are going to be a content creator, what value is your content providing to your customers that they cannot obtain elsewhere?

- **Communicating:** Once you have created your valuable products and services, you have to communicate this to your potential customers. You cannot use an "If you build it, they will come" strategy here. After spending weeks, months, and maybe even years creating, you want to attract the right customers who are going to pay for your products and services. You will need to develop a message that is going to resonate with your potential customers about why they should buy from you instead of your competitors.

- **Delivering:** Once you've gotten your customers (yay!), you are going to actually deliver the product or service to them. If you are providing speech and language intervention, for example, you are actually meeting with your clients to deliver the intervention. If you are selling digital materials, you are going to provide the materials, files, or downloads to your customers. This process should be as easy as possible for the customer. This is where you are going to build lasting relationships with your customers and hopefully have them tell all of their family and friends about it.

- **Exchanging:** This is the part of the definition that stumps a lot of entrepreneurs. Exchange is the act of giving one thing and receiving another. This definition implies that your customers are giving you something in return. This may defy conventional wisdom for many new business owners. If you are providing the service, what are your customers offering you in return? First of all, unless you are running a non-profit organization, your customers are providing you a fee for your product or service. Secondly, let's talk about data. Beginning with the evaluation process, speech-language pathologists are trained to collect data. You are trying to establish a baseline, deliver an intervention, and monitor progress to determine the effectiveness of your intervention.

    Regardless of the type of business you start, you will obtain some sort of data from your customers. For example, as a content creator, you will collect reviews from your customers to determine their satisfaction with your products. If you are a blogger, you will see which posts are read the most, which have the most comments, how many social media posts are liked and shared, and so on. All of this data is going to help you not only shape your content but also determine which marketing strategies are most effective.

This sums up the definition of marketing, which hopefully has given you a bigger picture of what marketing actually is. Now, let's look at the four elements required to create an effective marketing strategy. If you attend business school or read any marketing textbook, you will read about the Marketing Mix (Figure 2–4). Also referred to as the 4 P's of marketing, the marketing mix consists of *product*, *price*, *place*, and *promotion* (American Marketing Association, n.d.).

Product: The term "product" refers to either products or services. For private practice owners, this may be speech and language intervention, whereas for content creators, this may include digital materials or membership subscriptions.

Price: This is how much the customer pays for the products or services. Determining your price will depend on a number of factors, which is explained in more detail in the *Costs and Revenue* section.

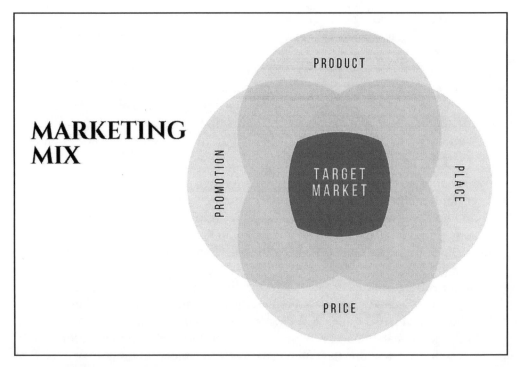

Figure 2–4. *Marketing Mix Model.*

Place: This refers to where and how products and services are delivered to customers. If you are in private practice, will you go to the client's home, or will they come to your clinic? If you are a content creator, will you sell on http://www.teacherspayteachers.com, or will you have your own online store? Refer to the distribution channels in the previous section.

Promotion: This refers to how to influence the purchase of your products and services in the short term. As a private practice owner, you may offer a prompt pay discount for private pay clients who pay for services in advance or at the time of service. On the other hand, as a content creator, you may offer a 50% discount on new digital products for the first 48 hours.

We discuss various marketing strategies in Chapter 6. For now, we'll shift our attention to costs and revenue.

COSTS AND REVENUE

When you start any new business, you are going to have startup costs, which will be different from your ongoing costs. Let's look at the type of costs that you might incur when starting a business, and whether these are only startup costs or also ongoing expenses (Table 2–1). Please note that this does not include the costs associated with renting an office. As discussed in the section on Service Delivery, there are alternatives for opening a brick-and-mortar location. We discuss specific costs for a traditional private practice in Chapter 4. For now, you can consider gathering information about how much the average rent is in your area. Use the blank worksheet (Table 2–2) to calculate your own business expenses. When considering your ongoing expenses, some expenses will be fixed (meaning that the cost is the same on a regular basis), whereas others will be variable (the cost changes). Some examples of fixed and variable expenses that you may incur monthly are provided in Table 2–3.

> **“**
> **The biggest benefit of running my own business is the independence to make my own schedule, adjust my days/hours as needed, and to raise my rates on a yearly schedule.**
>
> *Jennifer Nonn-Murphy*
> *Communication Building Blocks*
> *Clear & Confident Speech Coaching* **”**

Table 2–1. *Sample Business Expenses*

Expenses	Startup Costs	Monthly Expenses	Annual Expenses
Domain name	$0	NA	$20
Website hosting	$25	$25	$300
Computer	$1,000	NA	NA
Email marketing software	$0	$30	$360
CRM	$0	$30	$360
Social media ads	$0	$300	$3,600
Phone	$0	$50	$600
Email	$6	$6	$72
PO Box	$80	$15	$180
LLC filing fees	$125	NA	$75
Accountant	$300	NA	$500
Attorney	$300	NA	NA
Total	**$1,836**	**$456**	**$6,067**

Table 2–2. *Business Expenses Worksheet*

Expenses	Startup Costs	Monthly Expenses	Annual Expenses
Domain name			
Website hosting			
Computer			
Email marketing software			
CRM			
Social media ads			
Phone			
Email			
PO Box			
LLC filing fees			
Accountant			
Attorney			
Total			

Table 2–3. *Fixed Versus Variable Business Expenses*

Expense	Expense Type
PO Box	Fixed
Liability Insurance	Fixed
Email	Fixed
Website hosting	Fixed
Utilities	Variable
Advertising	Variable

Now let's take a look at possible sources of revenue for your business. As we've already addressed, in a traditional private practice, your services will typically include assessment and intervention, at a minimum. If you also serve as a consultant or conduct paid inservices for schools or organizations, those would be additional revenue sources for your business. You may categorize these as "speaking fees" or "consultant fees."

We will help you develop a marketing strategy for your business in Chapter 6, but for now, let's look at what you will need to do to have a *profitable* business. Every business owner should set goals for their projected revenue. After you've set your prices, you can easily calculate how many sessions you need to have or how many products you need to sell to meet your revenue goals.

Let's say that you are opening a traditional private practice, and your rate is $100 per hour. As the sole provider in your practice, you want to gross (before taxes and expenses) $100,000 per year. You will need to bring in $8,333 each month to reach your annual goal ($8,333.33 × 12 = $100,000). In order to make $8,333 per month, you need to have 83 billable hours in the month ($8,333 ÷ $100 = 83). That is approximately 21 billable hours per week (83 ÷ 4 = 20.75). When you are just starting your practice, unless you have a contract with a school or another facility, you will likely not have 20 billable hours on day one. While that would be great, realistically it will take some time to build up a private caseload. How much time depends on your target market and your marketing efforts. If you have strong relationships in your community, several referral sources, or potential clients waiting for your doors to open, then it may happen. However, it is best to be conservative in your revenue projections so you do not get into a situation where you are unable to sustain your business and have to close your doors. Another caution is to be sure that you have enough of a cushion in case your payors do not pay on time. If you have a 60-day billing cycle, this will affect your cash flow, which is discussed further in Chapter 7. Table 2–4 illustrates the scenario with an annual salary of $108,000.

Just for fun, let's double the numbers and say that you want to gross $200,000 per year. Because we've already done the math, we know that you will need

Table 2–4. *Sample Revenue Goal Worksheet*

	Worst-Case Scenario	Best-Case Scenario	Average of Best- and Worst-Case
a. How many billable hours you work per week	15	30	22.5
b. Your hourly rate	$100	$100	$100
c. Total (a×b=c)	$1,500	$3,000	$2,250
d. Number of weeks you expect to work per year	48	48	48
e. Total Revenue (c×d=e)	$72,000	$144,000	$108,000
f. Expenses and taxes ($6,000 + 33% of revenue)	$30,000	$54,000	$42,000
g. Net income (e-f=g)	**$42,000**	**$90,000**	**$66,000**

Please note that all numbers are approximate and this is for illustration purposes only. Your numbers will depend on several factors, including but not limited to, your actual business expenses, business structure, and tax filing status.

approximately 42 billable hours per week. Unless you hire someone to do all of the administrative work for you, 40 hours of direct time per week may be more work than one person can handle. In that case, you will need to look into hiring additional service providers to reach that goal. The great thing about being an entrepreneur is that you can work as much or as little as you want. You have to decide what is important to you, what your financial goals are, and what it will take to meet those goals.

If we look at this from a content creator's perspective, we will do the math in the same way. However, instead of calculating billable hours, you will calculate how many products you will need to sell. For example, if you are selling a digital download at $9.99 each, and you want to make $100,000 in a year from sales, you will need to sell 10,000 units in a year. That's 833 units per month (10,000 ÷ 12 = 833). If you sell a bundle for $49.99 each, you will only need to sell 2,000 units in a year, or 167 per month. These numbers are only for illustration purposes. Now it's your turn! Use this Revenue Goal Worksheet to determine what it will take for you to reach your target revenue. Keep in mind that your business may have more than one revenue source. You can customize a revenue goal worksheet that meets your needs, but we are providing you with one in Table 2–5 as a starting point.

Once you set your goals, you can work backward to see what it will take to get there. You can then develop a marketing plan to reach your target customers and

Table 2–5. *Revenue Goal Worksheet*

	Worst-Case Scenario	Best-Case Scenario	Average of Best- and Worst-Case
a. How many billable hours you work per week			
b. Your hourly rate			
c. Total (a×b=c)			
d. Number of weeks you expect to work per year			
e. Total Revenue (c×d=e)			
f. Expenses and taxes ($6,000 + 33% of revenue)			
g. Net income (e-f=g)			

achieve those goals! Do not get discouraged if you have to tweak your plan or if it takes a little longer than you hoped to reach your goals. As long as you do not give up, you will get there.

NETWORK

Your consistent and intentional engagement within your network is going to be a vital tool when establishing or growing and expanding your business. Of all the many steps that it takes to establish, grow, or expand a business, networking is one of the most crucial steps you can take. Word of mouth referrals to your private practice can help make or break a practice. Being introduced to or connecting with referral sources or potential collaborators in and around your practice area can only happen if you are intentional about the connections you make, and you are clear about what your mission is. Let people know what you do. Let people know who you are and how you can help them or someone they know. We will talk more in depth about ways to connect with your network when we discuss establishing a more specific framework for your private practice business in Chapter 4 and when we discuss marketing your business in Chapter 6. Regardless of whether your business is a traditional private practice, or something that is SLP-related but not a traditional practice, the most important point to remember regarding networking is that your goal is to build relationships in order to: (1) build a network of potential referral sources for your business, (2) engage with potential collaborators for your business, and, in certain cases, (3) gain exposure with potential investors or interested parties for your business. At networking events, you should always be prepared with a concise, confident, and clear message to introduce yourself. This is referred to as an elevator pitch, which we discuss in more detail in Chapter 6. Taking the time to network and prepare your elevator pitch will help you to expand your network, which is essential to establishing and growing your business.

REGULATORY CONSIDERATIONS

As a certified speech-language pathologist, you should already have your mandatory licenses/certifications achieved and registered. As you transition into the role of a business owner and entrepreneur, there are additional regulatory considerations that you will have to consider and adhere to. Given the changing landscape of our field, and of the world as a whole, it would be impossible to specifically list all of the appropriate legal certifications and regulations that are necessary for an SLP Entrepreneur to abide by. Even within the field of speech-language pathology, in the United States, for example, each state has variable rules and regulations in terms of what type of licensure and qualifications are deemed necessary to uphold that license on an annual basis. If you provide services via telepractice, you may have several state licenses and certifications to keep track of. Given the global scope of the corporate world and business world, as well as the influx of e-commerce and virtual business negotiations, there are many other regulations related to not having a brick-and-mortar space and instead conducting business online. The item checklist in Figure 2–5 (see p. 42) is not exhaustive, but does list some important regulatory considerations. Some of these items should be thought of as must-haves, while others can be thought of as nice-to-haves.

66

The hardest part of starting a business is transitioning from idea to action.

Lisa Kathman
SLP Toolkit
Bright Ideas

99

In closing, we suggest that you get started on your business plan now. While we have developed The SLP Entrepreneur Business Model that includes the elements we think are most relevant for your business, this is intended to serve as a summary of the key elements you will need for your plan. There are more traditional business plans, which are much longer, such as one by the Small Business Administration (Small Business Administration, n.d.), that enable you to dive deeper into each section from the onset of your business. A more detailed business plan is a necessity if and when you pursue loans or investors. In contrast, your internal plan is for your eyes only, as it helps you answer important questions about your business and stay on track toward reaching that Mission, Vision, and Value Proposition (MVVP) that you created to guide all of your future decisions. While there is no right or wrong way to write a business plan, just be sure that it meets your needs. Take a look at our sample business model in Figure 2–6 (see p. 45), and then create your own in the blank template provided in Figure 2–7 (see p. 46).

REGULATORY-ADMINISTRATIVE CONSIDERATIONS

	MUST HAVE:
☐	Professional Liability Insurance
☐	Federal Tax Identification Number (EIN)
☐	Business Registration (e.g., LLC, Sole Proprietorship, Corporation, etc.)
☐	General Liability Insurance* (Brick & Mortar)
☐	Secure Payment System
☐	Secure/Privacy Compliant Method of Obtaining Signatures/Obtaining Confidential Information
☐	Website/Digital Media Regulatory/Compliance Regulations (e.g., Statement about use of Cookies, etc.)
☐	Any regulatory compliance for Grants/Loans received*
☐	
☐	
☐	*Not applicable for all situations
☐	

Figure 2–5. *Regulatory-Administrative Considerations.* continues

REGULATORY-ADMINISTRATIVE CONSIDERATIONS
(CONTINUED-PAGE 2)

	NICE TO HAVE:
☐	Cyber-Security Liability Insurance
☐	Woman/Minority/Disabled/Veteran-owned enterprise certification specialties {Governmental or Private}
☐	Business Registration (e.g., LLC, Sole Proprietorship, Corporation, etc.)
☐	General Liability Insurance* (Brick & Mortar)
☐	Specialty certifications/training or specialty area certification beyond professional certification (e.g., Diversity, Equity, & Inclusion; Leadership, etc.)
☐	
☐	
☐	
☐	
☐	
☐	
☐	

Figure 2–5. continues

REGULATORY-ADMINISTRATIVE CONSIDERATIONS

☐	
☐	
☐	
☐	
☐	
☐	
☐	
☐	
☐	
☐	
☐	
☐	
☐	

Figure 2–5. continued

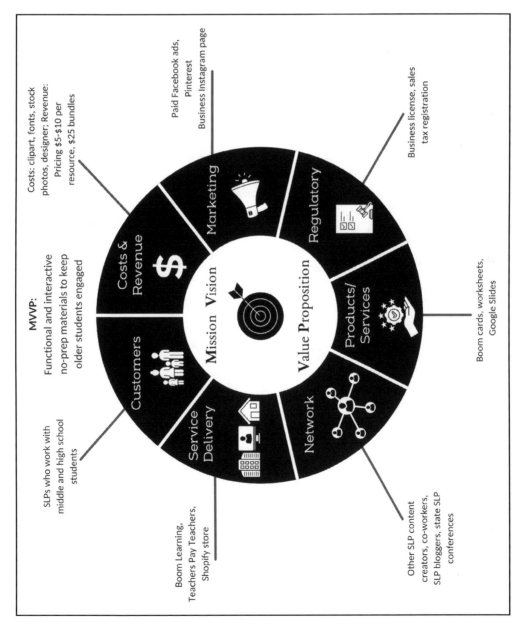

Figure 2–6. The SLP Entrepreneur Business Model—Sample Business Model for Content Creators.

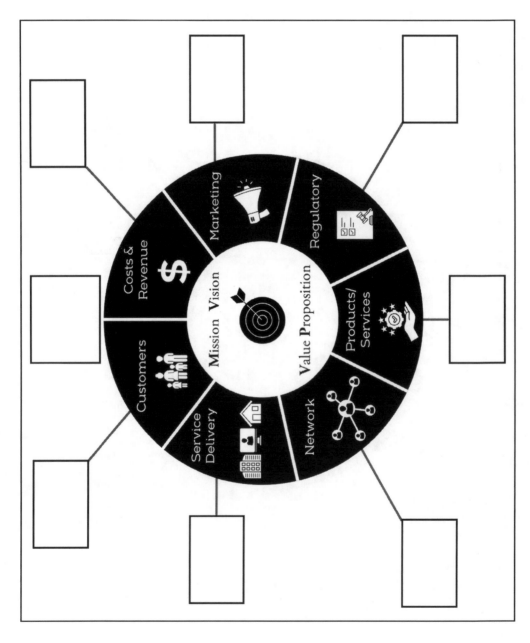

Figure 2–7. The SLP Entrepreneur Business Model—Blank Business Model Template.

CHAPTER CHECKLIST

☐ Write your mission, vision, and value proposition (Figure 2–2)

☐ Identify your primary and secondary target audiences (Figure 2–3)

☐ Determine your products and services

☐ Decide how you will deliver your products and services to your target audience

☐ Brainstorm some marketing strategies for your business

☐ Determine the costs of your business

☐ Identify your potential revenue sources

☐ Complete your Business Expenses Worksheet (Table 2–2)

☐ Complete your Revenue Goal Worksheet (Table 2–5)

☐ Identify potential referral sources in your network

☐ Complete your Regulatory-Administrative Considerations Checklist (Figure 2–5)

☐ Create your SLP Entrepreneur Business Model (Figure 2–7)

REFERENCES

American Marketing Association. (n.d.). *Definitions of marketing*. Retrieved July 1, 2021, from https://www.ama.org/the-definition-of-marketing-what-is-marketing/

American Speech-Language-Hearing Association. (2020). *ASHA COVID-19 Survey Results—May 2020*. Retrieved from http://www.asha.org

Lilyquist, M. (2020, July 20). *What is direct selling?* The Balance Small Business. Retrieved September 7, 2021, from https://www.thebalancesmb.com/what-is-direct-selling-1794391

Scott, C. (2019, June 21). *What is retail? What is wholesale? A guide for small business owners*. QuickBooks. Retrieved September 7, 2021, from https://quickbooks.intuit.com/r/selling/retail-vs-wholesale-business-models-whats-best-business/

U.S. Small Business Administration (n.d.). *Write your business plan*. Retrieved September 7, 2021, from https://www.sba.gov/business-guide/plan-your-business/write-your-business-plan

CHAPTER 3

Thinking Like an
SLP Entrepreneur

Mindset Matters Related to
Executive Presence and Self-Care

A large part of entrepreneurship is your mindset. The way that you think about yourself, your business, your purpose, your fulfillment, your expectations, your strategy, and your planning, all play an incredibly vital role in navigating the business framework that we previously laid out in Chapter 2. While your mindset is not listed under the SLP Entrepreneur model, please note that it is a strong underlying foundation of all of those elements that we just dissected. In this chapter, we've tried to separate some of the elements of your mindset that need to be in place, and a plan to help you improve in these areas, as you embark on this journey of entrepreneurship and establish or grow your business.

SHIFTING YOUR MINDSET FROM SLP TO SLP ENTREPRENEUR

One of the hardest things that you'll do as an SLP Entrepreneur is shifting your mindset from being the clinician, caregiver, or service provider, to being all of those things *and* the business owner, founder, president, CEO, and entrepreneur. What does that mean? Does that mean that you stop caring? No. Does that mean that you stop providing excellent service? No. Even more, it means that you continue to provide quality products or services and work in an ethical, effective manner. However, there are contrasts in your response to certain scenarios as an SLP employee in either a health care or educational setting, compared to providing services within your own business as an SLP entrepreneur. For example, as an employee, you might find yourself working extra hours to get documentation completed. That will still most likely happen in your own business. However, as an entrepreneur, you also need to start thinking about how that impacts your overall business cost/benefit and what you can do to minimize extra time spent on documentation, without compromising on quality, thoroughness, and the legal/ethical obligations of your completed documentation. As an employee, the extra time you take to complete that documentation extends your workday and work-related stress without any positive or negative fiscal impact. As a business owner, however, you now need to consider that beyond adding to the workday stress levels of the individual putting in additional hours to complete documentation, there is also a fiscal impact. This is especially true if you are paying an employee/contractor by the number of hours worked, compared to a flat salary. Additionally, you will need to look into processes that are less efficient and contribute to your or your employee/contractors' work-life balance and stress levels within your organization.

> **66**
> **In many ways, our profession has ideally prepared us to approach a start-up endeavor. We rely on evidence-based practice, diagnose situations and treat accordingly, and we constantly have to pivot when challenges arise.**
>
> *Tia Bagan*
> *theEATBar* **99**

Consider how it will impact your *bottom line* if a client is running 15 minutes late or someone cancels with only 2 hours' notice. Your bottom line can be defined as what your revenue and cost are for a certain transaction. The cost portion of your bottom line also includes the time that it took you to prepare and the time that you set aside for an appointment. If you were not able to schedule anything else in that time slot because you were expecting a client and they canceled with only 2 hours' notice, you have lost all of that valuable time and revenue. As an SLP employee, you might take the time that was allotted for that appointment to catch up on documentation or administrative tasks for other clients; you most likely will not directly feel the financial impact of the canceled visit. In contrast, as a business owner, you need to not only make use of that "lost time," but you also need to acknowledge and address the financial impact of the missed visit. You *should* have a client cancellation policy in place that you need to enforce, which may include a monetary fee for the late cancellation. While that may feel uncomfortable, it is a necessary piece of business ownership, in order to recover a piece of the loss of revenue for the canceled session, and to also prevent the recurrence of late cancellations. Even though each business owner may have a different level of "flexibility" in terms of their policy and/or enforcement of that policy, it is an important example of the mindset shift that must take place when you transition from being an employed SLP to an SLP Entrepreneur.

Take a look at Table 3–1 to reflect on the contrast between the mindset or reaction you might have in certain scenarios as an SLP employee compared to an SLP Entrepreneur. Starting to reflect on various aspects of potential mindset shifts is an essential building block to your transformation from an SLP to an SLP Entrepreneur. This shift in mindset is important regardless of whether you are establishing a private practice or have plans to pursue another SLP-related business venture.

Table 3–1. Mindset Shift From SLP to SLP Entrepreneur

Hypothetical Scenario	Clinician/SLP Response	SLP Entrepreneur Response
Client/Patient is late	Still see Patient/Client/Student and may even extend session to cover missed minutes, possibly extending your work day because you still needed to finish paperwork	Need to ensure Client has signed Attendance/Late Arrival Policy, which is revisited as needed.
Cancellation at the last minute	Don't necessarily feel financial impact; provides extra time to see another client/catch up on calls, documentation, etc.	Need to ensure Client has signed and understands consequences of last-minute cancellation (e.g. verbal/written warning, cancellation fee, etc.)
Not paying bills	Don't necessarily know financial/payment status of copays/balances or feel financial impact of nonpayment	Need to ensure that invoices are sent out regularly, along with notices via written/phone to collect payment. Consideration of discontinuing services/need for potential legal action to recover funds.
Prep/ Documentation time	Because of the expectation within a salaried position and/or [billable] productivity expectations of your employer, you stay late to do paperwork and/or prepare for sessions at home/away from work prior to sessions with no change in pay scale/grade.	Consideration of the time it takes for prep/documentation and accounting for that in pricing/scheduling/volume of clients on caseload.

GROWTH MINDSET

As you embark on this journey of entrepreneurship, there is going to be a great deal of learning ahead of you. This learning will continue throughout your entire journey of business ownership—from the planning stage, to the pursuing stage, establishing and growing stage, and then your "exiting" (i.e., retiring/selling/closing your business) stage as well. As speech-language pathologists, we are not taught business practices, how to create business policies, or how to conduct business engagements. Much of this you will have to do on your own through various resources. Reading this book is a good first step. It is also recommended to seek guidance from other business coaches, mentors, or other fellow SLPs for support as you embark on this journey. Just as the concept of having a *growth* versus a *fixed* mindset is being taught as a part of school curriculums to children, it is relevant that we keep this in mind as professionals and entrepreneurs as well. A *growth mindset* can be described as having the belief that through hard work, perseverance, and learning from one's own challenges and others' successes, intelligence/talent/skill can be improved. On the contrary, a *fixed mindset* is one that believes intelligence is static, avoids challenges, gives up easily, and believes that putting in extra effort will not result in desirable rewards (Dweck, 2016; Hughes, 2021). You will find challenges, obstacles, and areas of running a business that seem daunting and virtually impossible to overcome and achieve. You need to keep working at it, to not only stretch your mind, but to also learn new skills that will tangibly align with your entrepreneurial success.

> **If you're not making mistakes and improving a ton when you start, you started too late!**
>
> *Shannon Werbeckes*
> *Speechy Musings*

This idea of struggling, yet persevering through challenges in order to attain success, or *productive struggle* is something that will be significantly important to remember throughout your entrepreneurship journey. You need to set yourself up knowing that it will feel challenging and some days overwhelming, but you will get through your obstacles as you build and grow your business, if you use the lessons you learned from making mistakes to grow, prosper, and do something differently in order to attain success. It's important to keep this in mind even when you're collaborating with another speech-language pathologist or related professional, or even when you are receiving feedback from a coach, mentor, or spouse when your business practices are impacting them or your family unit. Use the feedback that you gain from making mistakes and learning from them, as well as the feedback that others around you provide in order to continue persevering.

Keeping your growth mindset and positive outlook, especially when you are facing several challenges either from a knowledge/expertise, confidence, and/or time/energy perspective will be vital to your continued progress and success. Don't give up. Many times you may feel "stuck" in terms of knowing you don't want to "go back to what you left behind" or *plan* to leave behind (i.e., in most cases your current or most recent SLP job); however, what lies in front of you seems daunting and overwhelming. Keep in mind that your struggles will *help* you learn, grow, and do better the next time around. With a creative and inspired mission, strategic planning, established support and resources, and ongoing review to learn, grow, and expand, you will succeed. When you read through the inspirational journeys of SLP Entrepreneurs that are highlighted in Chapter 8, an ongoing theme you will notice is that many felt overwhelmed and unsure if they would be able to learn how to run a business successfully; they now have feelings of confidence and pride when reflecting on the amount of growth that resulted from perseverance and use of all of the tools available to them.

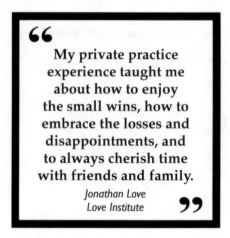

> **66**
> **My private practice experience taught me about how to enjoy the small wins, how to embrace the losses and disappointments, and to always cherish time with friends and family.**
> Jonathan Love
> Love Institute **99**

EXECUTIVE PRESENCE

Executive presence, simply put, refers to being able to demonstrate your product/service/leadership value for an individual or organization through your confidence, communication, and expertise. This might initially feel uncomfortable, or you might have a difficult time believing in yourself and your capabilities as an entrepreneur. Even though you feel confident in your clinical expertise and knowledge base, will you be manipulating people to believe something that is not true, given your inexperience as a business owner? Absolutely not. Given the preparation and strategic planning that you will invest into launching your business, and by continuing to maintain a growth mindset, you will gain knowledge and expertise that will aid in building your confidence and allow your executive presence to surface.

As an SLP Entrepreneur, you will constantly be challenged to know your worth, believe in your skillset and expertise, and inspire confidence in others by doing so (Valentine, 2018). Remember that one of the most important things that you can do as you're establishing, growing, and expanding your business is network, network, network. Therefore, you must be willing to share this belief in yourself and confidence that you can add value as a leader with others. As you do this, you want to be seen as the go-to professional or the go-to business to help individuals, families, and even organizations with their biggest pain points. In order to obtain executive presence, Valentine (2018) suggests that you take these steps:

1. *"Have a vision and articulate it well."* Consider your MVVP in Chapter 2 and creating your Elevator Pitch in Chapter 6.

2. *"Understand how others experience you."* Consider the Westfall (2018) exercise later in this chapter. It is important to understand how your target customers view you/your offerings. It is also important to reflect on how you are viewed by other stakeholders in your organization—colleagues, collaborative business partners, employees/contractors, vendors, the general public, and your personal stakeholders (i.e., family and friends).

3. *"Build your communication skills."* You are a communication expert by trade, but even the best communicators need to rehearse before entering new situations. Practice your elevator pitch. Make your presentation skills and storytelling engaging for target audiences. Invest in your leadership communication skills training.

4. *"Become an excellent listener."* As SLPs, we are already trained to be very astute listeners. You may use your expertise in this area to train others (in nonclinical contexts) at enhancing their listening skills.

5. *"Cultivate your network."* This is a crucial element of your business framework, which we discuss in more depth in Chapters 2 and 6.

6. *"Learn to operate effectively under stress."* As a business owner, you will have a fair amount of stress; however, learning to cope with stress and implementing strategies to prevent and lessen your stress level will be essential in creating a sustainable business model. Refer to the upcoming Self-Care section in this chapter for more guidance and perspective.

Learning to build your executive presence can feel like somewhat of a challenge at times, given that as SLPs in health care or educational settings, we are typically given the role of serving and helping as caregivers, without needing to "sell" or "market" our services. When you are running a business, a foundational necessity is letting people know you exist, and, more importantly, that you can positively impact them with your skillset and expertise, i.e., make them aware of your value proposition that we discussed in Chapter 2. As an entrepreneur and leader, you need to take stock of all of your strengths, and determine what value that strength will provide to various individuals, organizations, and any potential stakeholders. Thinking a step further, take the perspective of your intended audience, target market, or stakeholder, and view your strengths and value proposition from *their* perspective. Determine how you will demonstrate and communicate this with them.

The exercise in Figure 3–1, adapted from an exercise presented in Westfall (2018), will help you do exactly that. Take a bit of time to fill out this chart specifically for each one of your stakeholders, clients, or customers. In doing so, you will gain perspective on your own strengths and how you can impact the lives of others, and, in turn, gain the confidence that will lead you to a strong sense of executive presence. For example, when thinking about how you communicate your value to a prospective private preschool's Executive Director in order to sign a contract with your business to offer services on an ongoing basis, you might want to consider the school you attended to obtain your graduate degree as a "strength" that you would enter in the first column on the left. While the Executive Director may find some relatable value-add in knowing that you went to a certain school with a certain reputation of training SLPs, that is not likely to be the factor that will resonate most with the Executive Director in order to get them to sign a contract with you. Instead, consider focusing on a strength such as having data-driven methods to identify those students that may need speech and language therapy through (possibly free) screenings that you could quickly generate, given your expertise and experience in conducting screenings. For the Executive Director, if you are able to offer that service and eventually serve the children in their school that could benefit from skilled therapeutic services, you have now offered them something of value. This strength demonstrates your expertise and builds confidence in your unique skillset. This, in turn, benefits the director, as they are able to include "free speech-language screenings and speech therapy as needed" to the list of advantages of attending that private school, and can market this feature to current and prospective parents.

This executive presence that you will carry with you and this framework of thinking about your value from your target audience's perspective will be

SPEAKING TO YOUR SPECIFIC AUDIENCE

Make note of all of your potential Customers/Clients/Stakeholders
(Think about your Primary/Secondary Target Audience/Customer Groups)

Complete this exercise for each Customer you listed

Client/Customer/Stakeholder : _____

What are my strengths & how does my client/stakeholder benefit from them?

WHAT ARE MY GREATEST STRENGTHS/MY VALUE PROPOSITION ?	METHOD OF DELIVERY-HOW BEST TO COMMUNICATE/DEMONSTRATE ?	HOW IS MY CLIENT/STAKEHOLDER BETTER OFF ?

Adapted from Westfall (2018)

Figure 3–1. *Speaking to Your Audience. Adapted from Westfall, C. (2018).* Leadership Language: Using Authentic Communication to Drive Results. *Wiley.*

extremely useful across various aspects of your business, including your marketing, networking efforts, brand awareness, service delivery, and eventually your overall business growth and success. What this means is that you need to consider how well you are able to confidently and clearly state what you can do and how you can help that individual, family, or organization. You must keep that belief in yourself, and let the confidence in your skillset and expertise show in order to inspire others to trust and invest in you.

GREG WHEELER JR.

Owner, Wheelhouse Marketers
www.wheelhousemarketers.com

I work with business owners who are looking to scale. I help them implement an evergreen funnel that is powered by paid advertising.

Important Considerations for Entrepreneurs

They should be clear on why they are starting their business. Times will get hard, and that's why systems need to be strong enough to see them through it.

To create an offer that people want and are willing to pay for, answer these 4 questions:

1. Who is your ideal client?
2. What high-value problem do you solve for them?
3. How do you communicate that?
4. Which segment of your audience can afford your price?

Pitfalls to Avoid

Don't try to sell to everyone. Niche down, at least at the beginning.

Advice for Entrepreneurs

There is a lot of noise out there when it comes to how to market your business. There are many methods. Pick a method, and stick to it for at least 6 months. Don't jump from shiny object to shiny object.

TIME MANAGEMENT

Time management refers to making decisions about how you spend your time. Making good decisions about how you spend your time should lead you to living a more productive, less stressful life. During the COVID-19 pandemic, time management took on an entirely new meaning for millions of working parents. Before the coronavirus pandemic, approximately 4% of Americans were working from home. In June 2020, that number increased to 40% (Shepherd, 2020). Individuals found themselves not only managing their own schedules, but also those of their significant others. Regardless of your familial status (e.g., spouse, kids, etc.), the basics of time management remain the same. Use Figure 3–2, and follow along with the Time Management Planner as you read this section.

TIME MANAGEMENT PLANNER

MON		DATE:
TUE		**PRIORITIES:**
WED		
THU		**TO DO:**
FRI		_____
SAT		_____
SUN		_____

Figure 3–2. *Time Management Planner.*

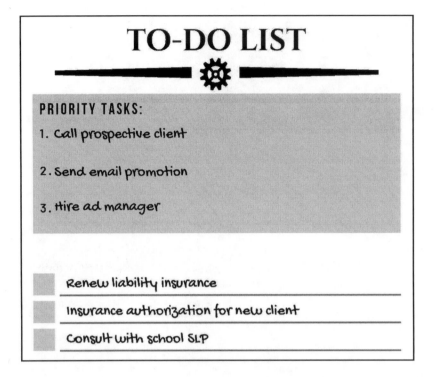

Figure 3–3.
Sample To-Do List.

We've developed a list of time-management strategies for SLP entrepreneurs.

1. Make lists.

2. Set deadlines.

3. Prioritize.

4. Do what you can when you can.

5. Ask for help.

1. Making Lists: Making lists is a way to ensure that you accomplish everything that you set out to do. An example of list items for a private practice owner might include collaborating with a school-based SLP of one of your private clients; submitting insurance authorization for a new client; and updating your professional liability insurance policy. For another type of business, you may have tasks such as returning a phone call to a potential client, sending an email with a new sales promotion, and running online ads. Let's use the second list to illustrate how you might implement the other time management strategies. We suggest making a list at the beginning of each week, and only including what needs to be done today, tomorrow, and by the end of the week. Save the long-term tasks for another list (i.e., Google Keep, Todoist). Your to-do list for the week might look a little like the one in Figure 3–3. Now use Figure 3–4 on the next page to write out your own to-do list.

TO-DO LIST

PRIORITY TASKS:

1.

2.

3.

Figure 3–4. *To-Do List Template.*

2. Setting Deadlines: Setting deadlines is going to help you with what comes next. On our sample list of three tasks, you may already have a deadline set for returning the phone call (i.e., aim for returning phone calls within 24 hours). Sending an email to promote your online course should be done as soon as possible, but definitely by the end of the week. Finally, finding someone to run your social media ads has been put off for too long, so that should be done no later than Wednesday. After you've set deadlines for each task on your list, move on to the third strategy.

3. Prioritizing: The process of prioritizing includes assigning importance to the tasks you need to complete to help you determine what needs to be done now and what can wait. The items on your "someday" list will slowly make their way to your priority list when you decide that it's time to act on them. The things that are on your priority list should be those that either have a deadline set by someone else (e.g., clients or business partners) or important things that you need to get done to reach your goals or help your family (even though they probably have their own lists). From our list of three tasks, prioritizing them may look something like Figure 3–5.

One way to prioritize is based on the deadlines you've set, but you can also prioritize the things that impact other people or that have negative consequences if you put them off. Think about what the consequences will be for not getting something done. If you don't return the phone call from a potential client, not only would you potentially be missing out on future revenue, but you could also give your business a negative image. On the other hand, there is probably some wiggle room in the timeline for finding someone to run your online ads (especially if you've been doing it yourself until now). If you have trouble prioritizing, use the priority matrix in Figure 3–6 on the next page.

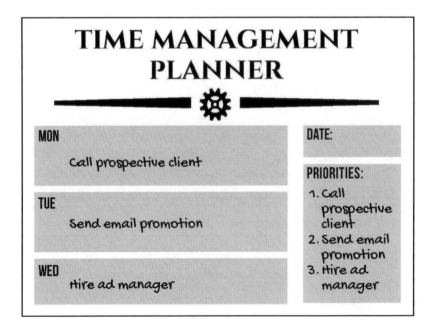

Figure 3–5. *Sample Time Management Planner.*

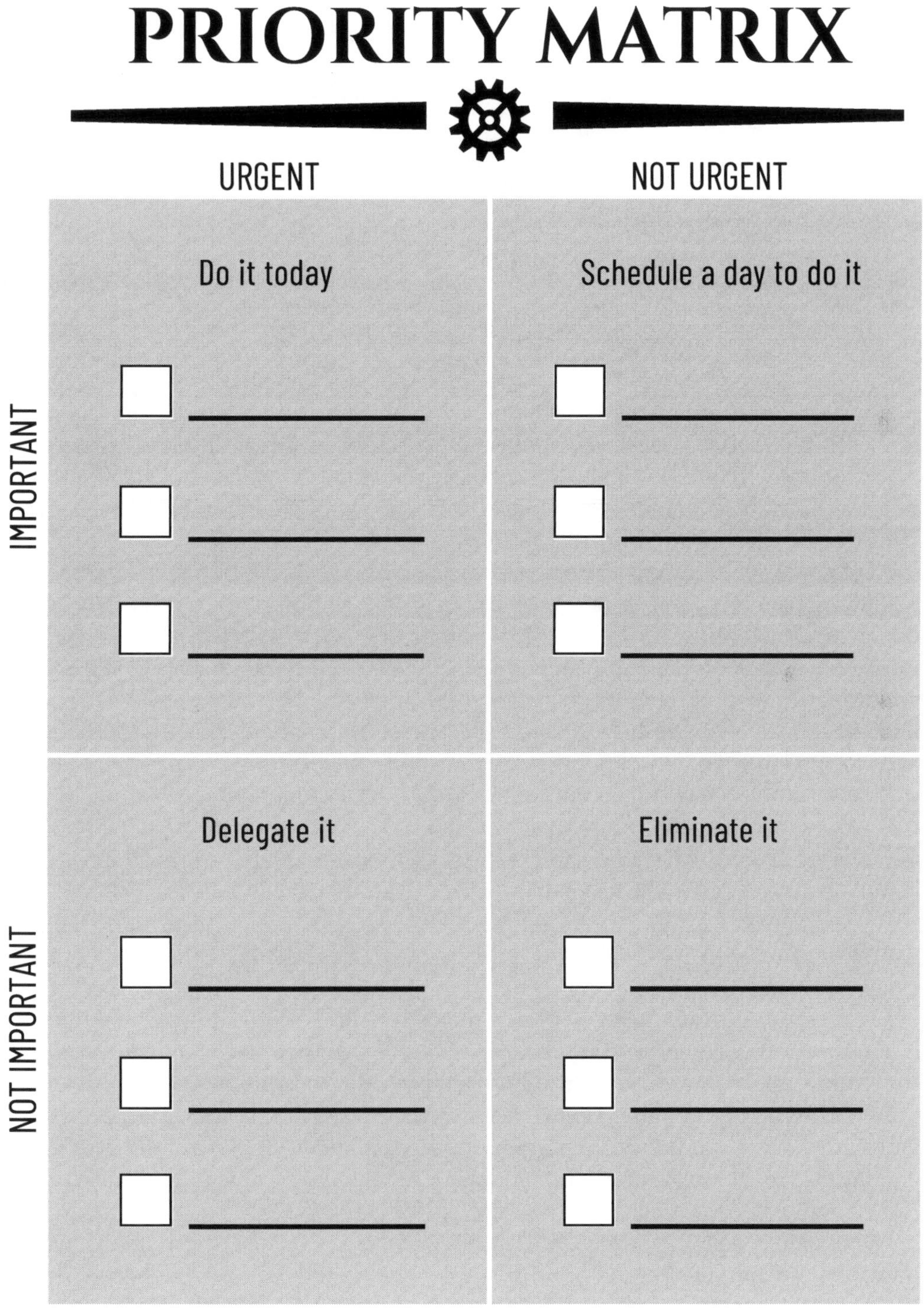

PRIORITY MATRIX

URGENT   NOT URGENT

Do it today   Schedule a day to do it

IMPORTANT

Delegate it   Eliminate it

NOT IMPORTANT

Figure 3–6. *Priority Matrix.*

When prioritizing, the first step is to determine whether a task is urgent. You will then decide what to do, based on if it is important or not. For things that are both urgent and important, you need to do them today! If something is urgent but not important to you, delegate it to someone else. Regarding items that are not urgent, if it is not urgent but is important, you can schedule a day to do it later. If it is neither urgent nor important, then eliminate it from your list. Here is a guide to help you after you've completed your priority matrix.

- Urgent and important: Do it today.

- Urgent, not important: Delegate it.

- Not urgent, but important: Schedule a day to do it.

- Not urgent or important: Eliminate it.

When you think about prioritizing your to-do list, there are more important things in life than just getting through your list. For example, if a family member needs your attention, you can always make a phone call or send an email later. When you are prioritizing, make sure that you don't neglect the things and people that you value most. This leads to our next strategy.

4. Doing *What* you can *When* you can: Everyone is different, so what works for one person may not work for the next. You have to know what works for you and when you will be the most productive. It's a waste of time to just stare at a screen and reread the same thing over and over because you aren't focused. It's also not best practice to try to multitask either. Just think, if you are working on five things at once, how much of your attention are they each *really* getting? And if you've done a little work on each task, you might not actually be accomplishing anything, which means your to-do list has not gotten any shorter. Just focus on doing what you can when you can, and what you can't do now will have to wait—unless you can ask someone else for help. This leads us to our fifth strategy.

5. Asking for Help: "Why isn't this #1 on the list?" you ask. Well, if you're an entrepreneur, there are only so many things you can actually get help with. After all, it is your vision, and you need to play a major role in carrying it out. For example, if you are having someone run ad campaigns for you, you need to make sure that they know what you are "selling." If you are providing a professional service where you work with high-paying clients directly, they want to talk to *you*, not a virtual assistant. And if you are hosting a Facebook Live with your loyal followers—can anyone else really do that for you? Though you may not be able to delegate certain tasks, you *can* ask for help at home, so you can get through those quick tasks that have been lingering on your to-do list since last week. Maybe your mom can watch the kids for a couple of hours or your spouse can do the homework check tonight. If there are things that you can delegate—do it! Know your limits. It's *okay* to ask for help. As an entrepreneur, we know what it's like to be a one-person show. In Chapter 7, we discuss preparing your business for growth. Outsourcing tasks where you can allows you to focus your time and energy on the big-picture decisions and setting your business up for future success.

DONNA LETTIERI-MARKS PSY.D., L.T.D.
Licensed Clinical Psychologist
www.NapervillePsychology.com

"Integrating **self-care** into our daily routines actually serves to **increase** both
our **efficiency** as well as our **therapeutic effectiveness.** "

Self-Care for the Entrepreneur

Many healthcare providers think of self-care as a selfish act or as a luxury that they just don't have time for. As an entrepreneur, we manage not only clinical but administrative responsibilities as well. Integrating self-care into our daily routines actually serves to increase both our efficiency as well as our therapeutic effectiveness. Taking a 5–10-minute walk and breathing deeply, for example, will help us to focus and sustain our attention and increase our efficiency in processing information. Making sure that we have healthy nutrition and hydration during the day provides necessary fueling of our brain. Mindful engagement in relaxing, just being, stretching, or doing something pleasurable charges our battery to have the energy we need to engage most effectively in our therapeutic work with clients and to meet our practice demands. Even a few minutes of self-care integrated into our schedule on a daily basis will make a positive impact, and more extended periods of time during our week can serve to increase our overall mental and physical health and promote resilience.

SELF-CARE

When you are a business owner, you could potentially work on something related to your business 24 hours a day, 7 days a week, easily. That's not practical, and that is absolutely not why you would want to go into private practice or other business ventures using your SLP expertise. It is vital that you put boundaries around your time and your space when you are an entrepreneur and operating your practice or other business venture. It is very easy to take calls during family time, or work on that social media post late at night, or take networking opportunities when you really should be developing your new program. All of it can be very exciting and allows you to have a creative outlet for yourself as your business can be seen as a passion project that you are building and investing in on your terms. Having said that, if you have significant others, you need to take care of yourself so that you can take care of them.

Remember that the reason you went down this path of SLP entrepreneurship was to either better serve individuals and organizations, give yourself more flexibility with your schedule, give yourself more lucrative financial opportunities, or give yourself more time to do other things that you enjoy. Keeping those things in mind, you need to make sure that you are setting those boundaries early on in your pursuit and stick to them! To illustrate this, think about when you're on a plane and they tell you to make sure you put on your own oxygen mask first before assisting anyone else. If you are not taking care of yourself from a mental, physical, and social-emotional perspective, then you will not be able to fully reap the benefits of owning your own business, nor will you be as likely to succeed in your business pursuits, or have the energy to give to your other life joys, responsibilities, and loved ones because you will be spread too thin. This is why self-care is a vital and necessary practice when you consider embarking on the journey of entrepreneurship.

We know that taking care of yourself is essential to ensure potential success for your business establishment in the beginning stages, as well as for future growth and expansion. We also know that those are the times when it might be the hardest to practice self-care. In order to incorporate self-care practices into your daily life while embarking on the journey of entrepreneurship, you must first take stock of your self-care attitudes, as well as your current practices of self-care, and your potential areas of needed improvement in certain aspects of self-care (Markway, 2014). Once you've taken stock and reflected on your areas of need, or what you are currently doing to promote self-care in your daily lifestyle, you need to create a plan that is manageable and consistent in order to incorporate self-care practices based on your initial assessment. Make sure to include potential action steps (even small ones) that are attainable and feasible, and will allow you to have success at incorporating self-care practices into your daily lifestyle, which are vital to your overall success as an SLP Entrepreneur.

> **❝**
> **Set your limits. Know where this path may negatively interfere with key factors in your life—like your family and your own personal health.**
>
> · A. Monique Portelli
> SaidHear   **❞**

Taking Inventory of Self-Care Attitudes and Practices

Markway (2014) suggests taking an assessment, which includes first determining what your self-care *attitudes* are.

- Do you have guilt with self-care, or are you alright with slowing down sometimes to incorporate self-care practices?

- Do you have a "go-to" list of self-care activities, and have you made it a habit to incorporate those on a regular basis?

Markway (2014) goes on to suggest taking stock of your different *areas* of self-care.

- If you look at interpersonal self-care, do you have a small group of people you can call on for support? Are you able to set appropriate limits in your relationships?

- In terms of physical self-care, here are some questions to ask: Are you moving and exercising enough to work up a sweat several times a week? Do you feel comfortable in your own body? Do you sleep and rest when you're tired?

- In terms of mental self-care: Do you regularly stimulate your brain by learning new things? Can you make a mistake without it being a catastrophe? Do you currently practice stress-reduction techniques such as deep breathing, mindfulness, or meditation?

- In terms of emotional self-care: Can you identify and acknowledge your feelings? Are you willing to express your feelings appropriately? Do you have a plan in place for when you feel overwhelmed with feelings? Do you practice self-compassion (which is extremely important)?

- In terms of spiritual self-care: Do you pray, meditate, or practice whatever feeds you spiritually? Do you make time for reflection and contemplation? Do you have a serene place of your own when you're feeling stressed? Do you have a gratitude practice? (Markway, 2014)

Setting Self-Care Goals and Establishing Habits

Now that you've assessed what your self-care attitudes are and what your different potential areas of need are related to self-care, it's important to create a plan for how you will incorporate making self-care a priority as you embark on this journey, transform into an entrepreneur, grow, and scale your business as an established entrepreneur. Being a professional in our field itself indicates that we wish to make an impact, and we want to take a solution-based approach to help others. Many times, however, we don't recognize that in helping others, we lose sight of helping ourselves. Self-care practices must be a priority in order to maintain control over the progression of your business and the way it impacts your life. There are numerous studies in positive psychology that suggest happiness leads to success versus what we typically think, which is that only hard work leads to success (Hughes, 2018, 2021).

A good way to incorporate self-care into your routine is to set some goals for yourself after completing an assessment of your needs. Make a list of what you will do today, in one week, in one month, or in one year in terms of your self-care regimen (Vibrant Emotional Health, 2019). Creating a habit of something can be challenging when you feel like you don't have enough time or feel guilty because of all of the other "to-do's" on your list. In those circumstances, you may have more success if you try engaging in the practice of *habit stacking* (Scott, S.J., 2017; Hughes, 2021). Habit stacking encourages you to make a small change, resulting in more productive outcomes because you are integrating it into your life on a consistent basis. An example of habit stacking would be if you wanted to document moments of gratitude for something that you accomplished today in order to keep a positive outlook on your day, or your life in general. It may be hard to always have your notebook nearby and write it down. However, if you get into the habit of journaling at the same time and in the same place every day, it will become easier for you to incorporate that as a daily ritual.

You can also incorporate this new habit with an activity that you already do unconsciously without even considering whether to do it. For example, you brush your teeth every day, so this would be a good time or place to put your gratitude journal next to the bathroom counter so you can take a minute and just jot something down when you brush your teeth. If you are someone who has a ritual that involves drinking tea or coffee in the morning, then perhaps you put your journal right next to your coffee maker so you can take that minute to write something down as your coffee or tea is brewing. By doing this on a regular basis, research has shown that you are more prone to make that habit stick. Making the habit of writing in your gratitude journal on a daily basis will make you feel more grateful, which in turn makes you happier, which changes your neurological makeup and eventually leads to more success in your entrepreneurship journey (Hughes, 2021). If you haven't already, take some time now to complete this inventory and set your own self-care goals in Figure 3–7.

Self-Care Considerations for Small Business Owners

Some considerations for possible self-care strategies to reflect on or incorporate as you establish or grow your business include:

- Setting Boundaries and Establishing Your Personal and Professional Priorities
  - Learning to say "no"
- Staying Organized with Systems in Place
  - Time Management
- Scheduling Self-Care Time
  - Physical
  - Mental
  - Emotional
  - Social/Interpersonal
  - Spiritual (Keeping an Attitude of Gratitude)

Self-Care FOR THE SLP ENTREPRENEUR

TAKE INVENTORY OF SELF-CARE ATTITUDES & CURRENT PRACTICES

Do I recognize the necessity of self-care?
Do I feel guilty or allow myself to practice self-care?
What am I doing for my Physical, Mental, Emotional,
Social/Interpersonal, & Spiritual Self-Care?

Am I treating
Self-Care as a
Necessity/Priority?

SET SELF-CARE GOALS & ESTABLISH HABITS

Today & every day, I will......
Every week, I will....
Once a month, I will...
Whenever I need to, I will...

I will engage in HABIT STACKING by
connecting a new small change with an
already established habit.

INCORPORATE SELF-CARE CONSIDERATIONS FOR THE SLP ENTREPRENEUR

Set Boundaries/Establish Personal & Professional Priorities
--Learn to say 'no'
Stay Organized with Systems in Place
--Manage My Time
Schedule Self-Care Time
*Physical *Mental *Emotional *Social/Interpersonal
*Spiritual (Keep An Attitude of Gratitude)
Manage My Expectations/Believe in My Ability to Overcome Challenges

Communicate
My Boundaries,
Expectations, &
Scheduled Self-Care Time
with Others

Figure 3–7. *Self-Care for the SLP Entrepreneur.* continues

FOR THE SLP ENTREPRENEUR

Take Inventory of Self-Care Attitudes & Current Practices

Set Self-Care Goals & Establish Habits

Incorporate Self-care Considerations for the SLP Entrepreneur

Figure 3–7. continued

- Communicating Your Boundaries, Expectations, and Scheduled Self-Care Time with Others

- Managing Expectations and Overcoming Challenges

Setting Boundaries and Priorities

As we discussed in Chapter 1, you took some time to reflect on your overarching *personal* priorities, goals, and aspirations. You are also working on establishing your *business* priorities, goals, and aspirations. In the context of self-care, you need to ensure that you are setting boundaries around taking on projects in terms of your physical space and time, in order to have scheduled time to work on establishing or growing your business, and scheduled time to incorporate self-care activities into your daily lifestyle. From a professional perspective, as you start to grow and gain more market exposure, you will need to determine if the projects, opportunities, and potential collaborations that people seek from you and your expertise truly serve you and your overall mission, vision, value proposition, and purpose. While certain opportunities might be beneficial for you in terms of a financial outcome, they may not serve you in terms of personal fulfillment, or your time for self-care or family responsibilities. It is going to be up to you to make sure you're setting those boundaries, setting those guidelines, and maintaining your priorities. It is perfectly acceptable to say "no" when it does not serve you in the greater picture of your overall personal or professional aspirations and goals. Perhaps it may serve you, but you don't have the capacity because something else is more pressing for your time, effort, energy, or money. Keeping both mental and written guidelines (if necessary) of what these boundaries, priorities, and expectations are, will help you be consistent in only signing up for those things that can serve you, or that you have the capacity for. This helps to shed light on your overall options and where you choose to set your priorities.

> **❝**
> **You have to be honest with yourself about whether or not what you're doing is worthwhile, and valuable. If no, ditch your bad ideas quickly, without shame or regret, and move on to new ones.**
> *Meredith P. Harold*
> *The Informed SLP* **❞**

Staying Organized with Systems in Place

Being organized in terms of your business practices, your division of time manage-ment, and your division of personal versus professional boundaries, will help you incorporate your self-care activities into your daily lifestyle, and keep them as a necessary priority. While it may initially take you some time, money, effort, and energy to establish and navigate a system to organize all of the different aspects of your life and career, it will be worth the investment if it allows you to continue to engage in the activities that serve you, fulfill you, and also bring you financial gain. If you're not sure where to start, take stock of what you're doing right now that works and what you're doing that doesn't work, and then make a plan to help better organize those areas of your life. You might have to do a bit of testing and narrowing down of your organization systems or automations to help you, but starting to put a plan in place is better than not having an organized plan or strategy at all. Time management is of the utmost importance when considering staying organized and initiating systems to help you maintain structure and ease of your daily activi-ties. This is also interconnected with learning to set boundaries, as previously mentioned, and learning to just say "no" if it doesn't serve your mission, vision, or overall purpose.

Scheduling Self-Care Time

A part of that time management is scheduling those very important self-care activi-ties. Take notice, assess, and create a plan to make sure that you're incorporating things to improve your physical well-being by incorporating exercise or taking better care of your physical self through nutritional choices. Being mindful and reflective in itself is a good practice to help you gain clarity into what needs to be done in order for you to be happier and, in turn, more successful. Engage in practices that help you clear your mental library and gain some moments of peace. As a business owner, you will have several occasions where your mind is filled with many different areas of concern, question, or visionary thoughts. This can get overwhelming and taxing for your mental state, and so it is vital that you continue to nourish and balance your mental well-being. Take stock of your emotional well-being and make sure that you have good connections in terms of being able to express your emotions, are allowing yourself to feel those emotions, and have ways to express your feelings and move through and move forward after getting those feelings out.

Your social and interpersonal network is vital to your overall well-being, growth, and success as an entrepreneur. We talked about the value of having a network and we will mention it again because it is a key element of your successful business practice. To attain success, having interpersonal connections that allow you to relieve some of your stress by either joining activities or having a confidant to express your feelings with is quite relevant. Having a network of colleagues in similar professional industries or entrepreneurial phases is also vital because you can't do this alone. Also, having that external network can potentially help to bring you referrals, generate leads, and create opportunities to work on collaborative projects. This enables you to fulfill your mission and vision while still collaborating and interacting with others. Keeping your spiritual self well-balanced and well-nourished is also important. Whether it is faith-based prayer, spiritual self-reflection, or keeping an "attitude of gratitude" in general, these can be positive ways to bring happiness, which in turn enhances your overall success and growth.

> **Make sure you take some time to rest and do something not related to your business.**
>
> *Beata Klarowska*
> *TheraPlatform*
> *Virtual Speech Center*

Try keeping *"An Attitude of Gratitude"* by noticing things that you appreciate on a daily basis. By changing our outlook, we can influence positive physiological neural/psychological activity to be more positive overall, and we know with evidence from the literature that being positive and being happy can lead to more success in multiple aspects of your life (Ackerman, 2021; Chowdhury, 2021; Hughes, 2021). If you are not already incorporating a practice of gratitude in some form, try to make it part of your daily life by engaging the *"habit stacking"* strategy that we discussed earlier. Use the Gratitude Journal in Figure 3–8 to challenge yourself to integrate this small change into your life by completing a 5-Day Gratitude Challenge. Choose five consecutive days to write, draw, or take a photo of something that you are grateful for. It could be something small, or a huge event. It can be something very personal, or it can be a professional triumph. Whatever you choose to be grateful for that day, put it in your journal. Now, try to figure out a time to write, draw, or take a photo of these five points of gratitude. Challenging yourself to make this small change over a 5-day period (and pairing it with something you already do habitually to make it more feasible to incorporate) may be a small piece of your self-care practice that doesn't require a great deal of effort, but has a huge payoff in multiple aspects as you build, grow, or expand your business.

Communicating Your Self-Care Time with Others

After you have established what areas of self-care you need to focus on and prioritize making a clear plan to incorporate those things into your life, you need to make

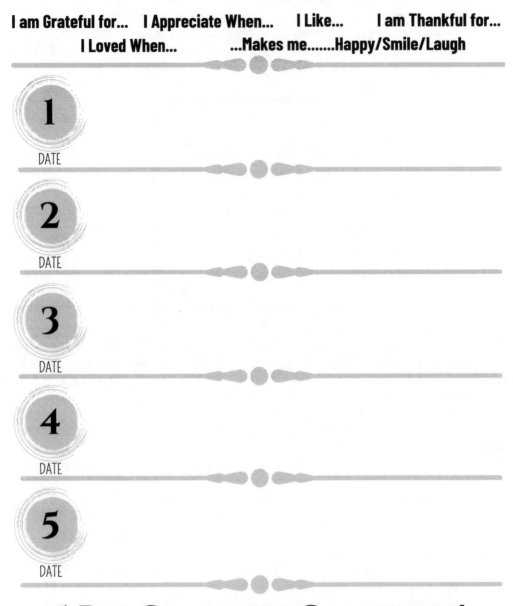

Figure 3–8. *Gratitude Journal.*

sure that you communicate these plans and efforts with others. In your efforts to set boundaries, and keeping in line with your priorities, communicating your need for an hour each day to do your mindfulness or meditation practice is something that you need to tell your loved ones in order to have more structure and peace in your home as well as successful business pursuits.

Managing Expectations and Overcoming Challenges

As we previously discussed, keep and maintain a growth mindset, knowing that you will have challenges to overcome, the first of which is being able to develop some basic business knowledge and business communication skills. As you establish, enhance, and grow your business, and as you transform into an entrepreneur, some challenges or obstacles might be small nuances, while others might be larger hurdles. Manage your expectations from the start, and know that you can overcome any challenges that are put in front of you. Help yourself by making a plan and strategy and working through your business framework, as this will help you manage your expectations. Having multiple supports in place, from social/interpersonal contacts, as well as from business and networking contacts, is vital to keep you from feeling like you are alone in this endeavor. This allows you to break away from work and maintain some of that social-emotional-interpersonal mental wellbeing. The more you break down all the elements to build your business, the easier it will be to tackle challenges that are headed your way. Your mindset of knowing that there will be challenges, managing your expectations, and knowing that you can successfully overcome those challenges and take it all in stride, is essential to maintaining a healthy balance.

When it comes to managing expectations, one of the biggest expectations to manage is that establishing a private practice or SLP-related business is not easy work, but it is rewarding and fulfilling work if you structure it to be. Establishing a private practice or an SLP-related business is not easy money, and you may not even make a lot of money initially; however, it can be quite lucrative if you plan, strategize, and execute your plan with intention. Keep in mind that you probably don't have a business degree and didn't take business courses in your graduate SLP program, which may put you at a disadvantage when selling your product or service. However, you have a skillset that is related to basic human function that is necessary for people's quality of life and fulfillment. You are an expert at communication, which lays the foundation at the base of any relationship, any industry, and any process or procedure. If you work with swallowing and feeding, and specifically, voice and respiratory retraining, then all of these are basic life functions that impact a variety of areas of one's personal and professional life, and you have a lot more expertise than the general public in these areas. Keeping the positive mindset of managing your expectations and keeping your executive presence in mind (knowing that you do have the skills and tools, or that you can gain the skills and tools, to overcome any challenge that is presented to you), will allow you to succeed in your business endeavors.

CHAPTER CHECKLIST

☐ Complete Speaking to Your Specific Audience Worksheet (Figure 3–1)

☐ Set self-care goals (Figure 3–7)

☐ Complete the Gratitude Challenge (Figure 3–8)

☐ Set priorities for your business this week (Figure 3–4)

REFERENCES

Ackerman, C. E., MA. (2021, September 10). 28 benefits of gratitude & most significant research findings. *PositivePsychology.Com.* https://positivepsychology.com/benefits-gratitude-research-questions/

Chowdhury, R. B. M. A. (2021, December 7). The neuroscience of gratitude and how it affects anxiety & grief. *PositivePsychology.Com.* Retrieved December 11, 2021, from https://positivepsychology.com/neuroscience-of-gratitude/

Dweck, C. (2016) What Having a "Growth Mindset" Actually Means. *Harvard Business Review.* Retrieved October 7, 2021, from https://hbr.org/2016/01/what-having-a-growth-mindset-actually-means

Fox, G. (2021, November 15). *What science reveals about gratitude's impact on the brain.* Mindful. https://www.mindful.org/what-the-brain-reveals-about-gratitude/

Fox G. R., Kaplan J., Damasio H., Damasio A. (2015). Neural correlates of gratitude. *Frontiers in Psychology, 6,* 1491. PMID: 26483740; PMCID: PMC4588123. https://doi.org/10.3389/fpsyg.2015.01491

Gambino, A. (2020, December 16). *Self-care for small business owners and entrepreneurs.* Entrepreneur. Retrieved July 13, 2021, from https://www.entrepreneur.com/article/361464

Hughes, D. C. (2018). *Simple tips to be a happier you: Scientifically proven to help you everyday.* Devin C. Hughes Enterprises, LLC.

Hughes, D. C. (2021, February.) *Finding gratitude in the face of uncertainty.* [Live virtual presentation] for Naperville Community School District 203. Naperville, IL.

Kini, P., Wong, J., McInnis, S., Gabana, N., Brown, J. W. (2016).The effects of gratitude expression on neural activity. *NeuroImage , 128,* 1–10. https://doi.org/10.1016/j.neuroimage.2015.12.040

Markway, B. (2014, March 16). Seven types of self-care activities for coping with stress. *Psychology Today.* Retrieved September 21, 2021, from https://www.psychologytoday.com/us/blog/shyness-is-nice/201403/seven-types-self-care-activities-coping-stress

SCORE. *5 practical self-care tips for small business owners during a pandemic.* SCORE. Retrieved August 13, 2021, from https://www.score.org/blog/5-practical-self-care-tips-small-business-owners-during-pandemic.

Scott, E. (2021, December 9). *5 self-care practices for every area of your life.* Verywell Mind. https://www.verywellmind.com/self-care-strategies-overall-stress-reduction-3144729

Scott, S. J. (2017). *Habit stacking: 127 small changes to improve your health, wealth, and happiness (most are five minutes or less)* (2nd ed.). CreateSpace Independent Publishing Platform.

Scott, S. J. (2021, October 21). *13 steps for building a habit stacking routine.* Develop Good Habits. Retrieved December 11, 2021, from https://www.developgoodhabits.com/building-habit-stacking-routine/

Shepherd, M. (2020, April 7). *28 surprising working from home statistics.* Fundera Ledger. Retrieved September 7, 2021, from https://www.fundera.com/resources/working-from-home-statistics

Sriram, R. (2020, April 13). *The neuroscience behind Productive Struggle.* Edutopia. Retrieved December 11, 2021, from https://www.edutopia.org/article/neuroscience-behind-productive-struggle

Valentine, G. (2018, July 31). Council post: Executive presence: What is it, why you need it and how to get it. *Forbes.* Retrieved August 13, 2021, from https://www.forbes.com/sites/forbescoaches council/2018/07/31/executive-presence-what-is-it-why-you-need-it-and-how-to-get-it/

Vibrant Emotional Health. (2019). *Self-care action plan.* Vibrant Emotional Health. Retrieved July 31, 2021, from https://www.vibrant.org/wp-content/uploads/2019/04/Vibrant_2019_Action Plan.pdf

Westfall, C. (2018). *Leadership language: Using authentic communication to drive results.* Wiley.

CHAPTER 4

Building a Traditional Private Practice

Elements of a Conventional Practice

WHAT A TRADITIONAL PRIVATE PRACTICE LOOKS LIKE

Given the changing landscape of our field, as well as the world as a whole, a traditional private practice may be something that is changing by definition itself. For the purposes of this text, we will label a traditional private practice as a brick-and-mortar space serving a certain type of clinical clientele. Now, however, given societal and circumstantial changes, telepractice options are plentiful, and, therefore, are a viable and reasonable method of owning and operating a private practice. There are still many private practitioners that choose a hybrid approach by having patients or clients come into their clinic space and also offering online services via a videoconferencing platform solution.

Setting up Your Practice (Brick-and-Mortar, In-Home/On-Site, Online, and Related Costs)

Service delivery refers to the method through which you are providing services to your customers (e.g., in person or online). When we talk about service delivery, we also need to define *where* you are going to meet your clients (e.g., home, school, clinic, etc.). For the purpose of this chapter, we will be using service delivery and setting interchangeably. Possible settings and service delivery options that we will discuss are:

- Brick and Mortar
- In-Home or On-Site
- Online

Brick-and-Mortar

A traditional brick-and-mortar private practice is an office, or multiple office spaces, which are designed to cater to the niche population that the private practitioner serves. Something to keep in mind when planning your private practice space is whether you will be seeing pediatric clients or an adult patient population, or a mixture of both. If serving both adults and pediatrics, it will be important to design your treatment areas to serve each population respectfully and in a manner that best meets their needs. For example, you would not want to have toys and sensory play areas in your treatment room for adults coming to you for dysphagia treatment. On the other hand, you would not want to have your young pediatric clients having to maneuver sitting at tables and chairs designed for the typical adult client. Physical materials that you would need to conduct your day-to-day assessments and treatment sessions would be stored in your physical brick-and-mortar space. Your physical space would need to have separators or dividers if there is more than one clinician working with clients, or if there is a waiting area for upcoming patients and their family/caregivers to wait in. With the traditional brick-and-mortar private practice, you need to also consider accessibility in terms of wheelchair-accessible parking/restrooms, as well as elevators (if necessary) for clients with limited mobility/endurance. Also considering whether your clinic space is accessible and visible from a main road or a shopping center with high traffic is necessary. Another consideration is having access to a sink (ideally inside your treatment space, especially if working with feeding/swallowing/toys or materials that require rinsing, etc.) and (accessible) restroom facilities designated for client and staff use. If you hire employees or contractors, you will need to make sure there is adequate space for administrative calls to be taken and documentation to be completed. If your plan includes adding related services such as physical therapy and/or occupational therapy, accounting for gym space, in addition to the supplies and materials needed for all three disciplines, will be important to consider. The following are some considerations when launching a private practice in a brick-and-mortar space:

- Storefront?
- Parking
- Wheelchair accessibility
- Client-specific environment (e.g., sensory pediatric space versus adult wheelchair accessible table space)
- Assessment and treatment supplies
- Storage for supplies (e.g., tests, treatment supplies)
- Sink
- Restroom for you, clients/patients, staff
- A place to lock up sensitive, private health information
- Computer
- Phone
- Fax/Copier
- Waiting room?
- COVID precautions/safety and sanitization supplies

In-Home or On-Site

Another traditional method of establishing a private practice is to offer in-home or on-site services. This is typically in the realm of in-home early intervention services, in-school to a pediatric population, and/or providing adult home health services to the adult population post-stroke, or any injury, disease, or progressive disease that makes them less mobile and warrants care and therapeutic interventions in their home. This type of private practice is often in high demand, and allows for flexibility in your schedule. However, the amount of travel, as well as the purchasing and transporting of materials for assessments and treatment need to be considered. There are certain precautions that one must take when thinking about the radius of areas that you will visit, the safety of going into people's homes, transportation costs, the intricacies of providing services with a client at their daycare or school, and having access to materials and the safety precautions readily available for your use on-site. Other factors to consider when providing services in-home/on-site:

- Transportation
- An accessible environment conducive to the client's attention and sensory needs
- Supplies
- Assessment and treatment supplies
- Personal protective equipment (e.g., face masks, gloves)
- GPS/navigation system (or phone)
- Computer (laptop/tablet)
- Phone (mobile)
- Fax (e-fax)

Telepractice

In more recent years, the ability to provide diagnostic assessments and therapeutic interventions over a computer with privacy-enabled videoconferencing has become increasingly popular and has demonstrated successful and similar outcomes to in-person services. Although telepractice services have been an option for several years for speech-language pathologists, during the COVID-19 global pandemic, as schools were forced to provide instruction via remote education, and hospitals/physician's offices relied more heavily on video visits for non-urgent appointments, there was also naturally a dramatic increase in the number of speech-language pathologists who found themselves successfully providing assessment and therapeutic services via videoconferencing platforms. In fact, according to a 2020 ASHA telepractice survey, 4.5% of speech-language pathologists reported that they routinely provided services via telepractice prior to the COVID-19 pandemic, compared to 62.2% routinely providing services after the pandemic began. There are many benefits in opting for this type of private practice or including this as a service provision within your in-person practice. There are also many cost benefits in terms of offering services via a virtual platform without many of the costs that we typically would incur in the brick-and-mortar or in-home/on-site settings. Here are some considerations when establishing an online private practice:

- Computer

- High-speed internet

- Additional monitor (optional, but useful)

- Lighting

- Microphone/Headset

- Document camera (optional, but useful)

- Actual supplies (e.g. toys, manipulatives, etc.)

- Digital assessment and treatment tools

- HIPAA-compliant videoconferencing platform

Comparing Settings and Service Delivery Options

SETTING/SERVICE DELIVERY CONSIDERATIONS

IN-PERSON/BRICK & MORTAR	ON-SITE/IN-HOME	ONLINE
• Storefront? • Parking • Wheelchair Accessibility • Client-specific environment (e.g. sensory pediatric space vs adult wheelchair accessible table space) • Assessment & Treatment Supplies • Storage for Supplies (Tests, Treatment Supplies) • Sink • Restroom for you, Clients/Patients, Staff • Place to lock up sensitive, private health information • Computer • Phone • Fax/copier • Waiting Room? • COVID Precautions/Safety-Sanitization Supplies	• Transportation • Accessible environment conducive to attention/sensory needs • Assessment & Treatment Supplies • Personal Protective Equipment (PPE) • GPS/Navigation System • Computer (laptop/tablet) • Phone (mobile) • Fax (e-fax)	• Computer • High-Speed Internet • Additional monitor* • Lighting • Microphone/Headset • Document Camera* • Actual supplies (e.g. toys, manipulatives, etc.) • Digital Assessment & Treatment Tools • Client with Accessible Internet *Optional

Figure 4–1. *Service Delivery/Settings Options Considerations.*

To compare all three types of settings and service delivery options, look at Figure 4–1. These lists are not exhaustive of all possible considerations, but it is a good starting point to consider which setting and service delivery model would best serve your needs and market when establishing your private practice. A combination or hybrid service delivery model is also very possible and can offer an expansion of the types and volume of clients that your private practice can cater to. For example, in addition to the pediatric patients that you see in your brick-and-mortar private clinic, you may also have a few afternoons a week where you offer telepractice sessions for patients that live in rural areas. In addition to these services, you may also offer assessments on a monthly basis to a local school that is in need of ongoing speech-language evaluations.

If you are starting a traditional private practice, there are pros and cons to each service delivery option. Let's look at the pros and cons in more detail (Table 4–1). As you can see in Table 4–1, there are also pros and cons of each service location (setting). As you are making this decision for your practice, keep your target clients in mind. If you will be working with kids in early intervention, a common model is parent coaching. This would lend itself well to home-based or telepractice services. If you are working with adults with limited mobility, they would also be appropriate for home-based or telepractice services. If your practice will be based upon obtaining mostly school contracts, it may not make sense to have the overhead of a brick-and-mortar office. In this case, you would be working with the client at their location.

Table 4–1. *Pros and Cons of Different Service Locations*

	Client's Location	**Clinic**	**Online**
Pros	Low overhead costs	No travel	Low overhead costs
	Natural environment	Possible foot traffic	No travel
	Family involvement	Safety	Flexible scheduling
		Access to all materials	Natural environment
			Family involvement
			Motivating technology
Cons	Travel time	High overhead (e.g., rent, utilities, security, office staff, etc.)	Client resistance
	Safety		Unable to use tactile cues

Related Costs

When considering the type of clients that you wish to serve and the setting in which you wish to offer services, it is vital that you also consider the cost and revenue related to offering these services to this target population in this setting. While we typically consider costs to be related to finances or money, we also need to think about cost in terms of time spent working, time spent preparing, and/or time spent not serving another client because your scheduled client canceled, all of which are indirectly related to your money and revenue. It is also related to your self-care and overall wellness which we discussed in Chapter 3. When you are an SLP Entrepreneur, you hold many roles that are vital to a successful business. Your main MVVP (that you established in Chapter 2) will guide you to providing the best quality services that improve your patient's/client's/student's communication/cognitive/swallowing function for improved quality of life. However, as a business owner, you need to be mindful (refer to Chapter 3) that you are also intending to make revenue and income to help support your lifestyle, and/or support your aspirational goals.

Revisiting Figure 4–1, you can see the comparison of potential items that you might need to consider and think about what that means in terms of cost. The financial cost will be there, but also think about time as a cost factor. For instance, if you decide that your private practice model is going to offer services to the early intervention population in their homes, you need to consider the driving and traveling time as a financial expense. In addition, the time you spend traveling needs to be considered in terms of the wear and tear on your vehicle and associated maintenance costs, as well as the time you are away from your family and other responsibilities. In contrast, if you were to provide telepractice services instead of in-home services, you would save on travel time. However, you will need to have a strong internet connection, videoconferencing platform, lighting, and other accessories needed for a successful telepractice session, as well as the expertise to skillfully assess and treat clients via this online service delivery model. While you might be saving time and money related to travel by offering sessions exclusively online, you might also be losing the potential volume of clients if they do not have access to internet connections or the required technology to attend telepractice sessions.

These are considerations for you to make when planning. They don't all have to be exact when you first start, however, but you will want to make sure that you are gathering some data and trialing various factors to expand your client volume or offer services in multiple settings. This again goes back to consideration of your service delivery, the costs involved, and the revenue that you can obtain from each setting or method of practice. Going in with a clear plan will help you navigate to find out what is working and what is not working. Remember that you can start small and do not have to do everything all at once when first starting out. Also, keep in mind your initial MVVP at all times. Do the related costs of a certain client population or setting outweigh the fulfillment and sense of purpose that you are receiving in return? Revise your MVVP to reflect what your potentially revised mission and vision might be.

TYPES OF CLIENTS SERVED

> **"**
>
> **One of the biggest benefits of starting my own clinic is that I get to choose what population I work with.**
>
> *Angela Chung*
> *Speak Fluent Inc.*
>
> **"**

You've decided what your mission, vision, and value proposition are. You have determined what your niche population is going to be. Having said that, this does not mean you are not able to take on other clients that come along your way, and/or actively seek out other client populations once you've established your niche market. We have listed potential client groups that you could serve in your traditional private practice. It is not exhaustive by any means, but it is a good starting point.

Potential Client Populations for a Conventional Private Practice

- Adult—Neurological (stroke, TBI), progressive (e.g., PD, Alzheimer's), head and neck cancer, voice-respiratory retraining, motor speech/fluency, dysphagia

- Pediatric—feeding/swallowing, reading specialist, neurodivergent, developmental speech and language, cleft lip and palate specialty, oromyofunctional therapy, fluency/voice

- Individual vs. group

- On-site contractual/consultancy

- Corporate speech clients—accent modification, business-professional communication enhancement (This client population can be included for elective services, not traditional clinical services.)

Figure 4–2 may look familiar to you, as we went through the exercise of writing down potential customer groups in Chapter 2. Take a bit of time to revisit the list you made in Chapter 2. If you have not completed this in Chapter 2, take some time now to jot down on Figure 4–2 who you would consider to be your ideal target customer

~MARKETING~
CUSTOMER GROUPS/TARGET AUDIENCES

PRIMARY	SECONDARY
• Niche Target Customer Group	• Broader Audience that includes niche Customer • Secondary Customer Group based off expansion of product line/service offerings

Figure 4–2. Blank Customer Groups/Primary and Secondary Target Audiences.

groups, as well as who might be listed in a secondary group of potential customers, if your expertise allows, when your primary target customer group is not producing the volume of clients and revenue you have projected. An example of a primary target audience might be infants and children (and their parents/caregivers) that have feeding/swallowing difficulties. A secondary target audience might be all parents/caregivers with children from a marketing perspective, and/or infants and children (and their parents/caregivers) with speech-language-literacy-cognitive-communicative disorders (to build your caseload).

While the field of Speech-Language Pathology offers many diverse service types within our scope of practice, this field also continues to see clinicians finding a specialty area of focus for their practice. However, when you are offering a specialized service to a niche population, you need to make sure that if you're establishing a brick-and-mortar space that your specialty market can access your practice easily for there to be a continuous volume of that particular clientele coming your way. The same holds true if you are establishing a private practice that is primarily conducted online via telepractice. You need to make sure that there is a market for your specialty service that will fill the volume needed with individuals who:

- are from that specific patient population,

- will be open to receiving services remotely, and

- also have insurance coverage for an online method of receiving services (if you plan on accepting insurance).

In both cases, if you don't have enough of a market for that particular niche population, you need to either consider expanding the market of your target customer or consider limiting your hours available for your in-person clinic offerings. If you will be providing services on-site at a school, health care facility, and/or in your clients' homes, you are more likely to find your volume of targeted population preemptively based on the contracts that you establish with organizations or through the early intervention/home health care systems.

If you continue to establish a more generalized practice, serving a variety of patient populations, you will need to make sure that your marketing and networking efforts speak to that, but don't get "diluted" without one specific niche area that you highlight. Of note, if you are going to set up a clinic that serves both adult and pediatric client populations, you need to make sure that your marketing, as well as your brick-and-mortar space, reflect the division of clinical services for these different client populations. In contrast, setting up your clinic and engaging in marketing efforts towards only one niche patient population may seem to be less complex at first glance, however, certain challenges could arise with this method of attracting customers as well. For example, if you establish your practice as one that serves primarily adult stroke or brain injury survivors with their speech/language/cognitive-communicative and swallowing needs, then you will need to be careful about where you open your practice. You want to make sure that there is not a large rehabilitation clinic that offers outpatient services or a large hospital system that has multiple locations where their patients from an acute care facility might feed into their inpatient rehabilitation unit, and then get discharged into their day rehabilitation or outpatient clinics.

Having said that, you can still serve that population—you simply need to be prepared for the potential of less volume if that patient population is getting absorbed elsewhere. In that case, you will want to consider marketing to other potential patient populations (if you are qualified in terms of experience and expertise to do so, and if it still aligns with your mission/your purpose/your fulfillment) to make up for the reduced volume of your target market. In doing your market research, however, you might find that even if you establish your brick-and-mortar practice close to an area where there are large hospital systems offering rehabilitation services (i.e., your competition), they may have long waiting lists, so establishing a relationship with those organizations will benefit both you and their patient pool. For instance, if they don't have an SLP to serve a Spanish-speaking adult with aphasia, you could reach out to those clinics and let them know that you exist and are fully capable of providing that specialty service. The hospital outpatient clinic appreciates being able to have a referral list of providers when they cannot meet the patient's needs themselves. Patients and their caregivers appreciate being able to come to a space that: (a) may not have a waiting list as long as the larger hospital system's list; (b) does not have facility fees that large hospital systems would charge on top of the service visit cost; (c) may offer more specialized services and scheduling options; and (d) may be in a location closer to their home and/or offer online services compared to the larger hospital system.

Don't be discouraged from going after your target customers, despite any "competition" that you have found in your local area. Take a look at the sample letter to a physician's office in Figure 4–3 to get some inspiration of how you could reach out to area physicians, schools, and clinics to broaden your referral base. In this sample letter, we have created a hypothetical scenario of a clinic that serves both adults and pediatric patient populations, takes insurance, and offers services in multiple languages. Make sure that when you reach out to physician's offices, schools, or clinics, you cater your messaging to speak to the type of client that particular location can refer to you, including details that describe the type of services you offer. Try to connect with the referral coordinator at various physician's offices to get into their system. If you drop off marketing material in person, be sure that the letter is on your branded letterhead, with business cards, referral pads, and other important informational materials readily available.

REVENUE SOURCES

In Chapter 2, we discussed possible revenue sources for private practice, such as assessments, intervention, and consultations. In addition to the type of service that you will be providing in exchange for revenue, you need to think about the payors of the revenue. For example, if you accept private pay clients only, the clients (e.g.,

YOUR LOGO
Your Website/Phone

Dear Dr. .... & MagnificentMedicalAssociates Referral Team-

We wanted to take the opportunity to introduce ourselves, as we are excited to open our doors to our comprehensive Speech-Language Pathology practice, the SuperStarSLP Clinic, located in downtown SuperStarvsville, next month. After working in the academic medical setting for 13 years, we decided that we wanted to create our own space for patients to receive evidence-based, high quality, individualized speech-language/cognitive-communicative/feeding-swallowing/voice assessment and treatment.

We have designed separate spaces for our adult patient population and the pediatric population that we serve, to meet each patient's needs with respect, dignity, accessibility, and quality care.

We are fortunate to have a team of multilingual Speech-Language Pathologists so that we can proudly offer services in English, Spanish, Polish, Hindi, and Mandarin.

We are currently accepting multiple private insurances, as well as Medicare/Medicaid.

We welcome you and your Team to attend our Open House that we are hosting on Oct 1. Details about our event are included in the enclosed flyer. We are also enclosing business cards, a referral pad, and informational pamphlets for our individual adult & pediatric services, as well as our group therapy and community enrichment class offerings.

We look forward to partnering with you to collectively serve our Community's health & wellness needs with the highest level of expertise and quality care.

Best,

SuperStarSLP1 & SuperStarSLP2
Co-Founders, SuperStarSLP Clinic
Email | Phone |Fax
Website

Figure 4–3. *Sample Letter to Physician's Office.*

adults or children's parents) are your payor. If you are credentialed with a private insurance company, such as Blue Cross Blue Shield, United Healthcare, or Cigna, the insurance company will be the payor. Some clients may have a deductible that has to be met prior to insurance paying for services. For example, your client has a $1,000 deductible and you see them for 10 sessions at $100 per session. They will have met their deductible by the 10th session. The 11th session is then covered by insurance. If the client has a co-pay, that will also be a payment source for the services rendered. Let's look at an illustration of this difference in Table 4–2. In this example, your 60-minute session rate is $100. If you are private pay, you can have different rates depending on the length of the session. You may have a fee schedule that includes 30-minute, 45-minute, and 90-minute sessions. In this scenario, your "session rate" will vary from client to client. If you are credentialed with an insurance company, you sign a contract that includes the amount that the insurance company agrees to pay for a given service (or CPT code).

We'll address CPT codes in the next section, but for now, we will focus on the difference between an hourly rate and session rate. If an insurance company agrees to pay $75 for CPT code 92507 (Treatment of speech, language, voice, communication, and/or auditory processing disorder), then you will get paid $75 regardless of the session length. If you have a 30-minute session, the insurance will pay $75; if you have a 60-minute session, the insurance will pay $75. Table 4–3 illustrates this scenario, where the contracted rate that the insurance pays will result in lower revenue for the same length of time. This is also true for assessments. When you own your own business, you are able to set your own prices. However, when you are contracted with an insurance company, you will only be paid the contracted rate. Some providers attempt to negotiate the contract, but not all insurance companies

Table 4–2. *Insurance vs. Private Pay Scenario 1*

	Billed Amount 45-Minute Session	Insurance	Client	Total
Private pay	$75	$0	$75	$75
Insurance	$75	$60	$15	$75

Table 4–3. *Insurance vs. Private Pay Scenario 2*

	Billed Amount 60-Minute Session	Insurance	Client	Total
Private pay	$100	$0	$100	$100
Insurance	$100	$60	$15	$75

are willing to negotiate. When setting your prices for assessments, you need to factor in the indirect time associated with preparing, conducting, scoring, and reporting the results. For example, the assessment does not begin and end with the test(s). You will need to collect the client's case history, administer the test(s), score each test, and write the report. Some SLPs can spend hours just drafting the report. If your practice is private pay, you set your rate based upon the amount of time it takes to complete the entire process (from start to finish). Your calculations may look something like Table 4–4.

If you are credentialed with insurance companies, the contracted rate is the most you will receive for the assessment based on the CPT code (e.g., 92523 Evaluation of speech sound production; with evaluation of language comprehension and expression). Table 4–5 shows the difference in pay for assessments. This example illustrates the lost revenue on assessments for the amount of time involved. Many providers justify the cost based on potential future revenue for a client who qualifies for services. If you consider the potential for lost revenue with longer sessions, it may appear that there is no long-term benefit in obtaining the client. However, let's revisit what we know about marketing. You need to think about who your target market is, in addition to what the market will bear. If all of your potential clients will want to use their insurance benefits and all of the other practices in the area accept insurance, you may find it a challenge to attract clients unless you offer a highly specialized service.

Table 4–4. Setting Rates for Assessments

Activity	Investment
Parent interview	30 minutes
Administer assessments	60 minutes
Score assessments	30 minutes
Write evaluation report	60 minutes
Total time	3 hours
Assessment fee	$100/hr × 3 hours= $300

Table 4–5. Insurance vs. Private Pay Scenario 3

	Billed Amount Assessment	Insurance	Client	Total
Private pay	$300	$0	$300	$300
Insurance	$300	$180	$20	$200

Another benefit of being in-network with insurance companies is the exposure. If you need to see a doctor, you usually start with your insurance directory of in-network providers. The same is true for specialists, i.e., speech-language pathologists. If you get your practice on the provider list, you will have another opportunity to increase exposure. More clients = more revenue. However, you need to determine whether that will translate to increased profit for your business.

> **"**
> **By accepting private pay only, I have been able to provide exactly what appears clinically necessary without the confines of insurance limitations.**
>
> *Ashley Parks Froats*
> *Versatile Speech Services* **"**

The final revenue source that we'll discuss is school contracts. As we discussed earlier in this chapter, if you have a traditional private practice, you may still choose to offer services at your clients' location. In the case of school contracts, the school (e.g., school or district) is your client. The benefits of contracting with schools are:

- Growing your business
- Having a steady stream of referrals
- Controlling where (in what states) and when you work
- Working on your terms

One of the challenges of contracting with schools is competing with larger contract companies that can offer lower rates. Schools across the country are dealing with staff shortages. In fact, according to the Bureau of Labor Statistics, the job outlook for speech pathologists is 25% growth for 2019–2029, which is much faster than the average growth rate of 4% for all occupations (U.S. Bureau of Labor Statistics, 2021). This leaves many schools to turn to independent contractors to fill these vacancies. An article by McKenzie and Bishop (n.d.) features an educational service agency in Massachusetts that outsourced its related services as a solution to concerns with special education services. Some of the benefits for the schools that they reported were:

- Decrease in costs
- Increase in quality of services

- Decrease in administrative overhead

- A more efficient delivery system

- Timely evaluations and reevaluations (McKenzie & Bishop, n.d.)

In addition to providing benefits for the schools, your business will also benefit from selling business-to-business (B2B). One of the main advantages of selling to schools is that it enables you to obtain a large client base with less effort. If you were marketing to individuals, you would receive one client for your efforts and marketing dollars. Whereas if you market to districts, you may receive 50 or more clients for your efforts, which stretches your marketing dollars. Acquiring school contracts is a great way to fill your caseload quickly, though your hourly rate may be less than private clients. If you obtain multiple contracts, you can then hire employees or independent contractors to provide services, which is a great way to grow your business. We discuss ways to grow your business in more detail in Chapter 7.

Looking at the possible payment sources (e.g., payors) for your speech and language services, you will have to decide if you want to accept private pay (e.g., paid directly by individual clients), insurance (e.g., paid primarily by insurance companies for individual clients), or contracts with schools or other organizations (e.g., paid by a school district for services rendered for multiple clients). Though your payors may be driven by your target clients, we break down the pros and cons of accepting each of these payment sources in Table 4–6.

As you can see in Table 4–6, each payment source has its pros and cons. Regardless of which options you choose for your business, you will need to determine your marketing strategy to drive revenue for your business. To make sure that your business is profitable, you will also have to determine the cost of operating your business. Let's look at the type of costs that you might incur when starting a traditional private practice, and whether these are only start-up costs or also ongoing

Table 4–6. *Pros and Cons of Different Payment Sources*

	Private Pay	**Insurance**	**Schools and Organizations**
Pros	You set your own rates Payment at time of service No additional paperwork	Free marketing More affordable for clients	Steady stream of clients B2B instead of B2C marketing
Cons	Clients are not always able to afford it	Insurance company determines rates Delayed payments Time spent filing and fighting for claims	Delayed payments A lot of competition in some regions Lower hourly rate than private pay

expenses (Figure 4–4). If you have already gathered information about how much the average rent is in your area while you read Chapter 2, you can enter that into the table below. If you will be working from a home office or only providing services via telepractice, you can leave that line blank.

Sample Private Practice Expenses

Expenses	Startup Costs	Ongoing expenses
Malpractice insurance	150	Annual
PO Box/UPS mailbox	20	Monthly
Videoconferencing platform	15	Monthly
Practice management (EMR)	40	Monthly
Email provider	6	Monthly
Phone line (Google voice)	0	Monthly
Fax line	4	Monthly
Website domain name	20	Annual
Website hosting	20	Monthly
Business cards	10	N/A
State Business Filing	150	Annual
Headset	30	N/A
Webcam	30	N/A
Registered agent (if applicable)	35 – 100	Annual
Advertising	Varies	Varies
Lawyer	Varies	N/A
Accountant	Varies	Varies
Computer	500 – 1,000	N/A
Assessment materials	Varies	Varies
Treatment materials	250	Varies
Rent	Varies	Varies
Total	1280 – 1845	
*Note: These expenses are meant to be an example, and are not an exhaustive list of all of your startup costs and ongoing expenses. The costs of starting and maintaining your practice will depend on your state's requirements, what services you decide to pay for, and the decisions that you make about your ongoing expenses (e.g., which videoconferencing platform and plan you choose).		

Figure 4–4. *Sample Private Practice Expenses.*

LICENSURE

When you are setting up your traditional private practice, it is important to ensure that you are following all local, state, and federal laws. As a speech-language pathologist, you need to have, at a minimum, your professional licenses from your state (e.g., Board of Examiners), and you may be required to obtain a teaching license if you will be providing services in schools. Be sure to check with the school that you are contracting with to find out their licensing requirements. When you are setting up your business, you will also need to comply with state and local business license requirements.

At the state level, you will need to register your business with the Secretary of State. There are several business structures that may be options for you when registering, and these vary from state to state. The most common business structures are sole proprietorship, partnership, Limited Liability Company (LLC), PLLC, and S-corporation. The Small Business Administration created a comparison chart, which we have summarized in Table 4–7. We recommend that you speak with an accountant or business lawyer to determine what type of business structure will be best for your business.

If you are forming a sole proprietorship, the process is fairly easy and requires minimal financial investment. For example, in the state of New Jersey, it is free to register a sole proprietorship, whereas in Illinois the cost varies by county. The Illinois Assumed Name Act requires sole proprietorships to register with their local County Clerk's Office (Illinois Department of Commerce, n.d.). For example, in 2021,

Table 4–7. *Business Structure Comparison Chart*

Business Structure	Ownership	Liability	Taxes
Sole proprietorship	One person	Unlimited personal liability	Self-employment tax Personal tax
Partnership	Two or more people	Unlimited personal liability	Self-employment tax Personal tax
LLC	One or more people	Owners are not personally liable	Self-employment tax Personal tax or Corporate tax
S Corporation	One or more people, but no more than 100	Owners are not personally liable	Personal tax

the cost to register an assumed name in Cook County was $50, whereas the fee was only $10 in DuPage County. In any state, if you are registering as an LLC, PLLC, or S Corporation, there is typically additional paperwork that needs to be completed, including an initial filing fee, renewal fees, and annual reporting requirements. At the local level, you will need to check with your county and municipality to see what is required for you to operate a business in that location. Some additional requirements may include zoning and liability insurance.

INSURANCE CREDENTIALING

As mentioned earlier, insurance companies are possible payors for your practice. This depends on whether you are credentialed with the insurance company. If you *are* credentialed, you are an in-network provider, and if you are not credentialed, you are considered an out-of-network (OON provider). If you are in-network, you will bill the insurance company directly for the services rendered to your patients. If you are out-of-network, you may provide your patients with a superbill, which they can then submit to their insurance company to request reimbursement. Even if you are an in-network provider, it does not guarantee payment for services, as it depends on the specifics of each patient's plan. For speech and language services, in-network providers are sometimes required to obtain a "pre-authorization" prior to beginning services with the patient. This typically entails you providing information in terms of your identifying information (e.g., practice and provider names, NPI billing number, Tax ID number, etc.), related CPT and ICD codes, as well as the requested number of sessions (visits). In some cases, in order to ensure reimbursement from their out-of-network benefit within their insurance plan, sometimes a patient's insurance company will still require a pre-authorization. While the patient will be the party responsible for paying you, in order for them to get reimbursed by their insurance company, they might ask you to fill out the pre-authorization before services ensue, in addition to providing the superbill after services have been rendered. ASHA has excellent resources and a free superbill template on its Practice Portal. View Figure 4–5 for the template. The Word document can also be downloaded from the Plural Plus companion website.

The two types of codes that you will need whether you are billing insurance directly or providing a superbill to clients are ICD codes and CPT codes. ICD codes classify the diagnoses and reason for visits, whereas CPT codes specify the "procedure" that was completed during the visit. For example, the ICD-10 code for an expressive language disorder would be F80.1, and the CPT code would be 92507 for "Treatment of speech, language, voice, communication, and/or auditory processing disorder." The common ICD codes for speech and language services can be found in Table 4–8. Please note that the ICD-11 codes are scheduled to be released in January 2022. As of the writing of this book, ICD-10 codes were still in use. ICD-11 may have slightly different descriptions and even additional codes that were not in use

SUPERBILL TEMPLATE for SPEECH-LANGUAGE PATHOLOGISTS

PATIENT:	ACCOUNT #:
DOB:	POLICY HOLDER:
ADDRESS:	INSURANCE PLAN:
	POLICY #:
REFERRING PHYSICIAN:	DATE INITIAL SYMPTOM:
DATE OF SERVICE:	DATE FIRST CONSULTATION:

PLACE OF SERVICE:　☐ HOME　　☐ OFFICE　　☐ OTHER: _____

DIAGNOSIS:

PRIMARY (Speech-Language Pathology):	ICD-10 CODE:
SECONDARY (Medical):	ICD-10 CODE:
ADDITIONAL:	ICD-10 CODE:
ADDITIONAL:	ICD-10 CODE:

SERVICES:

☐ DESCRIPTION	CODE	CHARGE
Swallowing Function		
☐ Treatment of swallowing dysfunction and/or oral function for feeding	92526	_____
☐ Evaluation of oral and pharyngeal swallowing function	92610	_____
☐ Motion fluoroscopic evaluation of swallowing function by cine or video recording	92611	_____
☐ Flexible fiberoptic endoscopic evaluation of swallowing by cine or video recording	92612	_____
☐ interpretation and report only	92613	_____
☐ Flexible fiberoptic endoscopic evaluation, laryngeal sensory testing by cine or video recording	92614	_____
☐ interpretation and report only	92615	_____
☐ Flexible fiberoptic endoscopic evaluation of swallowing and laryngeal sensory testing	92616	_____
☐ interpretation and report only	92617	_____
Speech, Language, Voice, and Cognition		
☐ Treatment of speech, language, voice, communication, and/or auditory processing disorder; individual	92507	_____
☐ group, two or more individuals	92508	_____
☐ Therapeutic interventions that focus on cognitive function (eg, attention, memory, reasoning, executive function, problem solving, and/or pragmatic functioning) and compensatory strategies to manage the performance of an activity (eg, managing time or schedules, initiating, organizing and sequencing tasks), direct (one-on-one) patient contact; initial 15 minutes	97129	_____
☐ each additional 15 minutes	97130	_____
☐ Nasopharyngoscopy with endoscope	92511	_____

☐ DESCRIPTION	CODE	CHARGE
☐ Laryngeal function studies	92520	_____
☐ Evaluation of speech fluency (eg, stuttering, cluttering)	92521	_____
☐ Evaluation of speech sound production (eg, articulation, phonological process, apraxia, dysarthria);	92522	_____
☐ with evaluation of language comprehension and expression (eg, receptive and expressive language)	92523	_____
☐ Behavioral and qualitative analysis of voice and resonance	92524	_____
☐ Evaluation of auditory function for surgically implanted device(s) candidacy or postoperative status of a surgically implanted device(s); first hour	92626	_____
☐ each additional 15 minutes	92627	_____
☐ Auditory rehabilitation; pre-lingual hearing loss	92630	
☐ post-lingual hearing loss	92633	
☐ Assessment of aphasia with interpretation and report, per hour	96105	_____
☐ Developmental screening, with interpretation and report, per standardized instrument form	96110	_____
☐ Developmental test administration (including assessment of fine and/or gross motor, language, cognitive level, social, memory and/or executive functions by standardized developmental instruments when performed), by physician or other qualified health care professional, with interpretation and report; first hour	96112	_____
☐ each additional 30 minutes	96113	_____

Disclaimer: ASHA's superbill template is only a model. It does not dictate which services should or should not be listed on the bill and does not imply coverage by payers. Some procedures, codes, or other pertinent information required by a payer may not be included in the model. See ASHA's website for additional information on this template.

Figure 4–5. ASHA Superbill. continues

	DESCRIPTION	CODE	CHARGE
☐	Standardized cognitive performance testing (eg, Ross Information Processing Assessment) per hour of a qualified health care professional's time, both face-to-face time administering tests to the patient and time interpreting these test results and preparing the report	96125	_____
☐	Laryngoscopy; flexible; diagnostic	31575	_____
☐	Laryngoscopy; flexible or rigid telescopic, with stroboscopy	31579	_____

Augmentative and Alternative Communication

	DESCRIPTION	CODE	CHARGE
☐	Evaluation for use/fitting of voice prosthetic device to supplement oral speech	92597	_____
☐	Evaluation for prescription of non-speech generating augmentative and alternative communication device, face-to-face with the patient; first hour	92605	_____
☐	each additional 30 minutes	92618	_____
☐	Therapeutic service(s) for the use of non-speech generating augmentative and alternative communication device, including programming and modification	92606	_____
☐	Evaluation for prescription for speech-generating augmentative and alternative communication device; face-to-face with the patient; first hour	92607	_____
☐	each additional 30 minutes	92608	_____
☐	Therapeutic services for the use of speech-generating device, including programming and modification	92609	_____
☐	Repair/modification of AAC system or device (excluding adaptive hearing aid)	V5336	_____

Other Procedures

	DESCRIPTION	CODE	CHARGE
☐	Unlisted otorhinolaryngological service or procedure	92700	_____
☐	Telephone assessment and management service provided by a qualified nonphysician health care professional to an established patient, parent, or guardian not originating from a related assessment and management service provided within the previous seven days nor leading to an assessment and management service or procedure with the next 24 hours or soonest available appointment; 5-10 minutes of medical discussion	98966	_____

	DESCRIPTION	CODE	CHARGE
☐	11-20 minutes of medical discussion	98967	_____
☐	21-30 minutes of medical discussion	98968	_____
☐	Qualified nonphysician health care professional online digital assessment and management service, for an established patient, for up to 7 days, cumulative time during the 7 days; 5-10 minutes	98970	_____
☐	11-20 minutes	98971	_____
☐	21 or more minutes	98972	_____
☐	Medical team conference with interdisciplinary team of health care professionals, face-to-face with patient and/or family, 30 minutes or more; participation by nonphysician qualified health care professional	99366	_____
☐	patient and/or family not present, 30 minutes or more; participation by nonphysician qualified health care professional	99368	_____
☐	Remote assessment of recorded video and/or images submitted by an established patient (e.g., store and forward), including interpretation with follow-up with the patient within 24 business hours, not originating from a related service provided within the previous 7 days nor leading to a service or procedure within the next 24 hours or soonest available appointment	G2250	_____
☐	Brief communication technology-based service, e.g. virtual check-in, by a qualified health care professional who cannot report evaluation and management services, provided to an established patient, not originating from a related service provided within the previous 7 days nor leading to a service or procedure within the next 24 hours or soonest available appointment; 5-10 minutes of clinical discussion	G2251	_____

Total Charges: $ _____

BILLING INFORMATION

PREVIOUS BALANCE:	$
TODAY'S CHARGES:	$
TOTAL DUE:	**$**
PAID TODAY:	$

PAID BY: ☐ CASH   ☐ CREDIT   ☐ CHECK
☐ VISA ☐ MC ☐ OTHER

BALANCE:	**$**

AUTHORIZATIONS

I hereby authorize direct payment of benefits to [Practice Name].

SIGNATURE: _____

DATE: _____

I hereby authorize [SLP's Full Name, Degree, CCC-SLP] to release any information acquired in the course of treatment.

SIGNATURE: _____

DATE: _____

SLP's Full Name, Degree, CCC-SLP
Practice Name | Street Address | City, State Zip
Youremail@email.com EMAIL | (999) 999-9999 PHONE | (888) 888-8888 FAX

Figure 4–5. continued *Used with permission from the American Speech-Language-Hearing Association. (n.d.-b). Superbill templates for audiologists and speech-language pathologists. American Speech-Language-Hearing Association. Retrieved August 8, 2021, from https://www .asha.org/practice/reimbursement/coding/superbill-templates-for-audiologists-and-speech-language-pathologists/*

Table 4–8. *Common ICD-10 Codes for Speech and Language Services*

Description	ICD-10 Code*
Dysphagia	R13.1
Aphasia	R47.01
Dysphonia	R49.0
Phonological disorder Speech-sound disorder	F80.0
Expressive language disorder	F80.1
Mixed receptive-expressive language disorder	F80.2
Other developmental disorders of speech and language Childhood onset fluency disorder	F80.8
Developmental disorder of speech and language, unspecified Communication disorder NOS Language disorder NOS	F80.9
Autistic disorder	F84.0

*Be sure to contact your payor to verify revised ICD-10 or updated codes per ICD-11 (2022). ASHA also regularly updates coding and reimbursement information at https://www.asha.org/practice/reimbursement/coding/

in ICD-10. We recommend that you confirm the appropriate ICD codes before you begin billing with the new codes. You may even consult with colleagues to inquire which codes are preferred.

Prior to taking the steps to get credentialed with insurance companies, you need to determine whether this is necessary for your business. If you are in an area where private pay is widely accepted, you may not need to accept insurance for your practice. If you do decide to begin the credentialing process, refer to our Insurance Credentialing Guide in Figure 4–6. Now let's look at the process required to become an in-network provider in more detail.

Before You Begin

Before you even begin the credentialing process, the prerequisites are an Employer Identification Number (EIN) (also referred to as "Tax ID Number") and National Provider Identifier (NPI). An EIN can be obtained from the IRS and can be completed online in a matter of minutes. You will be assigned your EIN immediately. Your EIN

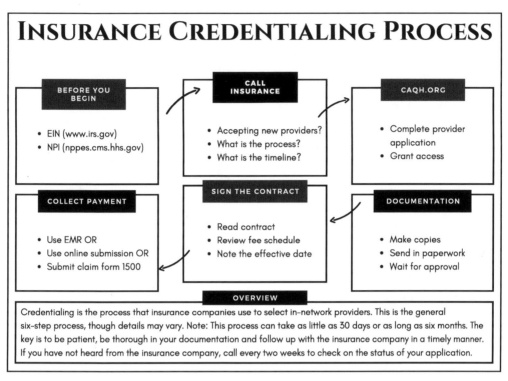

Figure 4–6. *Insurance Credentialing Guide.*

is a way of identifying your business, in the same way that your social security number identifies you as an individual. If your business will be a sole proprietorship, you can and should still apply for an EIN for billing purposes.

The next identifier, the NPI, is obtained from the National Plan and Provider Enumeration System (NPPES). You may have two NPI numbers: one for you as an individual, and one for your practice. If you have been working as an SLP in private practice, medical settings, and in some cases, schools, you may already have an NPI. This number follows you wherever you go. However, when you start your own practice, you can then apply for an NPI for your business, which is also known as a "Group NPI" (Entity Type 2) or "Billing NPI." The NPI application is completed online, and you will be provided with an NPI number in a matter of minutes. You can edit your information later if you need to switch over to a group and then associate yourself (the individual) with your group NPI number (your business).

NPI Types

NPI Entity Type 1: Individual provider (you)

NPI Entity Type 2: Organization (your business)

Step 1: Call Insurance Companies

We have already mentioned the importance of conducting your market research to determine the needs of your target market. We will examine marketing more closely in Chapter 6, but let's say you have already made the decision to begin the credentialing process. Another important step is to determine *which* insurance companies you want to get credentialed with. This should be determined based on which insurance companies your target clients will likely have. Some ways to determine this are to ask your potential clients directly (if you already have a waiting list), call and ask the large employers in your area, or find out what insurance companies other practices in your area are in-network with.

After you decide which insurance company to get credentialed with, you should call the company's provider line to gather information. In that call, you want to find out three things: whether they are accepting new providers, what the process is to apply, and an estimate of how long it takes to get credentialed (Table 4–9). You may also ask for reimbursement rates during this step, but not all insurance companies will provide them. Be prepared that you may not know the rates until after you have completed the application process and are sent the contract to sign. If part of the application process is to complete a CAQH profile, then proceed to Step 2. If this is not required, skip to Step 3.

Step 2: Complete CAQH ProView Profile

CAQH ProView enables you to enter your information into a central database in an effort to reduce redundant paperwork when going through the credentialing process. Once you complete your CAQH provider application, you authorize the insurance companies of your choice to access your information. They will then be able to access your information electronically, thus reducing the amount of paperwork that you need to send in. The CAQH application is very comprehensive and, thus, time-consuming to complete. It does not need to be completed in one sitting, but having access to the required information before you begin will make the process much faster for you. Also, be sure to download the Provider Quick Reference Guide and Frequently Asked Questions page to help you along the way. A few tips we suggest to help you complete this application are:

- Have your information handy before you begin.

- Don't complete it all in one sitting.

- Only complete the required fields. Skip the ones that are not marked required.

- Be sure to grant access to all providers so they don't need to individually request access and cause delays in the credentialing process.

Table 4–9. *Insurance Company Data Collection Sheet*

My NPI: _____   My EIN: _____

Insurance Company	Provider Line (Phone #)	Date	Name of Representative	Accepting Providers (Yes/No)	Application Process	Timeline	Follow-Up Steps	Notes

CAQH ProView Application Information Needed

- Educational background
- Employment history for the past 10 years
- Two professional references
- Identification numbers (e.g., NPI, ASHA license, state SLP license)
- Malpractice Insurance Policy Face Sheet

Step 3: Complete Required Documentation

If the insurance companies that you called to request information from send you an application, be sure to complete it and send it in as soon as possible. You do not want to cause any delays in an already lengthy process. Even though some information may still be redundant, having completed the CAQH application first should make this step in the process much easier. There may be certain pieces of information that are not applicable to you if your practice will not have clients visiting your office location. After you've completed the forms, be sure to make copies of everything before you submit them.

While the process may take upwards of six months or more to complete, you can start calling in to check on the status of your application after about 30 days. Then keep calling every couple of weeks to check in. If the insurance company gives you suggestions of when or how to follow up, be sure to make note of these and follow the instructions carefully. You should receive a welcome packet electronically or by postal mail. However, you may be credentialed before this arrives, so just be sure that you obtain the effective date when you call.

Step 4: Sign the Contract

Make sure that you thoroughly review your participating provider contract before you sign it. This may be the first time you are viewing the insurance company's reimbursement rates, as these are not publicly available. If the rates are lower than financially feasible for your business, you can try to negotiate the rates. Some insurance companies will be willing to negotiate, but others will not. For many commercial insurance companies, the rates are "per-session" and are not timed. This means that you will be reimbursed the same for a 30-minute session as you would be for a one-hour session. You will also receive a flat rate for assessments, no matter how long it takes to complete them. As we discussed earlier in this chapter, rates for assessments are typically not adequate compensation for the length of time it takes to complete the entire evaluation process from start to finish. However, many private practice owners look at assessments as long-term investments because you are able to generate future revenue if the client qualifies for services.

If insurance companies choose to classify or pay speech and language-related CPT codes on a per-unit basis, with a unit being equal to 15 minutes, you should consider whether this aligns with your service delivery model. In addition to determining whether the rates are acceptable, you also want to ensure that you can agree to the other terms of the contract. If you cannot, now is the time to walk away! You would think that signing the contract would signify that you are able to start submitting claims right away. However, some insurance companies will have an effective date set for a future date (e.g., in 30 days). Be sure to make note of this date. If the idea of going through the insurance credentialing process seems overwhelming to you, you can hire someone to do this for you. Be sure that you select a reputable credentialing service by requesting recommendations from other private practice SLPs.

Step 5: Submit Claims and Get Paid

You are officially an in-network provider! Congratulations! One of the major benefits of being in-network is that you will be listed in the provider directory. You can consider this "free" advertising, though you will spend many hours and months to get to this point. Most companies have electronic claims filing and you will need to ask how to access the website. This may take some additional processing time, though it is typically a matter of days instead of months.

One of the options for submitting claims and getting paid is to use a clearinghouse. A clearinghouse, in simple terms, is a portal in which you can receive electronic funds for services rendered, and/or you can receive information in terms of your patients' contact information and their eligibility of benefits within their insurance systems. For example, Blue Cross and Blue Shield of Illinois (BCBSIL) uses Availity. Once you become credentialed with Blue Cross and Blue Shield of Illinois, you will be issued login information to use Availity. Availity allows you to look up information related to your patient eligibility and what their tentative out-of-pocket cost may be for a visit or multiple visits, as well as serves as the portal to put in charges that will be conveyed to Blue Cross and Blue Shield of Illinois for the visits that you have rendered. After claims have been processed and (hopefully) paid by the insurance company, both the client and provider receive an Explanation of Benefits (EOB). This statement outlines the costs of the insured's health care services, lets you know whether a claim has been paid, and lists the patient's financial responsibility.

Many online telepractice platforms that also function as an electronic medical record (EMR) system already have billing to insurance included in their platforms, so signing up with a clearinghouse is something you may or may not need to do on your own. An EMR is also a great way to organize your client's information and manage your practice. All EMRs are HIPAA compliant, so you can protect your clients' protected health information (PHI). There are many EMR options, but not all of them cater to private practices for speech-language pathologists. If you are deciding on which EMR to use for your practice, you can usually get a free trial of 7 to 30 days. This allows you time to try out the features of the EMR and see if it will fit the needs of your practice. Here are some features to look for in an EMR:

> **Features to Look For in an EMR:**
>
> - Daily notes
> - Templates
> - Paperless intake
> - Claim submissions
> - File sharing
> - Secure messaging
> - Scheduling
> - Automated reminders
> - Billing

If you are just starting your practice, you may not see the need for an EMR until you build up your client base to justify the cost. An alternative is to use a local or cloud-based record-keeping option, as long as you are following necessary procedures to keep your clients' information secure. HIPAA basics will be covered in more detail in the next section. If you use Google Workspace, Google will provide a Business Associate Agreement (BAA) that enables you to use Google Forms, Google Docs, Google Sheets, and Google Drive. Many small private practice owners use this until their business grows. If you choose this method, you will still need a program to bill insurance.

While you have completed the credentialing process, this is likely only the beginning of a relationship between you and the insurance company. Be sure that you read all correspondence, document every phone call, and follow up in a timely manner. Staying organized and keeping thorough documentation will be the key to ensuring that all of your claims get paid. Some practices hire an in-house biller, or outsource to a billing company. Just be sure that you ask for recommendations before you take this step. You will also need to do a cost-benefit analysis to determine whether it makes sense for your business from a financial standpoint.

HIPAA BASICS

The Health Insurance Portability and Accountability Act (HIPAA) Rules provide federal protections for patient health information held by covered entities and business associates and give patients an array of rights with respect to that information (Office for Civil Rights, 2021). The Privacy Rule sets the standards for *who* may have access to PHI, while the Security Rule sets the standards for ensuring that only those who should have access to electronic protected health information (ePHI) will actually have access.

Privacy Rule

The Privacy Rule applies to any health care provider who transmits health information in electronic form in connection with certain transactions that are listed below (also known as a "covered entity"). The Privacy Rule protects all "individually identifiable health information" held or transmitted by a covered entity or its business associate, in any form or media, whether electronic, paper, or oral. The Privacy Rule calls this information "Protected Health Information" or PHI.

"Individually identifiable health information" is information, including demographic data, that relates to:

- the individual's past, present, or future physical or mental health or condition,

- the provision of health care to the individual, or

- the past, present, or future payment for the provision of health care to the individual,

and that identifies the individual or for which there is a reasonable basis to believe can be used to identify the individual." (Office for Civil Rights, 2021)

Individually identifiable health information includes many common identifiers, such as:

- Name

- Address

- Date of birth

- Social security number (Office for Civil Rights, 2021)

Security Rule

The Security Rule applies to electronic protected health information (ePHI). There are three parts to this rule:

1. **Administrative safeguards:** In general, these are the administrative functions that should be implemented to meet the security standards. These include

assignment or delegation of security responsibility to an individual and security training requirements.

2. **Physical safeguards:** In general, these are the mechanisms required to protect electronic systems, equipment, and the data they hold, from threats, environmental hazards, and unauthorized intrusion. They include restricting access to ePHI and retaining off-site computer backups.

3. **Technical safeguards:** In general, these are primarily the automated processes used to protect data and control access to data. They include using authentication controls to verify that the person signing onto a computer is authorized to access that ePHI, or encrypting and decrypting data as it is being stored and/or transmitted. (Office for Civil Rights, 2021)

Risk analysis is the first step in an organization's Security Rule compliance efforts. Risk analysis is also an ongoing process. The U.S. Department of Health and Human Services provides resources for organizations to complete this analysis, including a Security Risk Assessment Tool. The link is listed in the Resource List at the end of this book.

HIPAA for Telepractice Providers

If you are providing speech and language services via telepractice, the telepractice treatment session and all related information and documentation are subject to the Privacy Rule provisions, while the transmission of client information is protected by the Security Rule. To ensure the client's privacy, clinicians should:

- Consider the use of private networks during treatment sessions.

- Use encrypted videoconferencing software. (American Speech-Language-Hearing Association, n.d.-a)

To ensure that client data is securely transmitted, clinicians should:

- Consider using email encryption.

- Upload client information to a secure client portal if they are using an electronic medical record (EMR) system.

Privacy Policy

Additionally, you should *always* password protect your computers on which client information is stored. The ASHA website lists additional options for protecting ePHI. Every health care provider who electronically transmits health information in connection with certain transactions is a covered entity. These transactions include claims, benefit eligibility inquiries, and referral authorization requests. In other words, if you communicate with health insurance companies on a client's behalf, you are a "covered entity." If you are a covered entity, you need to provide your clients with a privacy policy and have them sign to acknowledge that they received it. There are many free online templates, including one from HHS.gov.

Business Associate Agreement

A BAA refers to a Business Associate Agreement. HIPAA rules state:

> If a covered entity engages a business associate to help it carry out its health care activities and functions, the covered entity must have a written business associate contract or another arrangement with the business associate that establishes specifically what the business associate has been engaged to do and requires the business associate to comply with the Rules' requirements to protect the privacy and security of protected health information (Office for Civil Rights, 2021).

A "business associate" is a person or entity that performs certain functions or activities that involve the use or disclosure of protected health information on behalf of or provides services to, a covered entity (Office for Civil Rights, 2021).

Examples related to services that telepractitioners may use include:

- Videoconferencing platform
- Electronic fax service
- Email provider (e.g., Google Workspace)

GROWING AND SCALING A PRIVATE PRACTICE TO ADD CLIENTS AND LOCATIONS

When you've established one brick-and-mortar location and then wish to expand, you need to revisit all of the steps when choosing what additional location and/or locations you may be interested in expanding to. For example, you will still need to make sure that there is accessibility, that it is an area where your target market will bring you a volume of clients, and that you will have the proper staffing to handle a second, third, or tenth location. Another consideration might be, instead of expanding physical locations, perhaps expanding into a different format. For instance, if you are currently serving clients within a physical brick-and-mortar space, you might expand your services to include teletherapy services, or you may start to expand by providing in-home or on-site services. In this way, you are growing and scaling, not with a replica of another brick-and-mortar space, but rather an expansion of the settings in which you provide services.

In Chapter 7, we discuss growing and scaling in more depth. As your practice continues to grow in terms of client volume, potentially hiring employees/contractors, and/or having collaborative business partnerships, you will want to ensure that your contracts, policies, and agreements continue to be aligned with the needs of your growing business. Refer to the *Contracting, Policies, and Procedures* section in Chapter 7 that takes a deeper dive into this topic.

SLP PRIVATE PRACTICE REGULATORY AND ADMINISTRATIVE MATTERS

In Chapter 2, we discussed all of the items to consider in terms of regulatory compliance when owning and operating a business. Again, it would be impossible to list all of the necessary documentation, certification, and registration legalities that are required state-by-state in the United States, let alone internationally. It is vital that you continue to check and recheck, keeping yourself updated on best business practices for your local area to ensure that you continue to be in regulatory compliance for your established business(es). As an SLP Entrepreneur and private practice owner, you not only need to consider the regulatory compliance of owning a small business, but now you also need to consider the regulatory compliance related to providing clinical services as a speech-language pathology business.

In addition to reviewing and maintaining all regulatory compliance efforts for an ongoing small business, you need to also be sure that your business is in compliance within the speech-language pathology professional field and industry. Considerations include: your license, (which will vary from state to state or internationally); your Certificate of Clinical Competence from ASHA (or similar equivalent in international cases); your school certifications (if your contracts with schools or educational organizations require it); your compliance measures for retaining your license in terms of continuing education credits and additional professional development courses (such as sexual harassment certification and ASHA's requirement for a course on ethics). You also need to consider that, if you are supervising students or a clinical fellow within your practice, you will need to complete professional development requirements related to supervision per ASHA's guidelines. These are "must haves" that are necessary when working as a clinical certified speech-language pathologist and, as such, you should have these regulatory pieces already in place even when working in the schools or within a health care setting. You will also most likely already have an NPI number, or your *National Provider Identification* number that is individually unique to you. As a private practice owner, who will have the potential to bill insurance and/or provide a *superbill* to private pay clients, you will also need to establish a *group NPI* number, which often serves as your "billing NPI number." The web address where this can be obtained is in the Resource List at the end of this book.

Another regulatory requirement that you will need to ensure you retain is your professional liability insurance. Within the United States, and as members of the American Speech-Language-Hearing Association (ASHA), we receive a professional discount from Mercer (Marsh) Pro Liability. This cost of professional liability/malpractice insurance is usually not significant, but it is necessary to protect yourself in case of legal disputes. Keep in mind that if you have registered yourself as a limited liability corporation (LLC), this may help protect your other assets outside of the business for instances of legal disagreement.

To maintain your contact information and provider information within insurance networks, you will regularly need to confirm that nothing has changed in terms of your business location, structure, services delivered, or managing business partners. You will typically get a reminder from the insurance company or from a service, such as Availity (clearinghouse to bill insurance) to confirm your credentials each quarter, or every 90 days. This is important for you to do so your practice can continue to be listed in the directory of in-network providers.

If you look at the checklist in Figure 4–7, we have kept all of the business regulatory compliance documents in the checklist that were shown in Chapter 2 initially, but have now added more regulatory compliance items that you should consider if owning and operating a traditional private practice. If you were to provide alternative services using your SLP expertise, such as business presentation skills training, these may or may not apply to you, depending on your state or local regulations. Additionally, if you are not providing clinical services, you will not be charging insurance companies and, therefore, the section on NPI and insurance credentialing through CAQH would not be pertinent to you. Again, remember this is a rough guide and each country, state, or province that you are practicing in might have additional requirements for you to consider when you are providing services.

Finally, a related compliance item to consider from your current or previous employer, if you have one, is a non-compete clause. If you are starting to establish your business while still working for another organization (school, hospital, private practice, etc.), you need to review any potential non-compete clauses that you may have agreed to when initially becoming an employee of that organization. For example, you may have signed a non-compete clause as a condition of your employment for another practice/business that indicates that for a given amount of time, you cannot market to or see a pediatric client within a certain radius. That is something that you will need to consider and adhere to, in order to avoid the risk of being out of compliance and having legal action brought against you or your business.

Once you have established a list of the registrations/certifications required to run your private practice, try to use a log such as the one provided in Figure 4–8 to help organize, document, and update when you earned the certification, when it is renewed and if you have renewed it for the year (or specified time period).

SLP PRIVATE PRACTICE
REGULATORY-ADMINISTRATIVE
CONSIDERATIONS

MUST HAVE:

*Not applicable for all situations

☐	Professional Liability Insurance
☐	Federal Tax Identification Number (EIN) // W-9 Form Annually
☐	Business Registration (e.g., LLC, Sole Proprietorship, Corporation, etc.)
☐	General Liability Insurance* (Brick & Mortar)
☐	Secure Payment System // HIPAA Compliant Billing/Payment System
☐	Secure/Privacy Compliant Method of Obtaining Signatures/Obtaining Confidential Information
☐	Website/Digital Media Regulatory/Compliance Regulations (e.g., Statement about use of Cookies, etc.)
☐	Any regulatory compliance for Grants/Loans received*
☐	State Professional License
☐	ASHA CCC (or International Equivalent)
☐	HIPAA Compliant Documentation System
☐	HIPAA Compliant Telehealth Conferencing Platform [Online/Telepractice] // Obtain BAA

Figure 4–7. *Regulatory-Administrative Matters for SLP Private Practice.* continues

SLP PRIVATE PRACTICE REGULATORY-ADMINISTRATIVE CONSIDERATIONS
(CONTINUED-PAGE 2)

	MUST HAVE:
☐	CAQH credentialing* [if credentialing with insurance]
☐	NPI Number (Individual)
☐	NPI Number (Group/Billing)* [will use this to bill if billing insurance]
☐	Continuing education credits for both state and national certification
☐	*Sexual Harassment Continuing Education Course
☐	*Ethics Continuing Education Course
☐	*Supervision Course (if planning on hosting Students for Clinical Placement Hours)
☐	*Any Continuing Education/Compliance Courses for Early Intervention, Local School District Requirements if contracting, etc.
☐	*Compliance/Continuing Education for Specialty clinical practice certifications/training (e.g., LSVT, PROMPT, DIR Floortime, etc.)
☐	
☐	
☐	

Figure 4–7. continues

SLP PRIVATE PRACTICE REGULATORY-ADMINISTRATIVE CONSIDERATIONS (CONTINUED-PAGE 3)

	NICE TO HAVE:
☐	Cyber-Security Liability Insurance
☐	Woman/Minority/Disabled/Veteran-owned enterprise certification specialties {Governmental or Private}
☐	General Liability Insurance* (Brick & Mortar)
☐	Specialty certifications/training or specialty area certification beyond professional certification (e.g., Diversity, Equity, & Inclusion; Leadership, etc.)
☐	
☐	
☐	
☐	
☐	
☐	
☐	

Figure 4–7. continued

SLP PRIVATE PRACTICE
REGULATORY-ADMINISTRATIVE
CONSIDERATIONS

Figure 4–8. Blank Template for Regulatory-Administrative Matters.

Keep this log handy at all times to add any additional certifications/documentation, and complete a log each year to keep track of whether you are updated on all requirements and renewals.

BUSINESS POLICIES AND PRACTICES

Before you open your doors to accept your first client, you will need to ensure that you have all of the necessary policies and procedures for your practice in place. The forms that you will need to create are standard, but the content will be based on the decisions that you've made for your business and what is legally acceptable in your state. Here is a list of forms that you will need to start your practice.

Private Practice Forms

- Client Case History Form
- Treatment Authorization Form
- Authorization for the Release of Information
- Cancellation Policy
- Payment Policy
- HIPAA Privacy Notice
- HIPAA Privacy Notice Acknowledgment
- Photo/Video Release (optional)

Client Case History Form: You will use this form to collect demographic and background information about your client. If you will serve both children and adults, you may opt to have two different forms.

Treatment Authorization Form: This is the form that your client or their parent/guardian must sign before you begin working with them. It grants you permission to evaluate or treat the client and informs the client of any potential risks of your treatment. If you are providing services via telepractice, you will need to make a specific form for Telehealth Treatment Authorization.

Authorization for the Release of Information: This is a form that you will have the client complete and sign to authorize you to share their medical information with other parties. For example, you may include the client's school SLP or primary care physician. You cannot discuss your client's condition without their consent.

Cancellation Policy: This outlines what happens in the event of client or clinician cancellation. Some practices will charge a cancellation fee if notification is not provided 24 hours in advance. This fee may be your full session rate or a portion thereof. It is up to you to decide what your cancellation policy will be for your practice.

Payment Policy: This should describe who bears financial responsibility for the client's services. You may choose to have separate policies for insurance clients and private pay if your practice will be accepting both. This also explains when payment is due (typically at the time of service) and how payments may be made. Do you do electronic billing? Do you accept credit card payments? Do you accept checks or money orders? Finally, what is the penalty for late payments?

HIPAA Privacy Notice and Acknowledgment: These are two separate forms. The notice outlines how client information is protected, and the acknowledgment is what you will have the client sign to acknowledge that they have received the privacy notice.

Photo/Video Release: If you will be taking photos or videos of your clients for promotional purposes, such as on your website or social media, you will need their written permission.

Good Faith Estimate (for self/private pay clients): Beginning January 1, 2022, under Section 2799B-6 of the Public Health Service Act, health care providers and health care facilities are required to provide a good faith estimate of expected charges for services to individuals who are not enrolled in a plan or coverage, or a Federal health care program (e.g., Medicare, Medicaid, etc.). The notice must be provided both orally and in writing, upon request, or at the time of scheduling services. The notice should be individualized for each patient and include the following information: patient name, contact information, diagnosis codes, and an estimated total cost for services. This information should be provided to new patients and current patients on an annual basis. To access customizable templates and learn more about the No Surprises Act, visit the Centers for Medicare and Medicaid Services (CMS). The website is in our Resources List at the end of the book.

While this list is not exhaustive, these are the forms that you will likely need before you accept your first client. As you establish and grow your practice, you may realize that you need to outline additional policies that are beyond the scope of the forms on this list. If you are using an EMR, there are often templates for the practice forms that you will need, which you can customize to suit your business needs. The best practice is to have your attorney review any forms that you will be using to ensure that they are in compliance with your state's laws and that they meet the needs of your private practice. Using The SLP Entrepreneur Business Model, review how a business framework for a traditional private practice may look in Figures 4–9 and 4–10. Then use the blank business model in Figure 4–11 to create your own business plan.

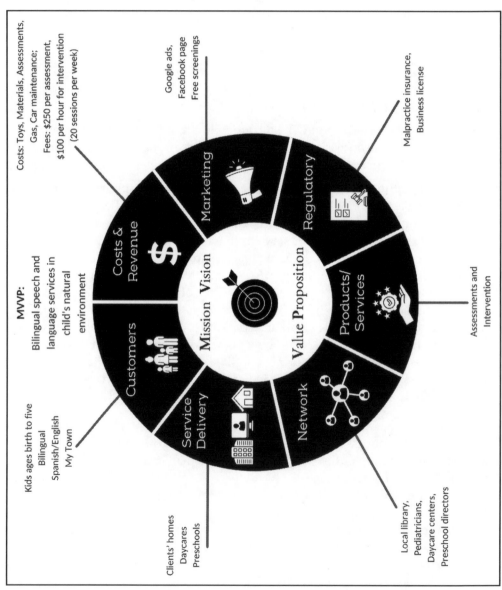

Figure 4–9. Sample Business Model for Pediatric Private Practice.

Costs: Toys, Materials, Assessments, Gas, Car maintenance;
Fees: $250 per assessment, $100 per hour for intervention (20 sessions per week)

Google ads, Facebook page Free screenings

Malpractice insurance, Business license

MVP:
Bilingual speech and language services in child's natural environment

Marketing

Regulatory

Costs & Revenue

$

Mission Vision

Value Proposition

Products/ Services

Customers

Service Delivery

Network

Assessments and Intervention

Kids ages birth to five Bilingual Spanish/English My Town

Clients' homes Daycares Preschools

Local library, Pediatricians, Daycare centers, Preschool directors

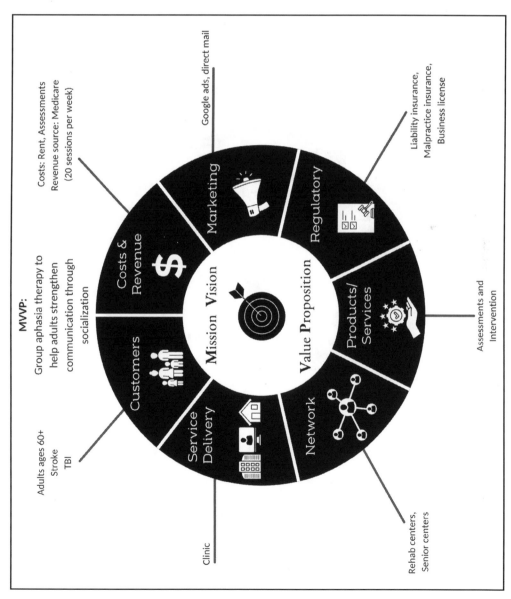

Figure 4–10. Sample Business Model for Adult Private Practice.

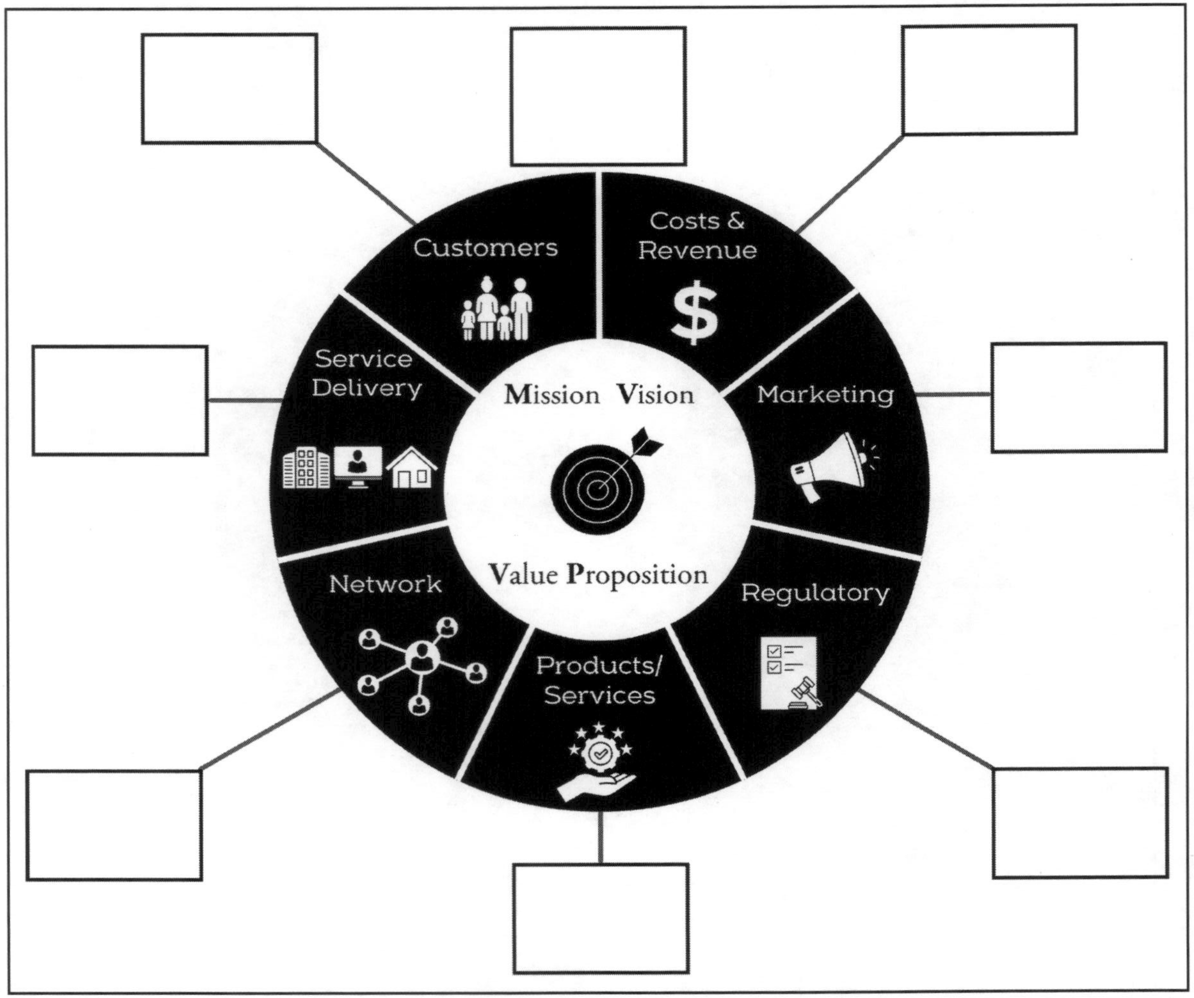

Figure 4–11. The SLP Entrepreneur Business Model Template.

120

CHAPTER CHECKLIST

☐ Determine what customers you will serve (Figure 4–2)

☐ Decide on your service delivery options

☐ Determine which payment sources you will accept

☐ Set your rates

☐ Write a letter to potential referral sources (e.g., physicians, schools)

☐ Determine your expenses

☐ Create your practice forms

☐ Complete your business model (Figure 4–11)

REFERENCES

American Marketing Association. (2017). *Definitions of marketing.* Retrieved September 30, 2021, from https://www.ama.org/the-definition-of-marketing-what-is-marketing/

American Medical Association. (n.d.). *CPT® Overview and Code Approval.* Retrieved August 11, 2021, from https://www.ama-assn.org/practice-management/cpt/cpt-overview-and-code-approval

American Speech-Language-Hearing Association. (n.d.-a). *HIPAA: Security rule: Frequently asked questions.* Retrieved July 8, 2021, from https://www.asha.org/practice/reimbursement/hipaa/securityrule/

American Speech-Language-Hearing Association. (n.d.-b). *Superbill templates for audiologists and speech-language pathologists.* Author. Retrieved August 8, 2021, from https://www.asha.org/practice/reimbursement/coding/superbill-templates-for-audiologists-and-speech-language-pathologists/

American Speech-Language-Hearing Association. (2020). *COVID-19 Tracker Survey Results May 2020.* Rockville, MD: Author.

Centers for Medicare and Medicaid Services. (n.d.). *ICD-10 resources.* Retrieved August 11, 2021, from https://www.cms.gov/Medicare/Coding/ICD10/ICD-10Resources

Cook County Clerk's Office. (n.d.). *Assumed Business Name Registration.* Cook County Clerk's Office. Retrieved September 8, 2021, from https://www.cookcountyclerkil.gov/

The County of DuPage, Wheaton, Illinois. (n.d.). *Assumed Business Names Registration.* DuPage County IL – County Clerk Home. Retrieved September 10, 2021, from https://www.dupageco.org/countyclerk/

Division of Revenue and Enterprise Services. (2020, October 27). *Getting Registered.* Official site of the State of New Jersey. Retrieved September 8, 2021, from https://www.state.nj.us/treasury/revenue/gettingregistered.shtml

Dotson, P. (2013, December). CPT® codes: What are they, why are they necessary, and how are they developed? *Advances in Wound Care.* Retrieved September 8, 2021, from https://www.ncbi.nlm.nih.gov/pmc/articles/PMC3865623/

Illinois Department of Commerce & Economic Opportunity. (n.d.). *Step by step guide.* Retrieved September 10, 2021 from https://www2.illinois.gov/dceo/SmallBizAssistance/BeginHere/Pages/StepByStepGuide.aspx

Internal Revenue Service. (n.d.-a). *Independent contractor (self-employed) or employee?* Retrieved September 18, 2021, from https://www.irs.gov/businesses/small-businesses-self-employed/independent-contractor-self-employed-or-employee

Internal Revenue Service. (n.d.-b). *Lesson 5 - Federal taxes when hiring employees or independent contractors.* [IRS Video Portal]. Retrieved August 18, 2021, from https://www.irsvideos.gov/SmallBusinessTaxpayer/virtualworkshop/Lesson6

McKenzie, A. S., & Bishop, A. M. (n.d.). *Outsourcing special education services.* AASA, The School Superintendents Association. Retrieved August 11, 2021, from https://www.aasa.org/SchoolAdministratorArticle.aspx?id=6940

nCred. (2018, November 15). *New to private practice and insurance billing?* National Credentialing Solutions. Retrieved August 11, 2021, from https://nationalcredentialing.com/how-do-i-get-credentialed-with-insurance-companies/

Office for Civil Rights. (2019, May 24). *Business Associates.* U.S. Department of Health and Human Services. Retrieved September 18, 2021, from https://www.hhs.gov/hipaa/for-professionals/privacy/guidance/business-associates/index.html

Office for Civil Rights. (2020, September 23). *The security rule.* U.S. Department of Health and Human Services. Retrieved September 8, 2021, from https://www.hhs.gov/hipaa/for-professionals/security/index.html

Office for Civil Rights. (2021). *The HIPAA Privacy Rule.* U.S. Department of Health and Human Services. Retrieved September 8, 2021, from https://www.hhs.gov/hipaa/for-professionals/privacy/index.html

Simon, B. (2019, February 15). *The quick guide to healthcare provider credentialing.* Smartsheet. Retrieved September 8, 2021, from https://www.smartsheet.com/medical-provider-credentialing-guide

U.S. Bureau of Labor Statistics. (2021, September 8). *Occupational outlook handbook. Speech-language pathologists.* Office of Occupational Statistics and Employment Projections. Retrieved September 20, 2021, from https://www.bls.gov/ooh/healthcare/speech-language-pathologists.htm

U.S. Small Business Administration. (n.d.). *Choose a business structure.* SBA. Retrieved November 30, 2021, from https://www.sba.gov/business-guide/launch-your-business/choose-business-structure

CHAPTER 5

Venturing Into Alternative Business Endeavors

Opportunities for Expansion and Creative Ways to Capitalize Your SLP Expertise

CORPORATE SPEECH PATHOLOGY (CORPORATE SLP)

KATIE SCHWARTZ MA, CCC-SLP

Director, Business Speech Improvement
www.businessspeechimprovement.com
Founder & President Emeritus, CORSPAN

Corporate Speech Pathology

combines the scientific and micro-skills of a speech-language pathologist with business communication. Communication drives business. Speech-language pathologists who are willing to expand their understanding of business language, and the business environment, and who are risk-takers find this to be an exciting sub-specialty.

We may work in areas such as public speaking, word-finding (due to lack of confidence), verbal networks, interpersonal communication with people who have different communication styles, and voice ergonomics.

We can translate these skills into many areas of business, such as working in call centers, sales communication, leadership communication, and communication between technical experts and their non-technical clients.

Speech-language pathologists who love variety and who want to believe that "the sky is the limit" would do well in corporate speech pathology.

The niche area of our field of that is referred to as Corporate Speech Pathology is growing. We did not put this type of service delivery in our previous chapters related to establishing a traditional private practice besides a mere mention because, while many of these elements of corporate speech pathology are listed in our scope of practice and can be included as a service offering in an established private practice, they are not clinically or developmentally/medically related communication challenges, and therefore should not be treated as such. It's important to know that as SLPs, we have a great deal of expertise and skillset that can be valuable to the mainstream professional or corporate world. Many SLPs that have not been exposed to corporate speech pathology service delivery either during their graduate clinical training or within previous places of employment choose to pursue further self-study and professional development in order to dive deeper into the technical nuances of these specialized services. Corporate speech pathology services include communication enhancement training or coaching, such as presentation skills, public speaking skills, accent modification/advanced pronunciation management, voice projection/vocal aesthetics training, and more. Many times, providing accent modification services seems to be the "easiest" or most relatable transition into offering corporate speech pathology services when initially pursuing expansion into this niche area of our field. The expansion into presentation skills or public speaking coaching seems to be another logical fit, and oftentimes is offered at the end of an accent modification training program, or a combined accent modification and presentation skills coaching program. Once established, corporate speech pathologists may choose to expand their practices of accent modification training and presentation skills coaching into offering other related services based on the needs of their clients. Related topics include interview coaching, professional writing guidance, leadership communication, executive presence coaching, cross-cultural/intercultural/interpersonal communication coaching, and cultural-linguistic diversity coaching and consulting. Many of these topics are related to our scope of practice; however, some of these potential coaching and consulting areas may take additional self-study and time to establish training programs for this particular niche market.

The potential market for this area is vast. There are several other non-SLP professionals that offer these types of services and have lucrative careers serving as trainers. Speech-language pathologists are uniquely positioned to serve as coaches/trainers in this capacity, given our broad knowledge base of speech-language-cognitive-communication systems, as well as our inherent ability to teach and train. One thing to delineate is that the clients that you serve as a corporate SLP/executive communication coach/leadership communication trainer are not individuals with medical/development/acquired communication disorders. These services are purely elective in nature and should be treated as such. In the United States, there is no insurance coverage for these types of training sessions, as you are not performing clinical speech-language pathology services. You are coaching/consulting/training, not treating. The individuals you serve are your clients/customers, not your patients. Therefore, SLPs that engage in corporate speech pathology service delivery have an ethical obligation to refer any individual that they suspect as having some sort of medically or developmentally related underlying clinical pathology to their communication patterns and function to a clinically-based SLP service.

Serving as a corporate speech pathologist is an interesting way to use your expertise as a speech-language pathologist in a non-clinical format. Our training and expertise as clinical SLPs allow us to broadly assess an individual's communication patterns, form a plan of areas to train with evidence-based methodologies to enhance functional communication, and modify goals/benchmarks as indicated. As we utilize that skillset in the corporate sector, we are uniquely positioned to provide this service as compared to professionals from other industries who offer similar corporate communication training services. Thus, being highly capable trainers and teachers, who are able to assess a situation or a communication challenge and plan accordingly, who know how to set short-term and long-term goals, who can modify their plan as a client progresses, and who know how to evaluate whether outcomes have been achieved, make us highly qualified, setting us apart from other professionals that do similar types of work in the corporate sector. This is an important distinction when establishing your value proposition for individuals or organizations related to corporate SLP services, as well as developing your framework for working with these individuals. Remember, these clients are typically successful in what they do, are typically high achievers in their field, and are motivated to enhance their effective communication practices in their professional lives. Here are some typical ways in which SLPs transition their skillset and expertise from clinical service delivery to corporate SLP services.

ROBERT MCKINNEY MA, CCC-SLP

CORSPAN President
www.CORSPAN.org

Author, Here's How to Do Accent Modification—
A Manual for Speech-Language Pathologists

Accent Modification

is a rewarding subfield that gives SLPs an opportunity to use their skills to help a highly motivated and engaging clientele. Learning to speak a new language involves acquiring its phonology, and, in most cases, direct instruction in the sounds and patterns of the spoken language is a part of the process. SLPs are highly trained communication specialists whose backgrounds are ideal for providing elective services to non-natives who wish to become more effective speakers. While this type of training is usually called "Pronunciation Instruction" by language teachers, SLPs commonly refer to it as "Accent Modification" because the unifying factor for their clients is that they speak with a non-native accent. However, services focus on intelligibility, naturalness, and other key factors that affect communication, and not the accent itself. Accents represent the beautiful linguistic diversity of our species, and over 25 years of research has shown that what makes someone sound different, the accent itself, can be separated from other factors which may interfere with communicative success. Several large studies have shown the benefits of these services, and clients report increased confidence, awareness, and proficiency. SLPs can also play a role in combatting the linguistic discrimination clients often face by counseling, promoting self-advocacy, and educating the community.

- **Accent Modification:** Accent modification is an elective training of segmental and suprasegmental pronunciation patterns with the goal of natural-sounding, clear, effective communication. Accent modification is typically the most direct and most natural transition when an SLP ventures from only clinical service delivery to offering corporate SLP services. Contrary to misconceptions, the goal of accent modification is NOT to eliminate an "accent" nor to make individuals all sound alike when speaking English. In stark contrast to that, SLPs work to provide accent modification services to *promote* diversity of talent and leadership and effective communication in the workplace. According to McKinney (2021), The SLP's role for accent modification training includes several aspects, including promoting *effective communication* (through training maintaining naturalness, working on intelligibility, and increasing communication confidence); *advocacy* (against linguistic discrimination), *raising awareness* (fostering self-learning, improved listening, and freedom of choice); *self-advocacy* (increasing confidence through role-playing); *counseling* (sets SLPs apart from other professionals that provide accent modification services, as we have counseling training as part of our graduate curriculum, as well as experiences in counseling patients within a clinical role); and *education* (for clients, communities, and peers).

- **Presentation Skills:** After engaging in further self-study and additional continuing education, SLPs can engage in coaching presentation skills to provide guidance on technical aspects of presentations (e.g., things such as clarity of speech, rate of speech, use of body language and gestures, voice projection and vocal variety [volume and intonation], eye contact/facial expressions, etc.), thought organization/thought cohesion, and storytelling skills.

- **Public Speaking/Business Communication/Communication Enhancement:** According to the ASHA Scope of Practice, SLPs may "Educate individuals about the importance of effective business communication, including oral, written, and interpersonal communication" (American Speech-Language-Hearing Association, 2016).

- **Leadership Communication/Executive Presence:** Given further self-study and professional development, SLPs may expand their business communication and presentation skills coaching to include specific coaching and consulting related to leadership communication/organizational communication/executive presence training.

- **Cross-Cultural/Intercultural Communication/Cultural-Linguistic Diversity Consultation:** SLPs with background knowledge and expertise and advanced self-study in the areas of linguistic/dialectal differences and cross-cultural/intercultural communication may expand their experiences and expertise and serve as a guide. Keep in mind that "diversity" does not necessarily only refer to aspects of a community based on race/ethnicity, and try to imagine SLPs as consultants/advisors for *communication* diversity. SLPs are well-positioned to be able to highlight facilitative communicative strategies and best practices within the workplace when communicating with a workforce that displays a variety of communication styles, abilities, dialects, and pragmatic functions, for example.

- **Interview Training:** SLPs can aid in interview preparation and increase confidence in clients through storytelling and thought organization coaching, as well as coaching through role-playing during "mock" interviews.

- **Professional Writing:** SLPs aid in the review of resumes, cover letters, essays, and professional documents, typically in conjunction with presentation skills/business communication/interview training services.

- **Professional Speaking Voice/Vocal Aesthetics:** SLPs can teach adequate voice projection, intonation, breath phrasing for increased vocal variety and clarity during presentations, as well as general vocal wellness techniques (not specific to any underlying clinical pathology).

ROBERT PORTNOY PhD, CCC-SLP, SHRM-SCP, CPLP

President & Chief Learning Officer, The Learn to Present Academy
www.LearnToPresent.com

"Presentation Skills are a business necessity.
   Presentation Skills Training is within speech-language pathologist's Scope of Practice.
   Presentation Skills Improvement can be guided with data and live coaching."

Speech-Language Pathologists

are uniquely qualified to design and deliver presentation skills training. Committed to professional standards, speech-language pathologists apply rigorous scientific, diagnostic, and treatment principles to help people speak clearly and effectively. And when barriers to effective communication signal underlying vocal pathology or other acoustically related medical problems, speech-language pathologists are the ones who can detect them and provide early intervention. Standing out among so many who offer presentation skills training, speech-language pathologists can be counted on as trusted and reliable communication experts.

When establishing a business, such as a clinical private practice, you have a general idea of where and who to market to. For example, there are schools, hospitals, physician's offices/medical clinics, parent groups, and if you are in-network and accept insurance, you will automatically be listed as a potential provider for people seeking these services. You also know which groups of SLPs to target your marketing efforts toward if your business offers teaching and training tools/apps/ products for speech-language pathologists to use in their clinical service delivery. However, when you are establishing a business in corporate speech pathology, your target markets are vast, and therefore potential customer groups are plentiful. This is an advantage, as there are multiple avenues in which we can utilize our skillset and expertise. However, it also creates an extra challenge and burden of focusing on a niche client market (that needs the communication enhancement services you are qualified and have expertise in providing) and executing marketing efforts toward that specific audience. While marketing, networking, and branding are important for any business, venturing into offering corporate SLP services will require a deeper marketing strategy and consistent networking efforts to gain a continuous and plentiful volume of clients.

ADVOCATE, ADVISOR, KEYNOTE SPEAKER

Now that you've established a good mission, vision, and value proposition for your intended business or private practice, it's a good time to revisit that MVVP. Also, revisit your overarching goals in terms of your professional mission and life aspirations. Keep your expertise in mind, and take inventory of all of your strengths and the potential value you could offer to different groups or different audiences, as we did in the Stakeholder Inventory-Speaking to Your Audience activity that we completed in Chapter 3. As speech-language pathologists, we have a wealth of information and expertise that could be very valuable for a multitude of individuals or community groups. For example, the global corporate world is now encouraging and embracing a more neurodiverse or neurodivergent workforce. If you have a skillset and expertise of working with individuals, especially adolescent or young adult individuals from the Autism/ADHD/Dyslexia communities, then who better to serve as an advisor or an expert consultant with an organization looking to increase their neurodiverse population of professionals? You are uniquely positioned to: help advise organizations and facilitate best inclusive and accessible communication practices within the workplace; perceive potential obstacles when selecting talent based on "traditional" in-person/video interviews; and possibly help to onboard those Neurodiverse professionals in getting situated within their new roles and responsibilities.

Other potential examples include:

- If you are someone that has worked with stroke or brain injury patients, you may serve as an advocate or have keynote speaking engagements about brain health, or advise organizations on the most accessible and facilitative communication practices within the workplace.

- If you are someone that is well versed in bilingual speech and language development or multilingual speech and language development, you may offer seminars for Pediatrician professional organizations or publications.

- If you are an Accent Modification/Advanced Pronunciation Training specialist, you may have speaking engagements and/or training workshops for organizations about promoting linguistic diversity and effective communication practices, including listener training workshops.

- If you are a fluency specialist, you may perform speaking engagements and workshops for organizations to advocate for inclusive workplaces that build awareness around fluency disorders and the stuttering community.

- If you have expertise in providing gender-affirming voice training, including having a deep understanding of the cultural-social-emotional aspects of individuals that you serve in this capacity, you might provide corporate training and consultancy to organizations to help educate and build awareness and acceptance of this community in professional settings.

- If you have expertise in augmentative and alternative communication (AAC), who better to serve as an advisor to local community park districts and/or governmental infrastructure agencies on having accessible communication available in parks/playgrounds and other public places?

You are that person who can advise and help establish more effective communication practices and awareness amongst the general public. Our knowledge base and experiences hold great value or potential value for other outside organizations. In order to engage in these types of activities as an alternate revenue stream, you need to explore opportunities and build connections through networking. If there are no opportunities visible to you, then you can create opportunities by highlighting your area of expertise and advocacy on your digital media pages. Perhaps offer to do a free talk about the subject and gain connections and potential leads from the audience that was interested enough to attend. If it's something that you want to build into a profitable alternative revenue stream while still accomplishing goals towards your mission, write down topics that you are passionate about, list them on your website in terms of workshops, advocacy engagements, or keynote speaking engagements that you are available for. This will help broaden the scope of acceptance, inclusivity, and functional gains for these specialized populations that you know very well how to work with. These engagements can come in the way of in-person speaking engagements, workshops, virtual webinars, meetings as an advisor with organizations, serving as a guest speaker on a podcast, writing related content on your own blog, serving as a guest post in a magazine, or writing an article for open op-ed opportunities.

Think outside the box and do not underestimate the value of your skills and expertise as an SLP. Now, as an SLP Entrepreneur, you also offer the perspective of a small business owner. You may also be well-versed within the educational or health care system, depending on where your current position is, and that offers you opportunities to share your perspective and experiences as an employee, a small business owner, or even as a consumer of services.

TRAINING OTHER SLPS

Do you have an area of expertise? Is there something that you are passionate about that you can teach others how to do? Then you can consider training other SLPs as part of or as your entire business. Training can take many forms, including hosting in-person trainings, live or recorded webinars, and even online courses.

Ways to Train Other SLPs

- In-person training
- Live webinars
- Prerecorded webinars
- Online courses

Regardless of which method you choose, the key is to first determine your niche. Will you teach topics related to pediatric school-based services, aphasia, or AAC? If you have a few specialty areas, consider conducting some market research to find out which topics are most in demand. You can search the CEU database on ASHA's website, or go directly to online CEU providers' websites to see what types of courses are being offered and how popular they are. If you already have a community of SLPs or are active on social media, those are also great places to start conducting your research. When surveying potential customers, consider asking questions such as:

- What are your professional goals?

- What is your biggest obstacle to you reaching your goals?

- What have you tried in the past?

- How can I help you facilitate these specific things in your practice?

From there, you can create a shared document in your Google Drive that outlines your course curriculum and involve your community in the course creation process by getting their feedback during the entire process.

Once you have selected your niche, you can then decide on the best way to conduct the training. If you are going to host your courses or webinars online, you will need to select a site to host them. There are many options for hosting online courses. The difference between courses and webinars is that courses can have a combination of different media types (e.g., text, downloads, video, and audio). You may provide assignments to your enrolled students or have specific milestones that you want them to meet along the way. In that way, courses provide much more flexibility. Webinars are timed and more structured, but you can decide whether you'd like to prerecord the webinar or present it live. The differences between webinars and online courses are provided in Table 5–1.

Table 5–1. *Webinar and Online Course Comparison Chart*

Feature	Live Webinar	Online Course
Live vs. On Demand	Live	On Demand
Interactive	Question and Answer	Worksheets, "homework" assignments
Access to instructor	Yes, if there is time	Offline
Timeline	Short (1 to 2 hours)	Can extend months (4 to 6 weeks)

Online Courses

According to an article written by Paul in 2021, the projected growth for the online learning industry went from $170 billion in 2017 to $350 billion in 2022. This makes online courses an excellent way to earn passive income. The initial work of creating the course may take days, weeks, or even months. However, after you've created a course, you can continue selling it for years to come, which is known as "evergreen" content. With online courses, you can update information as needed over time, and you can add interactive components to communicate with your students.

If you are going to create online courses, you will want to choose a place to house your courses. Think of it as a virtual classroom. This is where you will be delivering the content to your "students," so it needs to have all of the necessary supplies. The features that you will want in your course creation platform will vary based on how interactive and how long your online course will be. Figure 5–1 shows some of the basic features that you should look for when choosing a host for your online courses:

- **Unlimited courses:** While you may select a niche for your online courses, you will likely want to create more than one course. If you want this to become a lucrative business opportunity, you may create several courses within the same content area. Therefore, you want to select a course creation platform that will allow room for you to grow and expand.

- **Unlimited students:** As you plan for your current and future success, you do not want your growth to be inhibited by your course creation platform. Make sure that you choose a platform that has plan options that allow you to have unlimited students enroll in your courses. Some platforms will have free options that are fine for when you are just getting started. It is easy to upgrade your plan later—what is not easy is switching platforms. Save your future, successful self some undue stress by choosing a platform that will support your growth.

- **Multiple content types:** One of the major differences between a webinar and an online course is the opportunity to have your students engaged and actively participating to obtain a given outcome over a period of time. Instead of just listening (or watching) a recording, you can use a variety of media types, such as text, audio, video, and downloads.

- **Student progress tracking:** You may wish to track your students' progress, especially if you will be awarding completion certificates. Progress can include seeing which lessons have been completed or how much of a course has been completed, expressed as a percentage. This also gives you an opportunity to identify students who may not have started your course or who need a little extra support.

- **Completion certificates:** Whether or not you are going to become an ASHA-approved CEU provider, your students will want some

ONLINE COURSE CREATION CHECKLIST

☐	Unlimited courses
☐	Unlimited students
☐	Multiple content types
☐	Student progress tracking
☐	Completion certificates
☐	Graded quizzes
☐	Drip content
☐	Student comments
☐	Email integration
☐	Affiliate marketing

Figure 5–1. *Online Course Creation Platform Checklist.*

documentation that shows they have completed your course. This can be in the form of a completion certificate that is automatically awarded upon completion of your course (which is where tracking student progress and completion comes in handy).

- **Graded quizzes:** If you are going to become an ASHA-approved CEU provider, course evaluations are mandatory. Even if you do not need the official documentation to submit to ASHA, graded quizzes are a great way to check that your learning objectives have been addressed and that students have grasped the most important concepts in your course. If graded quizzes are not included in your course creation platform, you can still accomplish this through other programs, such as Google Forms or Survey Monkey.

- **Drip content:** This feature allows you to release course content one lesson at a time on a predetermined schedule. This is perfect for online courses that have a specified start and end date, or for those that will extend over a period of weeks. For example, if you have a four-week course, you can schedule a new lesson to be released each week, regardless of which date the student purchases the course.

- **Student comments:** When you do not have the benefit of a live webinar, you still want to provide your students with a way to communicate with you to ask questions and receive support. There are a number of ways to do this. You can provide students with your email address, create a private Facebook Group, or enable comments directly within your course. The benefit of allowing comments directly in the course is that students can ask their questions as they arise, instead of needing to remember to do it later. This enhances the student experience. Whichever method you choose, be sure to respond promptly to student questions (within 24 hours is ideal).

- **Email integration:** There are a couple of ways in which you can have email integrated into your course creation software. In the first option, you have the ability to email students directly from your course instead of using your email account. In the second option, you are able to link your email provider (e.g., Mailchimp, Constant Contact, etc.) into your course creation software. When someone enrolls in one of your courses, they are then added to the email list of your third-party account. Both of these options are useful, and you should look for at least the first option when selecting your course creation software.

- **Affiliate marketing:** An affiliate marketing program is a great way to grow your business. You will see this term again when we discuss blogging later in this chapter. However, if you are a course creator, you are on the other side of the affiliate marketing program. You can choose who you would like to be an affiliate for your courses, and they can drive more traffic and sales on your behalf. If you select an online course creation software with a built-in affiliate program, they will handle all of the reporting and pay your affiliates automatically.

Now that you know what features to look for in online course creation software, you may be interested in knowing which options are available. With the recent explosion of the online course market, there are many companies at work building their own course hosting platforms. A few of the most popular hosting options as of the date of this publication are Teachable, Thinkific, Kajabi, and Podia. These sites are built for delivering online content in a user-friendly way. They are also highly automated, which minimizes the manual work that you need to do, yielding the most potential for passive income. While you are responsible for creating all of the course content, including sales pages and curriculum, these platforms do the heavy lifting in terms of checkout, sending automated emails, and delivering the course content at your predetermined schedule.

If you are new to creating courses and want to get started by offering a free course, this will allow you to test the waters before you launch your first paid course. Any of the quality course creation platforms offer free training and support to their course creators. You should learn all that you can about the platform of your choice by taking advantage of the live and recorded training options. Also consider joining their online community, which may be directly on their website or in a private Facebook Group.

Webinars

Another option for training other professionals is to host live webinars. As mentioned earlier in the chapter, there are some differences between online courses and webinars. You can choose to host live webinars (in real-time) or prerecord webinars for participants to view later. The second option is considered an on-demand webinar. Another popular option is to host a live webinar and also record it for people to purchase on-demand. This way, you are maximizing your time and offering an alternative for those customers who may not be available at the scheduled time of your live webinar.

If you are going to present live or prerecorded webinars, you can sell them directly on your own blog or website. Another option is to record a webinar for a well-known company, such as Northern Speech Services or SpeechPathology.com. This is a great option for people who do not already have a large following and want to increase brand exposure. One major advantage of hosting your webinar on another platform is that you do not have to worry about upfront costs, such as website development, website hosting, and marketing. One of the major disadvantages is that you do not get to keep all of the profits earned from the sale of your webinars. However, with the potential for a larger audience reach, the benefits may outweigh the costs for you. The pros and cons of hosting on your own website are listed in Table 5–2.

Online Community Groups

Facebook groups have been growing in popularity over the last few years. In fact, a report from NYU's The Governance Lab (2021) found that 1.8 billion people use Facebook Groups every month. Additionally, more than half of all users are in five or more groups. Consider which Facebook Groups you belong to. What value do you derive from those groups? Is there a gap that you can fill that will align with your

Table 5–2. *Pros and Cons of Self-Hosting Webinars*

Pros	Cons
Maximize profit	Limited audience reach
Instant payouts	High up-front costs
Control over content	Responsible for marketing
Set your own price	
Generate email list	

niche and your passion? If you create a Group where you are deemed the "expert," that is another way for people to begin to know, like, and trust you. Those are the people who will eventually buy from you. Additionally, you can use the Group to drive traffic to your website, products, and services. Keep in mind that a Facebook Group does not equal an email list. No matter how many people are members of your Group, if Facebook crashes, you will have no way of reaching your Group members. Therefore, the key is to also find a way to obtain the contact information from members of your Group so you "own" the mailing list and can contact them in another way of your choice at any time.

Once you have established a Facebook Group, you will need to spread the word so people will actually join your Group. There are a number of ways to do this, which are listed in the box below.

Ways to Grow Your Facebook Group

- Post the link to your Group in other Groups
- Email the link to your Group to your email list
- Email the link to your Group to colleagues
- Invite Facebook friends to join your Group directly

Once you've established your online community, you will need to set the rules of engagement. If you are the only administrator, manually approving members can become quite tedious. However, you can set a list of criteria that will enable automatic member approval. After you've determined membership criteria, you will want to make sure that your rules are clear and easy to locate. Pinning the rules as an announcement at the top of your group page is a great way to achieve this. Some examples of group rules outline who can post, what they can post, and how often they can post. For example, do you want the administrator (you) to review every post before it is made public? Are people able to promote their own products and services? How often are members allowed to self-promote? All of these rules will set the stage for how much open discussion you want in your group and how much time you will need to invest in moderating the group.

After you've determined membership criteria and rules, you will need to create a plan for keeping your members engaged. Some ways to boost engagement are by regularly posting relevant content, giving away free resources, hosting Facebook Live broadcasts, and running contests, challenges, or giveaways. Managing an online community can become very time-consuming for a solo entrepreneur, so enlisting help from a digital marketing firm or virtual assistant can definitely help your efforts. Before you make the decision to hire someone to help manage your online community, however, consider whether the benefits outweigh the costs.

> **Ways to Boost Engagement in an Online Community**
> - Regularly post relevant content
> - Give away free resources
> - Host Facebook, Instagram, or LinkedIn Live events
> - Run contests, challenges, or giveaways

COLLABORATION

Collaborating with other professionals can be of great benefit to you and your collaborative partner's respective businesses. You may even decide to venture into business with another partner from the start and build it together. Beyond the potential benefit in the way of revenue or market exposure for the collaborative partners' businesses, collaborating on a project can be personally satisfying. Many times, being a solopreneur can get a bit "lonely" when new learning, decision-making, risk-taking, and success-celebrating happens by yourself. It is important to broaden your community and network to allow for you to share your questions, challenges, and successes with other SLP and non-SLP entrepreneurs, but engaging with others to collaborate on a project or business venture together can be exhilarating, allowing for a personal and professional return on investment.

Whether you decide to collaborate with a fellow SLP or another related professional, such as an occupational therapist, physical therapist, or someone from a less-related field, it is always a vital step to make sure that roles, responsibilities, and rights of your collaboration are delineated in detail. It is important that a framework for working together (or if you choose to end your working relationship together for any reason) is set, regardless of whether you have a personal relationship with that individual/entity. It is also important to know what your own strengths and areas of needed improvement and/or less preferred tasks are when joining a collaboration or partnership. Open and consistent communication are key to a healthy and profitable relationship and partnership. Many of the SLP Entrepreneurs that we've highlighted in Chapter 8 demonstrate the value of collaboration with other SLPs or related professionals for their business.

> **"**
> **If we weren't on the same page, we knew we couldn't move forward with teaming together. We have a relationship based on trust and full communication.**
>
> *Rene Robles*
> *Five Oaks Speech Therapy Services* **"**

A large consideration when collaborating with others is defining or assigning what your typical working and communication styles are *at the initiation* of working together. This can sometimes become tricky if you are working with someone who you are socially friendly with and then decide to collaborate with them on a professional project. Make sure that you help yourselves by clearly defining roles and workflow expectations together. You will always need to be a bit flexible, but also be aware of when your colleague or partner is not contributing what was expected or promised, and be upfront and communicate openly about it. If you don't, it could spiral into an unsuccessful and/or unfinished project that you're collaborating on and/or create undue stress. Furthermore, if this type of interaction is not fully transparent, and therefore leads to miscommunication and misunderstandings, it can leave you feeling neither fulfilled about your collaborative project nor positive about your interaction/relationship. Keep in mind that the same holds true when a family member or close friend chooses to help you, or you choose to go into business with them, seek advice from them, or ask someone who you already have a personal relationship with to complete tasks for you. You still need to be open to feedback and difficult conversations, honest, and consistently transparent about communicating, setting boundaries, and managing expectations on both ends. You must recognize and delineate between your business interactions and your social/personal relationship.

Beyond the communication and decision-making aspects of the business relationship between you and your collaborative partner, finding the right tools to efficiently communicate and keep you on track with your collaborative project(s) is another important aspect that requires some planning and decision-making. Given the advances in digital technologies, there is a wide array of tools that you can use to connect and collaborate with colleagues/partners on projects, regardless of whether you are in the same physical location. In addition to communicating via phone, email, and/or video conference, you need to decide which tools are most accessible and best serve your needs in accomplishing tasks related to your collaborative project. In the following section, we have highlighted some tools that are effective for collaborating, including Google Drive, Google Forms, Trello, and Canva.

- **Google Drive:** This can be used to collaborate on content in a shared folder. Changes are made in real-time, which eliminates the need for sending email attachments. Any file type can be uploaded into Google Drive, and you can also create documents directly in Google Drive using Google Docs (comparable to Microsoft Word), Google Sheets (comparable to Microsoft Excel), and Google Slides (comparable to Microsoft PowerPoint). These allow you to view changes that your partner may be making to a document in "real-time" as you are talking over the phone or having a video conference and simultaneously looking at the document in the Google Drive. You can also make edits and comments on any documents that you've created and assign tasks to each collaborator. In Google Docs, there are highlights for action items that are pending, as well as threads of specific comments/tasks that need to be completed. Dropbox is another option for sharing content, and like Google Drive, an efficient way to share large files, though the free version does not have the depth of collaborative features like Google offers, as of the writing of this book.

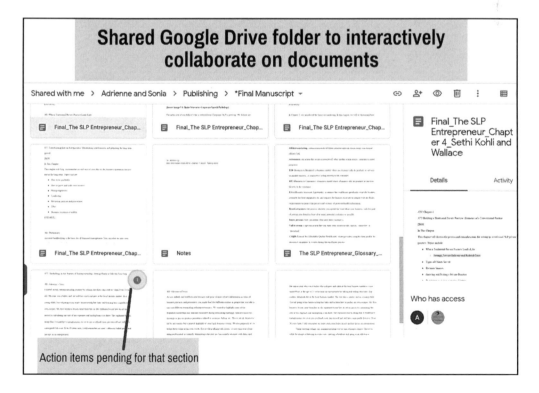

- **Google Forms:** This can be used to send feedback forms or surveys, just as you would use SurveyMonkey or Doodle Poll. This can also be used to gather information from potential clients and customers, even if you are not working on a business collaboration. However, when you are collaborating with a business partner, it updates the results of your surveys in real time, which also allows everyone to have access to the same information at all times. It allows you to view your results collectively (all responses for one specific question), or you can view each respondent's individual responses for all questions.

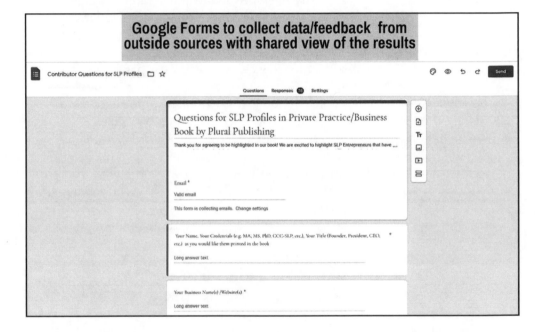

- **Trello:** This helps with managing your project by showing you a broad view of all of the tasks left to do for a collaborative project. You can invite multiple collaborative partners to have access to the project board and assign specific tasks accordingly. Once tasks are done, you can "close" them so the board reflects a visual representation of what is still pending.

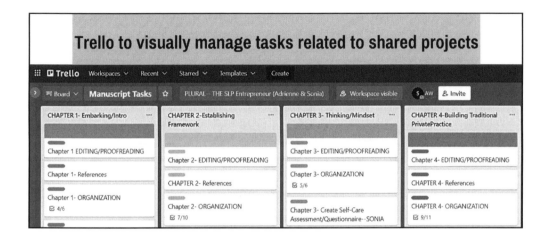

- **Canva:** Though this is not only for collaborative projects, Canva is a useful tool for collaborating on creative and design projects. With Canva, you have the potential to create virtually any creative design visual project that you need for your business, such as logos, graphics, worksheets, and marketing materials (digital or print). It also has an option to "share," which makes it easy to collaborate and make changes to each other's work in real-time as needed.

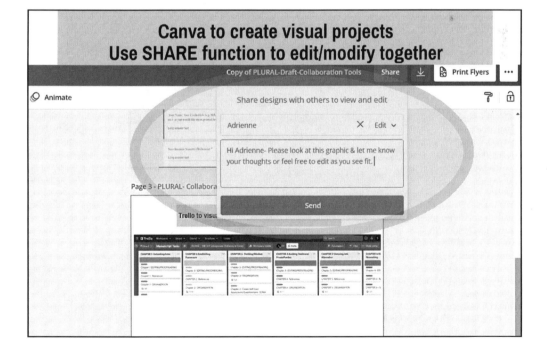

We chose to mention and share the above collaborative tools, as these are the specific tools that *we* have found to be the most helpful during our collaborative projects. However, please remember that there are many other tools available, which are very similar to the ones we've listed. As such, it is important to do your own research and communicate with your partner(s) to discover which tools may be the most beneficial and user-friendly options for *your* collaborative projects.

> **66**
> **I have been able to meet so many wonderful professionals, whether through collaborative projects or as clients, that my business really doesn't feel like work.**
>
> *Ann M. Pannell*
> *Clarity Speech Coaching* **99**

BLOGGING

According to the Hosting Tribunal, there are over 600 million blogs worldwide. The first well-known blog was created in 1994. Though many bloggers start blogging as a hobby, about 10% of bloggers make over $10,000 per year. Many bloggers boast six-figure sales annually, and the top .06% of bloggers earn over $1 million per year (Ch., 2021). Why do people choose to start blogging? It is no longer just a "hobby," but blogging can be a legitimate business, with many ways to earn revenue. Remember our business model from Chapter 2? Some of the revenue sources from blogging are listed below.

> **Five Ways to Earn Money as a Blogger**
>
> 1. Paid advertisements
> 2. Affiliate marketing
> 3. Sponsorships
> 4. Selling products
> 5. Selling services related to your niche

Paid Advertisements

One of the most popular ways to earn revenue for a blog is to use display ads by enrolling in an ad network, such as Google AdSense or Mediavine. You earn revenue when users view, click, and/or make a purchase through the ads. The main benefit of joining an ad network is that it is an easy way to earn passive income from your blog. The word "easy" does not equal lucrative. Though there is minimal effort on your part after the initial setup, you need to have a large enough audience for paid ads to be a major source of income for your blog. If you are interested in running display ads, you will need to make sure that it is compatible with your website host.

There are several disadvantages to posting ads on your blog through an ad network. For starters, some people do not like the aesthetics of paid ads. These tend to clutter your blog if not carefully placed. Though this may impair the user experience for your readers, ads are common on most websites that you may visit. Another downside to joining an ad network is that most programs require a minimum number of page views or "blog sessions" per month to qualify. This means that ads will not be an option for you when you are just starting out, but it is definitely a goal to aim for as your number of site visitors grows. For example, Mediavine increased its minimum number of blog sessions from 25,000 to 50,000 views for the previous 30 days (as of 2020), whereas Monumetric requires 10,000 monthly views. While you will need to drive traffic to your website in order to qualify for these programs, there are other ways to earn income from your blog until that milestone is reached.

Affiliate Marketing

If you join an affiliate program, you receive a commission when someone takes an action using your unique affiliate link. Some affiliate programs pay commissions simply for clicks, some for sign-ups, and others for purchases. One of the most popular affiliate programs is the Amazon Associates Program. This is likely due to the ease with which you can join the program and the wide variety of products that you can promote through the program. Additionally, you receive a commission for any product that is purchased through your affiliate link, not just the products that you directly link to.

Affiliate programs require little effort to earn revenue for your blog. It is as simple as sharing your affiliate link in your blog posts, social media, or emails, people clicking on your link, and you getting paid a commission if there is some action resulting from that click. Amazon reduced their commissions paid to their affiliates in 2020, with their current commissions ranging from 1% to 10%. To protect yourself from future commission cuts and maximize your earning potential, you can consider contacting brands directly to inquire about joining their affiliate program. Your earning potential will depend on the size of your audience and how much traffic you're able to drive to your blog. More traffic = more clicks = more commission.

Sponsorships

A sponsorship is when a company pays you to represent their product, talk about it, and promote it to your readers. Though this sounds similar to affiliate marketing, sponsored posts are paid a flat rate instead of a commission. Therefore, your revenue is not dependent on blog traffic, though qualifying for a sponsorship may be. Sponsorships are an attempt to promote brand awareness through one or a combination of the following methods: articles, videos, email marketing, and more. Brands select sponsors who align with their values and who they think will represent their brand well. Think about Nike and Gatorade's sponsorship of athletes. These are ideal pairings because the target market of Nike and Gatorade are athletes, and the audience of the NFL and NBA (for example) are athletes and their fans.

Even though brands such as Nike or Gatorade may not align with your niche, think about which brands appeal to your target audience and which brands they are likely to buy. To obtain a sponsored post, you will have to demonstrate who your audience is, including their demographics, and demonstrate that your blog is a good fit for the brand. An easy way to start is to join a sponsored post network or to contact brands directly. You should charge a flat rate for your sponsored posts. For example, you may charge $250 when you are just starting out. However, when your blog takes off and your number of site visitors is exponentially higher, you may be charging upwards of $1,000 to $2,500 per sponsored post.

Selling Products

While ads, affiliate marketing, and sponsorships are all viable sources of revenue for your blog, they all have one thing in common—you are promoting someone else's products. When promoting another brand's products, you can only earn a commission from that company, which is a small fraction of the revenue that your referrals actually bring to the company. Think about display ads, where each impression or click may only earn you a fraction of a penny on the dollar. An impression is the number of times a piece of content is viewed. This does not mean that someone has clicked on the content, but simply that it has appeared on their screen. According to Paulson (2016), in less lucrative niches, you may be able to earn $3.00 to $10.00 for every 1,000 people that visit your website compared to $25.00 to $40.00 for every 1,000 people that visit your website in more lucrative niches. Let's say you have an ad that earns $10 for 1,000 impressions. In this example, you earn $0.01 per impression, but it may earn the company $30 when a sale is made. If your conversion rate is 1%, you would have potentially made 10 sales of the product for that company, which equals $300 in revenue ($30 × 10) for *their business*. Instead, you only earned just over 3% of the revenue for that product ($10 ÷ $300 = 3.33%).

What if that was *your own* product that received the click and resulted in a sale for *your* product? Let's say you have a $30 digital product listed for sale on your blog that *you* created, such as an e-book or downloadable worksheet bundle—you not only *earn* $30, but you *keep* all of the revenue ($30 × 10 = $300)! In this example, digital products have the lowest costs to produce, but will yield you the highest profit. You can consider selling physical products instead, like mugs or t-shirts, but your cost of goods sold will be much higher. Let's use a t-shirt as an example. You sell your own brand's t-shirts for $30. After the costs to make, package, and ship the shirt, you may end up with a $10 profit for one shirt ($10 × 10 = $100). While that is still much higher than the $10 in the display ad example, it is significantly less than the profit from the digital product example. Though there are costs associated with creating your digital products, they are much lower than the costs of physical goods. This is an important consideration to keep in mind when deciding which types of products to sell.

Selling Services Related to Your Niche

We've restated the importance of having a niche for your business, whether you are developing online courses or starting a blog. An additional revenue source for your blog can come from selling your services related to that niche. Let's say that you've started a blog about AAC for pediatric clients. If you want to earn additional revenue, you can sell your consulting services to school districts. You start by using your blog posts to position yourself as an expert in this area, and then use your blog as a way for school districts to contact you to purchase your consulting services. In Table 5–3, we summarize the various blog revenue sources.

Table 5–3. *Blogging Revenue Comparison Chart*

	Display Ads	**Affiliate Marketing**	**Sponsor-ships**	**Selling Products**	**Selling Services**
Set up requirements	Ad network	Affiliate program	You seek sponsors	You create products	You create packages
Maintenance requirements	None	Write blog posts, post links	Write blog posts, create demo videos	Automated sales funnel	Self-promotion
Reader requirements	10K or more	None	None	None	None
Revenue	$3 to $40 per 1,000 site visits	1% to 30% of the product price	Flat rate $250 to $2,500	30% (physical products) 100% (digital products)	100% of your hourly rate or consulting fees

If you've decided that blogging is the route you'd like to pursue, you need to decide on your niche. Let's revisit *The SLP Entrepreneur Business Model* from Chapter 2. You have to determine who your ideal customers are (in this case, your ideal readers). What are their pain points, and how are you going to solve them? Your readers need to be at the forefront of your mind before you sit down to begin to write. Once again, you can conduct some market research to find out what people are struggling with and what they are looking for.

Begin by thinking about your areas of expertise, then find out what already exists related to your niche. What gaps are there? What could you add to the existing market? For example, if your specialty is AAC, and there is already a popular AAC blogger, do not be discouraged. This demonstrates that there is a demand for that topic. You can also think about what is missing from that blog or what you might do differently. Regardless of whether there are two or two hundred blogs in your area of expertise, there is only one you. This means that your writing style and your perspective will be different from any of your competitors. Another benefit of having other bloggers in your niche is that you can collaborate with other bloggers, which can help drive traffic to each of your websites.

As with any business, what you put into it is what you will get out of it. You cannot write one post a year and expect to rake in tens of thousands of dollars. In fact, most blogging experts suggest that you don't even launch your blog until you have at least 10 posts written. Once you have started your blog, you need to keep it updated with new, relevant content to keep your readers interested and coming back for more. QuickSprout has a list of 35 ideas for blog topics, which includes guides, frequently asked questions, interviews, personal stories, and best-of lists (QuickSprout, 2021).

Blog Topics

- Guides (e.g., How-to, Beginner, Ultimate)
- Frequently Asked Questions
- Interviews
- Stories
- Best-ofs

BECOMING A CONTENT CREATOR

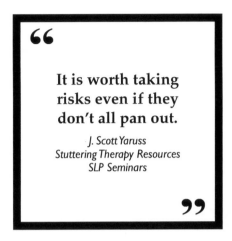

> **It is worth taking risks even if they don't all pan out.**
>
> J. Scott Yaruss
> Stuttering Therapy Resources
> SLP Seminars

Another way to use your expertise as an SLP is to create and sell content. It's hard to find an SLP who has never created an activity or resource to use with their clients. Whether it's customizing flashcards, creating a flowchart, or putting together PowerPoint/Google Slides, SLPs tend to be creators by nature. Recently there have been online marketplaces that enable SLPs and other content creators to share and sell their content to others. Teachers Pay Teachers and Boom Learning are two of the most popular sites as of the writing of this book. Teachers Pay Teachers was originally created in 2006, as you may have guessed, for teachers. Think about in-person learning where teachers and SLPs would print worksheets and laminator-friendly games and cards.

As of 2021, Teachers Pay Teachers has a membership of over 7 million educators who have downloaded over 1 billion resources (Teachers Pay Teachers, 2021). With the growth of digital learning options, Boom Learning has become a leader in online materials. These can be described as flashcards for your iPad (or computer). Boom Learning was founded in 2012. If you have not yet used either of these sites, you should definitely do your homework to see what it is like from the buyers' perspective before you consider becoming a seller. If you are thinking about creating materials to sell on either one of these platforms or your own website, follow the steps that we've written in Figure 5–2 when creating your content.

1. **Plan the activity type:** Whether you are creating a printable download or a digital resource, such as Boom Cards or Google Slides, you will need to decide what type of activity you are going to create. Will it be a board game, a matching game, a minimal pairs activity?

2. **Find relevant images and stimulus items:** Once you've decided on the type of activity, you will need to gather the list of stimulus items and corresponding images (if you will be using any). You may create your own list of stimulus

10 STEP PLANNING PROCESS FOR CONTENT CREATORS

1	Plan activity type.
2	Find relevant images and stimulus items.
3	Create a content mockup.
4	Choose a response method.
5	Test the activity.
6	Finalize document with details and directions.
7	Create cover art.
8	Write a description for your sales page.
9	Publish your product.
10	Promote your product.

Figure 5–2. *Ten-Step Planning Process for Content Creators.*

items, use grade-level vocabulary terms, or choose from the available clipart bundles on Teachers Pay Teachers. Where will you obtain the images that you will need? Will you be using clipart or photos? Do you want to pay someone to create custom illustrations, or will you find free stock photos online? Some places to find quality images are Pixabay.com, Pexels.com, Istockphoto.com and Shutterstock.com. Regardless of which method you choose, make sure that you are not infringing on any copyright laws and that you have permission to use the images you choose. Many TPT sellers require that credit be given with a link back to their store.

3. **Create a content mockup:** Now that you know what your plan is and have your stimulus items, you are ready to create! You can create most products using Microsoft PowerPoint or Google Slides. If you are creating a worksheet, Microsoft Word may be more appropriate. Think about whether your product will include more text or images. If you will have more images than text, opt for PowerPoint or Google Slides. If your product will consist of mostly text, consider using Microsoft Word or Google Docs. If you have the ideas for creating quality content and just need help with the aesthetics, there are many options for that. You can hire designers to create content for you on Fiverr.com or Upwork.com.

4. **Choose the response method:** For digital activities, you need to decide how the user will interact with the activity. If it is a Google Slides activity, will users drag pictures? If you are creating Boom Cards, will the user tap the correct answer from a field of two or three options or drag and drop their responses?

5. **Test the activity:** Once you have created your activity, you will need to test it to ensure that it works the way you intended. Consider having someone else try it out for you. They can provide valuable feedback regarding the ease of use and clarity of directions.

6. **Finalize the document with details and directions:** If you are creating a digital download, one option is to use Adobe Acrobat software to secure the document so others cannot copy or edit your content. There are many online tutorials available that will walk you through this process.

7. **Create cover art:** Even though this is one of the last steps in the process, it is one of the most important steps. Your cover art will be the first impression you present to your potential customers and can make your products stand out from the competition (especially if you are listed in seller marketplaces such as Teachers Pay Teachers or Boom Learning). If you are selling a book, the cover is the visual representation of its contents. When selling a digital product, you also need an image that represents what you are selling. This typically includes the title of the product and artwork. You want your cover art to appropriately reflect your brand, give buyers a preview of the activity, and align with the target audience. For example, if you are creating an activity for preschoolers in a classroom, you should not use an image of adults on a computer in your cover art.

8. **Write a description for your sales page:** The sales page should include the title, price, and description of what you are selling. As with cover art, your product description should adequately describe the product type and intended audience. Your description should be thorough and include keywords related to the activity. You can further enhance the description with a file or video preview of the activity.

9. **Publish your product:** After you have the finished the product, cover art, and product description, you are ready to publish your product and start earning sales. You will publish your product to your preferred selling platform or your own website. Part of this step is determining the price for your product and ensuring that you follow publishing guidelines for the platform.

10. **Promote your product:** Unfortunately, the quote, "If you build it, they will come" does not apply here. Once you publish your products, you need to spread the word! How will your potential customers find you— on social media, your email list, paid advertisements? You should have a marketing strategy in place before you get to this step, and this step is more about implementing that strategy than developing one.

As we mentioned earlier, sales from digital and physical products are also potential revenue sources for bloggers. In this way, you may be a blogger *and* content creator. There are many types of digital products that you can sell, whether on a blog, your website, social media, or another platform. Cochran (2019) separates digital products into several categories, which include printables, e-books, and video/audio files.

Five Types of Digital Products

1. Workbooks

2. Flashcards

3. E-books

4. How-to videos

5. Audiobooks

If you're considering starting your own blog or website, you can sell directly to consumers and avoid marketplaces altogether. In Figure 5–3, we demonstrate some of the costs of selling on each of these platforms, including Boom Learning, Teachers Pay Teachers, and Shopify.

As you will see in Figure 5–3, selling on your own website yields the highest profit. The downsides are that you do not get as much organic traffic, which means you are responsible for your own marketing, you have to do your own programming (or hire someone else to do it for you), and you are responsible for collecting/remitting sales tax. On the other hand, Boom Learning and Teachers Pay Teachers have the option of collecting and remitting sales tax on behalf of sellers.

Ultimately, the decision of which site to sell your digital products on is an important one, but this is one decision that you can change mid-stream. If you start selling Boom Cards exclusively on Boom Learning, for example, you can later

ONLINE STORE COMPARISON CHART

	BOOM	TPT	SHOPIFY	YOUR WEBSITE
ANNUAL PRICE	$35/year	$59.95/year	$348/year	$33-$99/year
SALES COMMISSION	85% + 2% Paypal fee	80% + 2% Paypal fee **Boom also takes 10% of sales**	100% -2.9%+.30 Paypal fee **Boom also takes 10% of sales**	100% -2.9%+.30 Paypal fee **Boom also takes 10% of sales**
PRODUCT TYPES	Only Boom Cards™	Boom Cards™ Google Slides Any type of digital download	Boom Cards™ Any type of digital download Physical products	Boom Cards™ Any type of digital download Physical products
MARKETPLACE	Yes	Yes	No	No

This comparison chart provides an overview of options available for selling your products online. Boom Learning℠ is best for selling Boom Cards™ with minimal setup. Teachers Pay Teachers (TPT) is best for selling a variety of digital products with minimal budget for advertising. Creating your own website is best for maximizing profits, customization and flexibility. However, you are responsible for your own advertising.

Figure 5–3. *Online Store Comparison Chart.*

decide to sell on Teachers Pay Teachers or even on your own website. At the risk of sounding like a broken record, think about who your customers are. Where are they shopping? How will they find you and your products? Then develop a plan with the answers to these questions in mind. We will help you develop your marketing plan in Chapter 6.

CHAPTER CHECKLIST

☐ Decide on revenue sources for your business

☐ Select a platform to sell your products or services

☐ Revisit the SMARTER goals for your business

☐ Create your content

REFERENCES

American Speech-Language-Hearing Association. (2016). *Scope of practice in speech-language pathology* [Scope of Practice]. Available from www.asha.org/policy/

BeaconLive. (n.d.). *What's the difference between a webinar vs. an online course?* BeaconLive. Retrieved September 9, 2021, from https://www.beaconlive.com/blog/whats-the-difference-between-a-webinar-vs.-an-online-course

Boom Learning Support. (n.d.). *Quick start for authors: Learn to sell boom cards.* Boom. Retrieved October 9, 2021, from https://help.boomlearning.com/en/support/solutions/articles/16000040502-quick-start-for-authors-learn-to-sell-boom-cards

Ch., R. (2021, September 6). *How many blogs are there in 2021? We counted them all!* Hosting Tribunal. Retrieved September 9, 2021, from https://hostingtribunal.com/blog/how-many-blogs/#gref

Cochran, L. (2021, May 18). *19 examples of profitable digital products to sell online.* Podia. Retrieved August 30, 2021, from https://www.podia.com/articles/examples-digital-products-for-download

McKinney, R. (2019). *Here's how to do accent modification: A manual for speech-language pathologists.* San Diego, CA: Plural Publishing.

McKinney, R. (2021, January 31). *Accent modification and linguistic discrimination.* [Live virtual presentation]. CORSPAN-The Corporate Speech Pathology Network. https://CORSPAN.org

Meyer, C. (2020, October 9). *How John D. Saunders made $100,000 with one online course.* Podia. Retrieved September 9, 2021, from https://www.podia.com/articles/john-d-saunders-case-study

Paul, J. (2021, June 26). *5 best online course hosting platforms for instructors and content creators in 2021.* Medium. Retrieved October 9, 2021, from https://medium.com/javarevisited/5-best-online-course-platforms-for-instructors-bloggers-teachers-and-creators-in-2021-84dd9cadd66f

Paulson, M. (2016, November 2). *How to make money by running display ads on your website.* Medium. Retrieved August 27, 2021, from https://medium.com/@matt_25083/how-to-make-money-by-running-display-ads-on-your-website-6f570ed6bda6

QuickSprout (Ed.). (2021, June 24). *35 blogging ideas that are guaranteed to be popular topics.* QuickSprout. Retrieved September 9, 2021, from https://www.quicksprout.com/blog-topics-and-ideas/

Teachers Pay Teachers. (2021). *About us.* Teachers Pay Teachers. Retrieved September 9, 2021, from https://www.teacherspayteachers.com/About-Us

The Governance Lab (2021, February). *The Power of Virtual Communities.* TheGovLab. Retrieved September 8, 2021, from https://virtual-communities.thegovlab.org/reports.html

WordStream. (n.d.). *Cost per click (CPC): Learn what cost per click means for PPC.* WordStream by LOCALiQ. Retrieved October 9, 2021, from https://www.wordstream.com/cost-per-click

CHAPTER 6

Marketing Your Business

An Introduction to Marketing, Networking, and Branding

In This Chapter

This chapter will help you create a marketing strategy and action plan. You will learn how to market your business using digital marketing, as well as understand the value of in-person marketing and networking.

Topics include:

- Creating a Brand
- Developing a Marketing Strategy
- Implementing a Marketing Action Plan
- Marketing Channels
    - Digital Marketing (Website, Email Marketing, and Social Media)
    - In-Person Marketing
    - Networking

In Chapter 2, we introduced the basics of marketing. In this chapter, we will be discussing how to develop a marketing strategy. As a refresher, marketing is defined as the "processes for creating, communicating, delivering, and exchanging offerings that have value for customers, clients, partners, and society at large" (American Marketing Association, n.d.). The action words in the definition are create, communicate, deliver, and exchange. In Chapter 5, we discussed *creating* offerings that provide value for customers. In this chapter, we will focus on *communicating* your message to your customers. If you used the business model template from Chapter 2, you have probably already started thinking about how you will market your business. Now it is time to dive into the details of your marketing strategy and marketing plan, which will turn your marketing strategy into action.

RAJ KASI MBA

Founder & CEO, speechx
www.speechx.tech

As the CEO of an early-stage tech company, I wear multiple hats and am responsible for setting the vision of the company, identifying and attracting talented professionals, acquiring users and ensuring a scorching growth rate, and raising capital.

Important Considerations for Entrepreneurs

The single most important consideration before starting any business is whether you know enough of the industry (segment) that you are looking to make an impact in. As the founder, it is crucial to display a deep understanding of the domain to which you cater in your new business.

Pitfalls to Avoid

Don't be afraid to hire people smarter than you. Don't hesitate to launch—launch fast, fail fast, learn faster. Don't ignore culture-building—this will make or break your business. Don't be afraid to pick up the phone and cold call your customers/prospects. Make sure to take some time out to recharge now and then— entrepreneurship is a 24x7 job.

Advice for Entrepreneurs

Make something people want—this is the classic Y Combinator advice, but it is much deeper than it sounds. You can have the best idea in the world, but if others don't buy it, then it just remains exactly what it is—an idea. Ideas are a dime a dozen (x1000s), execution matters. Make something scrappy, validate, make it better, validate, make it even better, validate, so on and forth until one day, you become a unicorn!

CREATING YOUR BRAND

A brand is an intangible marketing concept that helps people identify a company, product, or individual (Kenton, 2021). In addition to being a visual representation of your business, a brand also includes your values and how you interact with your target audience. When creating your brand, start with your target audience in mind. Then design a brand around the experience that you want your potential customers to have when they interact with your business. Finally, be sure to maintain consistency across all of your marketing channels.

You and your overall executive presence also contribute to your "brand." As a business owner and a service provider, for many, you are your business. As such, you must be thoughtful in delivering the quality product or service as promised. Be an effective and engaged communicator with clients, as well as potential customers and collaborators. Offer the best standard of customer service possible. Offer value with insights, perspectives, or basic guidance (free of cost), no matter whether you are at a networking event, having a "discovery" call with a potential client, and/or doing an inservice with a physician's group. These can all help to build your brand as the "go-to," confident, and skilled expert. Make connections and always have a business card (at the very least) ready to share, no matter where you are, to get brand exposure. Offer insights on your digital media pages and never shy away from connecting with individuals/organizations that contact you—it is another opportunity to gain exposure and build your brand's awareness.

Forbes suggests six brand-building strategies for small businesses and startups (Barker, 2019):

1. Choose a memorable name.
2. Evoke emotion in your audience.
3. Develop a visual identity.
4. Align your website with your brand identity.
5. Build your social media presence.
6. Align your promotions with your brand's voice.

Let's look at each of these in more detail:

Choosing a Name

When you are deciding on a business name, make sure that it reflects your target audience, represents what you do, and will be flexible enough to accommodate the future growth of your business. If you are opening a pediatric speech and language practice, but you have aspirations of adding occupational therapists, you may want to keep "Speech Therapy" out of the name. Instead of ABC Speech Therapy, maybe you will choose ABC Center. Before you register your business name, you also want to check that your business name and domain name (website address) are not already taken in your state. You can do a business name search on your state's Secretary of State website (or international equivalent). If you would like to trademark your business someday, also conduct a search of U.S. registered trademarks at USPTO.gov. In addition, search for available domain names on a website such as

GoDaddy.com or Domains.com. These sites will show you whether a domain name is available and how much it will cost to purchase it if it is.

Evoking Emotion

Maya Angelou said, "People will forget what you said, people will forget what you did, but people will never forget how you made them feel." Tapping into human emotion is the key to making a connection with your audience. Entrepreneur.com suggests three simple strategies for evoking emotion: tell your story, broadcast your values, and be yourself (Dodhia, 2021).

Developing Visuals

Your brand's visuals include your logo, colors, and fonts. Think about who you want your business to attract, then, how your brand elements will be consistent. If your target audience is children (and their parents), you may want to use a variety of bright colors and playful fonts. Whereas, if your target audience is business professionals, you want to stick to blues and grays and more traditional fonts. Matt Ellis, from 99 Designs, wrote an article about branding colors, which is listed in the Resource List at the end of this book. Think about the brands that you use, whether it's your car, shoes, or cell phone. Your logo should become easily recognizable by your potential customers, like Nike's swoosh or Apple's iconic apple logo.

Many graphic design programs and/or individuals now offer branding kits to allow you to maintain consistency in terms of your color palette, logo, a stylistic way of presenting information, linguistic nuances, fonts, as well as the graphics that you choose to use. For more reasonable pricing options, you can visit websites such as Fiverr or Upwork where you can receive different pricing and service options from a wide variety of freelancers to assist you with design elements for your business. You can also create your own logo using tools such as Canva or Hatchful by Shopify.

Aligning Your Website

Your website is an extension of your brand, so be sure to use the same or complementary colors and fonts that you used to create your logo throughout your website. More than the visual elements of your brand, your website is where potential customers are able to start making those connections with your brand. This is where you can share your story and your values. It's also a great opportunity to give customers a look into your personality. If your tone is serious and professional, you should make sure that your writing is formal. If your tone is fun and playful, consider incorporating some humor into your writing. Think about the subscribe option on your website (more about that later in this chapter). Do you want to invite visitors to "Join the club" or "Become an exclusive member?" Does your contact form say, "Drop us a line" or "Send us a message?" All of these are important decisions that you will need to make as you're building your brand's identity.

Building Your Social Media Presence

We will get into the details of incorporating social media into your marketing strategy later in this chapter. For now, let's think about how your brand can connect with potential customers on social media. It starts with your brand's images, including your profile picture and cover photo. Then consider every post on your business page. Make sure that the visuals and posts are complementary and consistent with your brand's message. You want your brand to consistently provide value and allow potential customers to interact with your business. For example, if someone sends you a message or comments on your social media account, be sure to acknowledge them. You can do this by quickly responding to their message or even liking their comments. You can even use the feature on Facebook that enables you to create sample questions and automated responses when someone messages your business page.

Aligning Your Promotions

Finally, align your promotions with your brand's voice. Think about where your target audience spends their time, and reach them where they are. This may be through social media, YouTube, or even local community events. As you are starting your business, you need to build awareness of your brand. It is important that your messaging is consistent so potential customers can easily identify your brand's values. Stephanie Schwab from Cracker Jack Marketing (2011) suggests four ways of developing your brand's voice by including tone, character, language, and purpose (Figure 6–1).

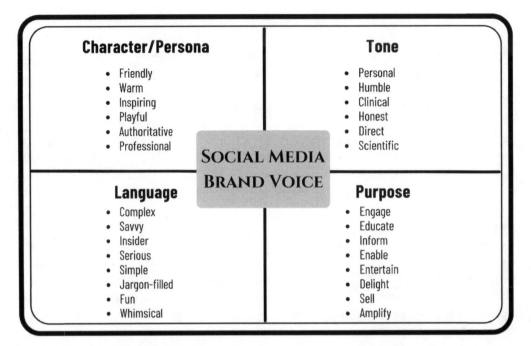

Figure 6–1. Social Media Brand Voice. Used with permission from Schwab, S. (2011, May). Finding your brand voice. *Crackerjack Marketing. https://crackerjackmarketing.com/blog/finding-brand-voice/*

MARKETING STRATEGY

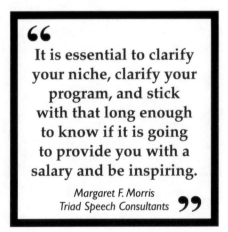

> **"**
> It is essential to clarify your niche, clarify your program, and stick with that long enough to know if it is going to provide you with a salary and be inspiring.
>
> *Margaret F. Morris*
> *Triad Speech Consultants* **"**

A marketing strategy is a key component of your business plan. You will develop a marketing strategy to highlight your goals and how you can achieve them. If you do a search for "marketing strategy," you will see a variety of examples and templates.

Based on our own experiences and research, these are the sections that we suggest including in your marketing strategy:

1. Company mission and goals
2. Market analysis
3. Target audience
4. Budget
5. Marketing action plan

Company Mission and Goals

If you've completed your business model, you have already written your vision. If not, pause now to make sure that you have clearly defined the mission and vision of your business, as these will guide all of your business decisions. This will help you develop a message that will resonate throughout your marketing materials. You should also have revenue goals for your business, which will then enable you to focus on marketing activities that are going to help you reach those goals.

Market Analysis

Conducting a market analysis is the process that is going to help you identify trends in your industry. This includes an analysis of your competitors and your target market. Your competitive analysis should identify your competition by product or service and market segment. For example, your market segment might be adults aged 60 and up who are recovering from a stroke. To organize this information, Parsons (2021) suggests breaking up your market research into four categories: industry overview, target market, competition, and pricing and forecast.

1. **Industry overview:** This is where you'll describe the current state of your industry and projected growth. Be sure to include the size of the industry and trends. A few places to get this type of information are the U.S. Census, Bureau of Labor Statistics, and Statista. For the field of speech-language pathology, ASHA has a lot of data about industry trends available at http://www.asha.org. Refer to the additional resources in the Resource List at the end of this book.

2. **Target market:** This describes who your customers are. How many are there? What are their needs? What are their demographics?

3. **Competition:** Analyzing your competition enables you to see where your business will fit within the market. Use this as an opportunity to examine your competitors' strengths and weaknesses. Think of what is unique about

your competitors and how you can fill the gaps that competitors have not yet addressed. What will set you apart from your competition? A great way to do this is to conduct a SWOT analysis. This acronym stands for strengths, weaknesses, opportunities, and threats. In the SWOT analysis, you are going to assess the internal strengths and weaknesses of your business in addition to the external opportunities and threats posed by your competitors. For strengths, you will include what your business does well and what unique resources your business has (e.g., staff or technology). For weaknesses, include what your competitors are doing better than you and any limitations in your resources. Opportunities would be the need for your product/service or which untapped markets you can serve. Threats relate to what your competition is doing and things that might harm your business. An example of a SWOT analysis for a pediatric private practice that provides home-based services is provided in Figure 6–2A. Use the template in Figure 6–2B to complete your own SWOT analysis.

4. **Pricing and forecast:** After you've set your pricing, you want to set a sales forecast for your business. Forecasting is the process where you determine what percentage of overall sales in your industry you hope to capture. For example, if you create and sell flashcards, "SLP flashcards" would be your industry. If you find that SLPs spend $1 million a year on flashcards, your sales forecast may be a goal of $100,000 in flashcards, which is 10% of the market ($100,000 ÷ $1,000,000 × 100 = 10%).

While the market analysis process can be time-consuming, it will allow you to answer questions about your specific business and what your potential customers are looking for. Some ways to gather information about what your potential customers are looking for is through surveys or focus groups. You can send surveys to those in your target audience through social media, or even host live webinars, to get input from potential customers. You will also need to identify your major competitors and compare your business to theirs. Use the information you gather to explain your competitive advantages and disadvantages. Your SWOT analysis is a great first step in conducting your competitive analysis. In addition, the non-profit organization, SCORE, provides several resources to help guide you through a competitive analysis, including a free on-demand course. The course is listed in our Resources list at the end of the book.

SWOT ANALYSIS

	HELPFUL	HARMFUL
INTERNAL	STRENGTHS PROMPT-certified SLP Evening and weekend hours In-home services	WEAKNESSES Small advertising budget
EXTERNAL	OPPORTUNITIES Another private practice owner is preparing to retire at the end of the year	THREATS 5 PROMPT-certified SLPs in my area running ads

Figure 6–2A. *Sample SWOT Analysis.*

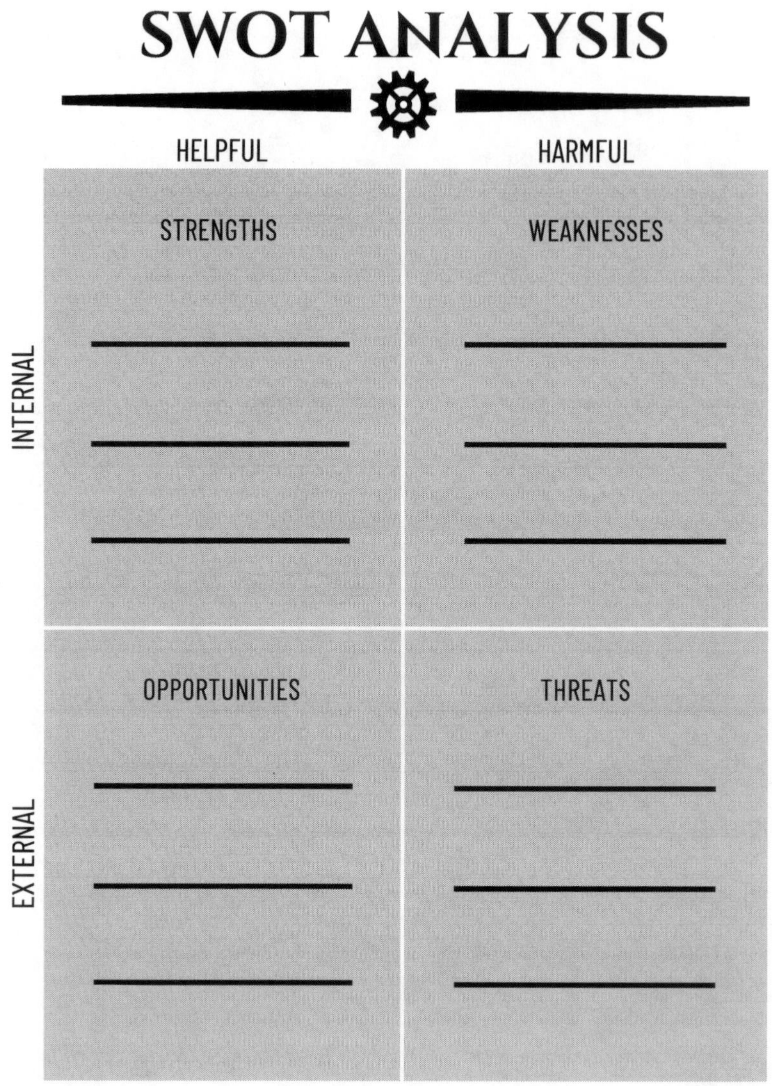

SWOT ANALYSIS

HELPFUL	HARMFUL
STRENGTHS	**WEAKNESSES**
OPPORTUNITIES	**THREATS**

INTERNAL

EXTERNAL

Figure 6–2B. *SWOT Analysis Template.*

Target Audience

When you are creating your marketing strategy, anticipate your customers' needs and determine how you can meet those needs. At this stage, you will identify your target audience and create what are referred to as "buyer personas." Completing this step will help you establish a plan that will effectively reach your target market. Use Table 6–1 to create your buyer personas, or use the free, editable template from Hootsuite, a social media management platform, which can be found in our Resources List at the end of the book.

Table 6–1. *Buyer Personas*

	Persona 1	Persona 2	Persona 3
Name			
Job Title			
Age			
Education			
Industry			
Income			
Family			
Location			
Hobbies			
Communication Preferences			
Goals			

Budget

Marketing is going to be an ongoing investment that you make in your business in order to create, communicate, deliver, and exchange value with your customers. Therefore, it is important to set a budget for how much you want to spend on your marketing activities. You can then measure whether you're getting a return on your investment (ROI) in terms of leads, new customers, and sales. WebStrategies, Inc. tracks trends in marketing budgets across a variety of industries and business sizes. They reported marketing spending as generally hovering between 6.5% to 10% of total business revenue. However, during the beginning of the COVID-19 pandemic, marketing spending actually increased from 11.3% in February 2020 to 12.6% in June 2020 (Leone, 2020). Companies that sell products to consumers (B2C) spend on average 11.9% of revenue on marketing, and companies that sell services only spend 4.8% of their revenue on marketing. Marketing spend also varies by industry, with health care companies spending about 9% of their revenue on marketing and retail companies spending about 4.4%. Table 6–2 lists some common marketing expenses and how they can be used to estimate your total marketing budget. As you create a marketing budget, you only need to use the expenses that are relevant to your business.

Customer acquisition cost refers to how much of your marketing budget is spent to acquire each customer. Calculating this amount will also help you determine

Table 6–2. Marketing Expenses

Expense	Monthly Budget
Website	
email marketing	
Pay-per-click advertising (e.g., Google)	
Social media advertising (e.g., Facebook)	
In person or online events	
Signage	
Giveaways	
Printed materials (e.g., flyers, brochures, postcards)	
Customer Relationship Management (CRM) Software (e.g., HubSpot, Pipedrive, Zoho)	
SEO tools (e.g., keyword research)	

whether you need to make adjustments to your marketing budget based on the return from each method. As you are running ads, there are two important metrics to track: the click-through rate (CTR) and cost per click (CPC). The CTR is the percentage of people who click on the link after seeing your ad, whereas the CPC is how much it cost you when that person clicked on your link. Your use of keywords, your actual ad, and how enticing the visuals are will impact your CTR, while a different set of factors influence CPC. The same ad can cost more on different days or even different times of day. It depends on how in-demand that advertising space is, which is related to what your competitors are doing. Think about the difference in ad spend between the high-ticket advertising space for the Super Bowl halftime show versus a Tuesday night at 11 pm during a replay of a golf tournament.

Keep a close eye on how much it costs to acquire a customer and adjust your ad budget accordingly. For example, if it costs you $100 to acquire a customer from Google ads, but only $40 to acquire customers from Facebook ads, you should allocate more of your budget to Facebook ads. Returns may or may not be financial. If you are aiming to generate a certain number of leads instead of sales, then your return will be measured in leads. For example, your Google ad yielded 100 new leads, whereas your Facebook ads yielded 20 new leads. You should focus more of your marketing dollars on Google ads. Look at the following example, then use Figure 6–3 to calculate your customer acquisition costs. In this figure, line "c" is the customer acquisition cost. You can then use this number to determine what your spending should be based on the goals you've set.

Here is an example:

1. Distribute (quantity of promotional effort) by Google Ads (medium)

2. At a total cost of $1,000

3. Acquire 10 new customers as a result

4. Divide the money spent by the number of new customers: $1,000 ÷ 10 = $100

5. By using this media message to reach this target market, the cost to acquire one new customer is $100

6. To get 100 (goal) customers, the budget would be 100 (number of customers) × $100 (cost per customer) = $10,000

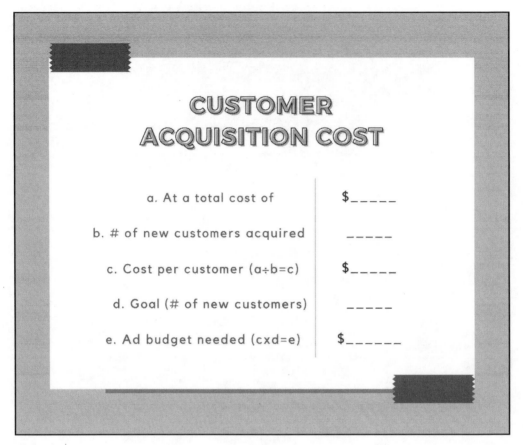

Figure 6–3. *Customer Acquisition Cost Calculator.*

After you've set your budget, it is time to develop your marketing action plan.

MARKETING ACTION PLAN

Creating a Marketing Action Plan includes the actionable steps that you will take to achieve your goals. We will break this into three components:

1. Marketing objectives

2. Marketing channels

3. Marketing tactics

Marketing Objectives

Your marketing objectives should align with your business's mission and goals. Think about when you are developing client goals for speech and language therapy. You first start with long-term goals, and then you create short-term objectives that will be your benchmarks toward reaching the long-term goals. These marketing objectives are intended to be short-term. What will you accomplish in the next 30 days? During this quarter? You can then see whether you've met the objectives and whether you need to change your tactics to keep you on track toward reaching your long-term goals. Just as you did in Chapter 1, be sure that you write SMART(ER) goals. It is not enough to say that you want to increase your number of followers on Instagram. Instead, a SMART(ER) goal would look more like this:

> ### SMART(ER) Marketing Goal
>
> *In order to increase brand awareness, ABC SLP will increase our number of Instagram followers from 100 to 1,000 by the end of the fourth quarter in 2022 through targeted marketing ads that include video demonstrations of our new product line.*

You can use our example and plug it into the SMART(ER) goal format to check that it meets our requirements.

- **S**pecific: targeted marketing ads that include video demonstrations of our new product line

- **M**easurable: 1,000 followers

- **A**ttainable: add 900 followers

- **R**elevant: increase brand awareness

- **T**imely: by the end of the fourth quarter in 2022

- **E**valuate: Did you meet your goal? What worked? What didn't work?

- **R**evise: Review your outcomes and revise your goal as needed.

While this was just one example of a marketing goal, there are other appropriate objectives that you may choose for your marketing action plan. HubSpot's "Not

Another State of Marketing" report in 2021 listed the top five marketing campaign goals (HubSpot, 2021). You can use this list as a guide to help you decide where to focus your efforts. Keep in mind what will be most relevant for your business based on your stated objectives, which should align with your overall mission and vision.

Top Marketing Objectives

1. **Brand awareness:** We discussed brand awareness earlier in this chapter. As a new business, your primary objective should be spreading the word about your business.

2. **Increase sales:** Whether you are selling a product or service, your goal is to make sales! You can calculate your sales conversion rate by how many sales you receive per visitor. For example, let's say you have an online store where you sell digital downloads. For every 100 people who visit your website, 5 people make a purchase. Your conversion rate is 5% (5 sales ÷ 100 visitors). If you want to double your sales conversion rate, you will aim to make 10 sales for every 100 visitors to your website (10% conversion rate).

3. **Increase engagement:** Social media engagement is a measure of how people are interacting with your social media accounts and content. The term can cover a broad range of actions across all social platforms. For example, engagement might include Likes, Favorites, Comments, Replies, DMs (direct messages), Shares, Retweets, Saves, Clicks, and Mentions (Eckstein, 2021).

4. **Lead generation:** A lead is a potential customer. One way to generate leads is to collect contact information from prospective customers, such as name, email address, and phone number. You are then able to follow up with a sequence of emails, phone calls, text messages, or other types of communication to provide value to those leads.

5. **Increase revenue:** Sales and revenue are two different metrics. You may aim for a higher sales conversion rate, which calculates the percentage of visitors purchasing your product or service. However, each visitor will spend a different amount. For example, if one sale is $10, and another sale is $100, you've only made two sales, but grossed $110 in revenue.

After you've written your marketing objectives, you can then decide which marketing channels are most appropriate to help you meet your objectives.

Marketing Channels

Your marketing channels are the methods through which you will communicate with your target audience. According to HubSpot (2021), social media was the #1 channel used in marketing in 2021. The other marketing channels that were among the most popular included website, email marketing, content marketing/SEO, and paid social media marketing. For your marketing action plan, we will focus on the top three digital marketing channels: social media, website, and email marketing. As you are creating your marketing action plan, you will likely begin with creating a website for your business. Even though social media is the #1 marketing channel, email marketing has a higher return on investment. Although you may use your social media marketing to build an email list, we will discuss email marketing second. Finally, we will help you create your social media accounts and use them to build brand awareness, increase SEO, and promote client engagement. We will round out this chapter by looking at in-person marketing strategies.

Website

According to a survey by Digital.com (2021), 77% of small businesses have a website. Of the 23% who did not have a website in 2021, only 33% said they never needed one. Driving traffic to your website can serve many purposes. For online businesses, this is your "virtual storefront." For businesses with a physical location, potential customers may visit your website to learn more about your business, including products, services, and contact information. You can also use your website to collect leads, which we will discuss in more detail later. For bloggers, website traffic is your key to generating revenue through any of your monetizing strategies, as we discussed in Chapter 5.

If you are just getting started, you will need to create a professional website, as this may be the first impression that your clients will have of your business. The branding that you chose will carry throughout your website and website design. This is going to be the central location where people can find information about you and your business or your product/service. Now, while you will also make considerable effort to gain exposure on social media networks, your website is your central location where you can guide anyone interested to come and find out more. Depending on what the call to action is on your website, you need to make the decision whether it's going to only provide information about your business, location, and contact information, or will you also be providing content related to your product or service? The content on your website might include articles, resource links, a blog, videos, or an email subscriber list sign-up. Another potential use for your website is for a payment portal (make sure to research the most functional and secure online payment methods to integrate into your website first). Determining the purpose of your website will help guide you in creating an effective design. An article in *Forbes* suggests ten steps for creating a small business website (Figure 6–4; AllBusiness Contributor Group, 2019).

1. **Obtain a domain name:** A domain name is your website address (e.g., www.TheSLPEntrepreneur.com). As we discussed in the branding section, you should research available domains when you are developing your brand name. When deciding on a domain name, you should choose one that reflects

10 STEPS TO CREATING A SMALL BUSINESS WEBSITE

1	Obtain a domain name.
2	Purchase website hosting.
3	Display a clear description of your business.
4	Implement a content management system.
5	Choose an e-commerce platform.
6	Create an engaging website user interface.
7	Optimize your website for search engines.
8	Regularly create and publish quality content.
9	Social media icons
10	Terms of Use

Figure 6–4. *10 Steps to Creating a Small Business Website. Adapted from AllBusiness Contributor Group. (2019, May 25).* 10 key steps to building a great small business website. Forbes.

your business name. If you can get your actual business name, that would be ideal. For long business names, you may shorten the domain to make it easy to remember. For example, Main Street Speech Associates could be shortened to MainStSpeech.com. Some places to purchase domain names are http://www.godaddy.com and http://www.domains.com. If you are purchasing a hosting package, it may include a free domain name. Be sure that you include your domain name in your marketing budget, as this is something that needs to be renewed every year. You can usually receive a discount for paying for several years in advance (e.g., purchasing a 3-year plan instead of a 1-year plan). Domains can start as low as "free" to thousands of dollars. It depends on how popular your desired domain name is. For example, as of the writing of this book, communicationnow.com would cost over $1,000, while communicationnowllc.com is less than $5. If a domain name does not appear to be available, you can attempt to purchase it for a broker fee plus the sales price of that domain if it is for sale. Also be sure to check periodically, as prices and availability of domain names change frequently.

2. **Purchase website hosting:** Website hosting is where your website will live on the internet. Your domain name means nothing if you do not purchase a hosting package. Purchasing your website hosting may occur simultaneously when purchasing a domain name. If you purchase a monthly subscription at an annual rate, you typically save over a monthly subscription price and have more "free" features included. For example, if you purchase a website hosting subscription at a rate of $10/month, that same package may be selling for $100 if the year is paid up front, and it may include a free domain name, or even free advertising credits for Google AdWords. Some popular options for website hosting are GoDaddy, Bluehost, and SiteGround. Website hosting can cost anywhere from $2 per month to over $100 per month. Regardless of which website host you choose, be sure to avoid selecting a free plan. These will typically have branded banners (e.g., "Created by Wix" at the top of your website), and have limits on the amount of content allowed. For example, you may only get five pages free or up to 1GB of media (e.g., pictures, files, and videos). If you hire a company to create your website for you, they may also have an option where they provide the hosting. These tend to be more expensive options, but you receive expert and individualized attention. Another benefit is obtaining a customized website to meet your unique business needs. If you are open to designing or maintaining your own website, you can definitely do this for less than $100 per month.

3. **Display a clear description of your business:** When you are designing the homepage of your website, be sure that the description of your business is prominently displayed. The top of your website is called the banner. Your banner can include your name, logo, and the slogan of your business. Take it one step further to include a welcome or introductory paragraph so visitors know what your business does. This may be a brief summary of your "About" section, which then links to your full bio or information about your business on another page.

4. **Implement a content management system:** A content management system (CMS) is what you will use to create and manage your website. For example, if your host is the building, your content management system is the furniture. Your host may serve dual purposes as both your website host and content

174 The SLP Entrepreneur: The Speech-Language Pathologist's Guide to Private Practice and Other Business Ventures

management system. Wix and GoDaddy are examples of all-in-one options. However, if you choose Bluehost or Siteground for your host, you will need a separate CMS, such as WordPress. According to HubSpot, the most popular content management systems in 2021 were WordPress (22%), Wix (15%), and Squarespace (13%) (HubSpot, 2021). If you are going to be designing your own website and you do not have programming experience, you probably want to choose a CMS that is user-friendly. These allow you to choose a template and then drag and drop your elements to easily customize your website. Wix and Squarespace were created for users with little design experience, whereas WordPress is not as user-friendly and requires a steep learning curve to become proficient in using it. However, you can hire someone to set up your WordPress website for you in a way that makes it easy for you to maintain and update yourself (more on that later).

5. **Choose an e-commerce platform:** Whether you will need an e-commerce platform depends on your products and services. For a traditional private practice, unless you are selling merchandise or classes, an e-commerce platform may not be necessary. You can choose a different billing system for therapy and assessments that is going to be HIPAA compliant, such as an EMR. However, if you are a blogger or content creator and will be selling physical or digital products, then you need to choose an e-commerce platform. As we discussed in Chapter 5, you may choose to only sell on a third-party platform, such as Teachers Pay Teachers or Boom Learning. If you want to create your own e-commerce store, then the most popular platforms in 2021 were WooCommerce, Shopify, and Squarespace. WooCommerce is a free plugin available for WordPress websites. This means there is no additional monthly fee for using WooCommerce. Shopify and Squarespace do have monthly plans, however. There are additional e-commerce options available, but you will need to decide what is going to suit your business needs while offering a user-friendly experience for your customers.

6. **Create an engaging website user interface:** Your customers should always be at the forefront of your mind when you are designing your website. Your goal should be to create a website that is visually appealing and easy to navigate for anyone who visits your website. Be sure that your website is easy to read, easy to use, and that your brand elements are consistent. This is a great time to visit other websites and critique them from the perspective of a customer. Think about the size of the font, the colors, and the use of video and images. Is the information easy to find? Do you know exactly what the purpose of the website is? Figure 6–5 is a website navigation checklist that will help you make sure that your website includes all of the basic components.

7. **Optimize your website for search engines:** SEO refers to search engine optimization. This ensures that search engines index and rank your site. To

WEBSITE NAVIGATION CHECKLIST

☐	Home
☐	About Us
☐	Products/Services
☐	Contact Us
☐	Pricing
☐	Value proposition
☐	Call to action
☐	Subscribe form
☐	Social media icons
☐	Terms of Use
☐	Privacy Policy

Figure 6–5. *Website Navigation Checklist.*

do this, search engines "crawl" your website's content, including keywords and images. Investing in SEO is one of the best ways to drive traffic to your website. Google tends to be the most popular search engine, and your website's performance on Google can tell you a good amount of information about what may need to change on your website in order to drive more traffic to your site, and ultimately to your business. With regard to SEO, you must keep in mind that in order to rank high on Google pages, it will not only take a great deal of market planning strategy and revisions (as needed), but it will also take a lot of time and patience to get there. Do keep in mind that you need to use keywords on each page that relate to things that your target audience is searching for. If you have a lead magnet, that will need to be updated regularly, and you will need to make sure that it's working properly as to not turn off potential customers. You also want to check that it is still relevant and bringing you the desired return on investment (ROI). According to HubSpot, using strategic keywords, localization, and optimizing for mobile were the top three SEO tactics in 2021 (HubSpot, 2021).

Keywords are the series of words that users enter on a search engine. Think about your target audience and what they are likely looking for when searching for the types of products and services that your business offers. For example, if your target audience is adults with aphasia, and you enter "aphasia," possible keywords might be expressive aphasia, aphasia stroke, stroke speech, or aphasia disorder. On the other hand, if you enter "aphasia" and "speech therapy," you will see keywords such as speech pathology, speech and language therapy, and speech-language therapist. Finally, if you enter "speech therapy for aphasia," related keywords are aphasia treatment, aphasia therapy, expressive aphasia treatment, and speech therapy for expressive aphasia. You can pay for a service or use a free service, such as Google's Keyword Planner, to find trending keywords for your target audience. Google has a list of do's and don'ts that should help your keyword planning, regardless of which keyword program you use (Google, n.d.; Table 6–3).

Table 6–3. *Do's and Don'ts of Keywords*

Do . . .	Don't . . .
Describe how your customers think of your product or service.	Don't be too specific.
Use the right amount of details.	Don't be overly general.
Use adjectives sparingly.	Don't start your keyword research with an adjective.
Use multiple keywords or phrases about your topic.	Don't use keywords about unrelated topics.
Use location if your customers aren't in the same location as your product or service.	Don't use location if you will use location targeting for your ads.

SEO is not a one-time activity, but something that you should be working on continuously. There are several ways to measure the effectiveness of your SEO strategy, including keyword rankings, organic traffic, time spent on a page, return and direct visitors, and domain authority. We will define these metrics next.

- **Keyword rankings:** You can track your Google ranking for keywords related to your business by doing a Google search. The results will show you where your website ranks for those keywords. The goal is to be the first listing, which would be a ranking of 1.

- **Organic traffic:** This is the traffic that comes from an online search versus a link from another source (e.g., social media, email campaign, or direct link).

- **Time spent on page:** As it sounds, this shows the average time a visitor spends on each page of your website. It measures the level of engagement visitors have with your site.

- **Returning and direct visitors:** This shows whether your visitors are new or returning.

- **Domain authority:** This is a search engine ranking score that predicts how likely a website is to rank in search engine result pages. Domain authority scores range from one to 100—the higher the score, the greater the likelihood of ranking (Moz, n.d.).

The next tactic is localization. Does your business have a brick-and-mortar location where your customers can find you? If so, you need to target potential customers in the surrounding area. One of the easiest ways to do this is to create a Google My Business (GMB) account. This is a free service that is separate from your website being indexed. Google My Business requires you to verify your physical address by mailing you a postcard with an access code. It only takes a few days to arrive, and then you enter the access code into your Google My Business account. You can then customize your GMB profile with information about your business, including products and services, contact information, and operating hours. Even if you are providing home-based services or do not have a location where clients can come to your office, you should set up a Google My Business account. Once you verify your address, you can then make it private and instead display a city or state(s) where your business operates and set a radius. You can even select multiple states in the Google My Business app.

The third SEO tactic is optimizing for mobile. According to Statista, mobile devices generate 54.8 percent of global website traffic (Clement, 2021). So when you design your website, be sure that the mobile version is as user-friendly as the desktop version. Additional ways of optimizing your website for search engines are to include internal links (links to other pages on your website) and backlinks (links on external websites with related content that lead to your site). If your website has a blog, you can link to your own blog posts. However, you also want to post links on social media back to your blog to drive traffic from external sources. Another way to drive traffic is to submit your website on directories, such as ASHA ProFind or websites related to your products and services. If you are a blogger, consider writing a guest post for another blogger; if you sell materials, contact bloggers to list your products on their website. Finally, be sure that your website is secured through an SSL certificate. This stands for secure sockets layer (SSL) and is intended to keep the connection secure (indicated by an "https" instead of "http" web address) (Vocell, 2020).

8. **Regularly create and publish quality content:** Once your website is published, you want to make sure to regularly update it. This will also help improve your search ranking. An easy way to create new content for your website is to create a blog page. This does not have to be a monetized blog like we discussed in Chapter 5. Instead, this is a way to provide useful information to your target audience to drive traffic to your website. Other ways to update your website include posting testimonials from customers and updating page content on a regular basis.

9. **Install webmaster tools:** Your webmaster tools will enable you to track which content is being viewed and the source of the website traffic. This also helps you measure the success of your SEO tactics. Two important webmaster tools that you will need for your website are Google Analytics and Google Search Console. You can install your own webmaster tools or hire someone to complete this step for you. If you have hired someone to design your website, ask them to complete this step for you. If not, you can consider hiring someone on Fiverr.com to set up your Google Analytics account. As of the writing of this book, both of these tools are free of charge if you have a Google account. Google Search Console will help you understand and improve how Google sees your site. There are step-by-step instructions for setting up and using both of these tools, which can be found on Google.com.

10. **Implement a website maintenance plan:** Once your website is up and running, be sure to create a plan to maintain your website. In addition to updating the content of your website, you need to make sure that your website continues to function well. Some things that you want to make sure to do at least on a monthly basis are:

- Keep software up to date
- Run security scans
- Back up your website
- Use traffic data to learn about your audience
- Use performance data to optimize and fix errors

Email Marketing

In 2020, the number of global email users amounted to four billion and is set to grow to 4.6 billion users in 2025. It is estimated that the average American spends nearly 2.5 hours a day in their personal email inbox. Additionally, in 2020, 78% of marketers said that email was important to overall company success, which was an increase from 71% in 2019 (Kirsch, 2021). This number was even higher for business-to-business (B2B) marketers, with 79% saying that their most used form of content marketing was email newsletters in 2020 (Content Marketing Institute, 2020). Email marketing is one of the best ways you can spend your marketing dollars. On average, it generates $36 for every $1 spent, which is a return on investment (ROI) of 3600%. Although it's true that social media is a great way to market your business, growing your email list should be one of your top priorities. You can then send relevant content that your audience will find valuable, which enables you to build a relationship and establish trust. Some ways to provide value to your target audience are to send newsletters, stories, and free resources. People buy from those who they know, like, and trust. So once you begin providing value to potential customers, they will be more likely to buy from you when you present a sales offer. In fact, *Forbes* reports that you are 40 times more likely to acquire new customers through email than through Facebook or Twitter (YEC Council, 2021).

Another advantage of growing an email list outside of social media is that you own the list. You can send an email directly to your audience however often you'd like and know that the content is getting directly to their inbox. With some of the algorithms on social media, marketers have to become more strategic to get their message in front of their target audience. Another advantage that email has over social media is that if you ever lose access to your social media account for some reason, you will still be able to communicate directly with your audience.

Now that you are convinced that you need an email list, let's talk about adding an email marketing program to your marketing budget. Instead of just sending emails directly from your inbox, such as Gmail, Outlook, or Yahoo!, you should use an email marketing system to organize your list and design your emails. When deciding on a program, you should look for the following features:

- **Number of contacts:** Most email marketing programs will have a free plan. If your number of contacts exceeds a certain number, then you will need to upgrade your plan. Be aware of how many contacts you have and how much more you are paying for the contacts on a monthly basis. If you are using your email campaigns effectively, you should see a positive ROI. Therefore, an increase in your email contacts should result in an increase in your revenue to offset the costs.

- **Number of emails per month:** Again, many email programs will have tiers based on the number of emails you send each month. If you have an email list of 10,000 subscribers and your maximum email send is 100,000 per month, you can only send 10 emails to your list in a given month. If you send an email every day, you will need a plan that allows for 300,000 emails per month (e.g., 10,000 × 30), plus the number of emails in your automation sequences. For example, you may send a series of emails whenever someone subscribes to your email list, or when someone abandons their shopping cart in your online store.

- **Templates:** One of the major benefits of using an email marketing program is the ability to design visually appealing emails. You want to choose a program that not only has email templates but is also user-friendly.

- **A/B testing:** This feature allows you to evaluate the effectiveness of your email campaigns. You can test two scenarios, such as subject line or send time, to see which has the better performance. This is usually a premium feature and can offer you valuable insights if used correctly.

- **Schedule emails:** You may notice that some of your marketing emails will come at one or three o'clock in the morning. *Do these people ever sleep? Who is up sending marketing emails at 3 am?* Chances are that the emails are scheduled in advance. While some marketers may just be in a different time zone or are truly burning the midnight oil, one of the most valuable features of email marketing programs (apart from automation) is the ability to schedule emails in advance. Coupled with A/B testing, you can optimize your send times to have the greatest likelihood of being opened by your audience.

- **Automations:** Did we mention that automations are the best feature of email marketing? This enables you to create an email that is sent *automatically* after an action occurs. Have you ever received an email urging you to come back and check out the items that you left in your cart? That's an automation.

- **Email sequences:** Email sequences are similar to automations, except they take it a step further. Your audience (or segments of your audience) will receive a series of emails based upon an action or lack of action. Using email sequences saves you time and money while allowing you to nurture your email list in your sleep.

- **Social media posting:** Earlier in this chapter, we stressed the importance of including social media as one of your marketing channels. There are a number of ways to do this, such as posting from Canva or sharing your latest blog post. Another easy way to create your social media posts is posting when you send email campaigns. Many of the popular email marketing programs have integrations for this process.

According to HubSpot's Not Another State of Marketing Report (2021), the most popular email programs in 2021 were MailChimp and Constant Contact. Additional programs on the list of those most used were ConvertKit and Active

Campaign. After you've chosen an email program, you will need to develop strategies for growing your email list. Here are ten ways to obtain more email subscribers.

1. **Embedded sign-up forms on your website:** You should strategically place a sign-up form in a prominent location on your website. This can be in the header, footer, or sidebar. The sign-up form should be on every page of your website so it is easy to find.

2. **Pop-ups and overlays on your website:** A pop-up is a great way to capture leads. Unlike an embedded sign-up form, a pop-up must be closed before visitors can view the other content on your website. When designing your pop-up, you want to make sure that it is clear what benefit email subscribers gain from joining your email list. Is it access to exclusive content? A monthly newsletter? A discount code to spend in your store?

3. **Loyalty/referral programs:** You can create a loyalty program for repeat customers, or a referral program where customers receive a discount if they refer a friend.

4. **Lead-generation offer:** A lead-generation offer is something that you create for the specific reason of collecting your customers' contact information. For example, you may request a name and email address in order to access the free offer. Some types of lead-generation offers are a free e-book, guide, or list.

5. **Offer an incentive:** Why should a visitor sign up for your email list? What can you offer that will incentivize your target audience to subscribe to your list? Consider offering a discount on their first purchase, such as 10% or 20% off. If you offer a subscription product, maybe you can enroll them in a free trial in exchange for their email address. Other incentives include limited-time offers, free shipping, and access to exclusive content. According to a survey from RetailMeNot, discounts encourage 67% of consumers to make a purchase they weren't originally planning to make. (RetailMeNot, 2018)

6. **Host a webinar:** In Chapter 5 we discussed hosting webinars as a way to generate income for your business. In this example, we are suggesting that you host a free webinar with the intention of collecting leads to grow and nurture your email list, which will result in future sales.

7. **Giveaway:** If you are trying to grow your email list, you can also get sign-ups from your social media accounts. Consider hosting a free giveaway of a product (e.g., free t-shirt) or service (e.g., free hour of coaching). Visitors must provide their email addresses to be entered into the drawing. You want to then drive traffic to your website for visitors to sign up and be entered into the drawing.

8. **Subscribe to your blog:** One of the SEO strategies that we mentioned earlier was to create a blog on your website. You can create a blog to provide value to your target audience, and if people like what they see, they will want to read more. Entice potential subscribers by offering to send an email notification whenever you write a new post.

9. **Call to action on your social media page:** A call to action is a specific action that you want your visitors to take, such as "subscribe" or "download." You can place links on your Facebook page or Instagram bio that will allow visitors to easily subscribe to your email list and receive the promised offer or benefit.

10. **Email newsletter:** As mentioned earlier, email newsletters are used by 79% of B2B marketers. Whether your business is B2B or B2C, your target audience will subscribe to your newsletter if there is enough value provided. You may consider posting snippets of your newsletter on social media and encourage people to subscribe to read more.

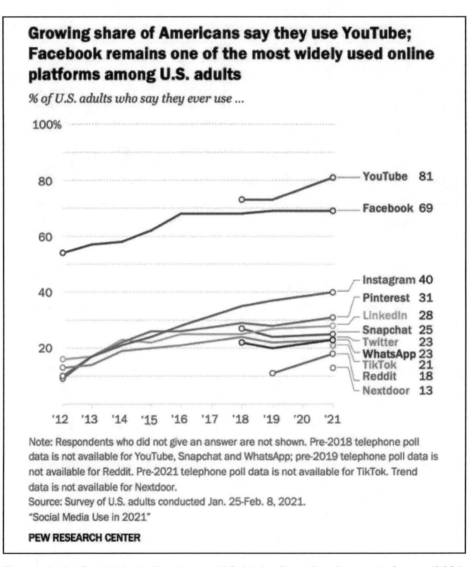

Figure 6–6. *Social Media Use Among U.S. Adults. From Pew Research Center. (2021, April 5). Social Media Use in 2021. Pew Research Center: Internet, Science & Tech.*

Social Media Marketing

According to Pew Research Center (2021), about 70% of adult Americans use any kind of social media. The most used platform is YouTube (81%), followed by Facebook (69%). Instagram (40%), Pinterest (31%), and LinkedIn (28%) round out the top five most commonly used social media platforms in the United States The use of social media has been steadily increasing over the past ten years, as shown in Figure 6–6. Though Facebook is still one of the most widely used social media platforms, its growth has stalled over the past two years. For businesses, some of the more popular social media channels are Facebook, LinkedIn, Twitter, and Instagram. Other platforms include Snapchat and TikTok for business. Pinterest has also gained considerable popularity in terms of being a viable option for businesses to market their offerings.

When you are posting on social media platforms, make sure that you take into consideration which social media platform your target audience is checking most frequently and what time they are typically online. In business-to-consumer (B2C) industries, marketers find Facebook (85%) and Instagram (78%) to be the most useful for their business. Whereas, in business-to-business (B2B) industries, 87% of marketers consider LinkedIn to be the most effective platform (Hootsuite, 2021). As you can see in Table 6–4, Twitter has a largely male audience (68%) and is popular among the 30- to 49-year age group (44%). If your target audience is female, you may consider Pinterest (78%) for the 30- to 49-year age group, though Instagram caters to a younger audience (25- to 34-year-olds). If you are a B2B marketer, LinkedIn dominates this space with its largest age group being 46 to 55 years old. Also, consider using something like SproutSocial.com to receive insights as to when the best days and times are to post your social media content. This will vary in terms of the season, as well as which platform you're using. For instance, we saw during the COVID-19 pandemic, that there was an influx of Instagram users by middle-aged adults which previously was reserved more for the millennial demographic or adults in their 20s (Barnhart, 2021).

When you are developing a social media strategy, be sure that you choose the platform(s) that work best for your business. Instead of trying to utilize all channels, initially, you should focus your marketing efforts on two or three platforms to effectively reach your target audience (Pew Research, 2021). There are certain consumer demographics that can help you decide on which social media platforms to focus your marketing efforts, namely age and gender. Figure 6–7 from Pew Research Center breaks down social media use by these demographics and more, including education and geographic location. For example, 67% of U.S. adults who live in rural areas use Facebook, whereas only 18% of adults who live in rural areas use Twitter (see Figure 6–7 on page 185).

Table 6–4. *Social Media Platform Comparison Chart*

	Facebook	Instagram	Twitter	Pinterest	YouTube	LinkedIn
# monthly active users	2.7 billion	1 billion	187 million	400 million	2 billion	738 million
Largest age group	25 to34 (26.3%)	25 to 34 (33.1%)	30 to 49 (44%)	30 to 49	15 to 25	46 to 55
Gender	44% female, 56% male	57% female, 43% male	32% female, 68% male	78% female, 22% male	72% of female internet users; 72% of male internet users	51% male, 49% female
Time spent per day	38 minutes	29 minutes	3.53 minutes/session	14.2 minutes	41.9 minutes	63% access monthly, 22% weekly
Used for	Posting and sharing photos and videos	Posting and sharing photos and videos	Short updates (280 characters or less)	Discovery		Business-to-business
Business uses	Keep up-to-date with news	Find information about products	Follow/find information about products & brands	Follow/find information about products & brands		Follow/find information about products & brands

Use of online platforms, apps varies – sometimes widely – by demographic group

% of U.S. adults in each demographic group who say they ever use …

0% 20 40 60 80 100

	YouTube	Facebook	Instagram	Pinterest	LinkedIn	Snapchat	Twitter	WhatsApp	TikTok	Reddit	Nextdoor
Total	81	69	40	31	28	25	23	23	21	18	13
Men	82	61	36	16	31	22	25	26	17	23	10
Women	80	77	44	46	26	28	22	21	24	12	16
White	79	67	35	34	29	23	22	16	18	17	15
Black	84	74	49	35	27	26	29	23	30	17	10
Hispanic	85	72	52	18	19	31	23	46	31	14	8
Ages 18-29	95	70	71	32	30	65	42	24	48	36	5
30-49	91	77	48	34	36	24	27	30	22	22	17
50-64	83	73	29	38	33	12	18	23	14	10	16
65+	49	50	13	18	11	2	7	10	4	3	8
<$30K	75	70	35	21	12	25	12	23	22	10	6
$30K-$49,999	83	76	45	33	21	27	29	20	29	17	11
$50K-$74,999	79	61	39	29	21	29	22	19	20	20	12
$75K+	90	70	47	40	50	28	34	29	20	26	20
HS or less	70	64	30	22	10	21	14	20	21	9	4
Some college	86	71	44	36	28	32	26	16	24	20	12
College+	89	73	49	37	51	23	33	33	19	26	24
Urban	84	70	45	30	30	28	27	28	24	18	17
Suburban	81	70	41	32	33	25	23	23	20	21	14
Rural	74	67	25	34	15	18	18	9	16	10	2

Note: White and Black adults include those who report being only one race and are not Hispanic. Hispanics are of any race. Not all numerical differences between groups shown are statistically significant (e.g., there are no statistically significant differences between the shares of White, Black or Hispanic Americans who say the use Facebook). Respondents who did not give an answer are not shown.

Source: Survey of U.S. adults conducted Jan. 25-Feb. 8, 2021.
"Social Media Use in 2021"

PEW RESEARCH CENTER

Figure 6-7. Use of Online Platforms by Demographic Group. From PEW Research Center. (2021, April 5). Social Media Use in 2021. Pew Research Center: Internet, Science & Tech.

After you've decided which social media platforms to use to reach your target audience, you will need to create your profiles. Each network requires different information for your business profile. For example, Facebook is the most comprehensive, and you need to include details such as your business hours and services. As of the writing of this book, Facebook limits the length of your bio to 255 characters, while Instagram, Twitter, and Pinterest limit the length of bios to 150 to 160 characters. Though the details may vary slightly for each platform, Rock Content suggests that your social media bio should have the three I's (Rock Content, 2021):

1. **Informative**: information about your business (e.g., What do you do?)

2. **Imaginative**: something to make your brand stand out (e.g., How do you do it?)

3. **Inviting**: include a call to action (e.g., What do you want the audience to do?)

Dara Fontein provides recommendations for social media bio templates for Facebook, Instagram, Twitter, and Pinterest, which we've summarized in Figure 6–8 on the next page. (Fontein, 2019).

After you've set up your social media profiles, you need to post relevant content on a regular basis to keep your followers engaged. Here are ten ideas for social media posts:

1. Have a contest where you give away an item that your audience deems valuable.

2. Share, Pin, and Tweet posts from others.

3. Post a recorded video or go live.

4. Repurpose your content by pulling a quote from a blog post and adding an image.

5. Create how-to's or tutorials about your product or service.

6. Post case studies about past customers.

7. Host interviews with industry experts.

8. Post memes.

9. Create a poll.

10. Share milestones, such as anniversaries, reaching a certain number of followers, etc.

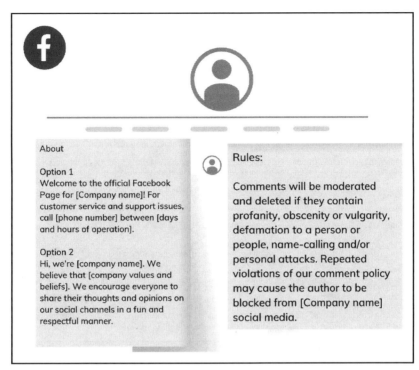

A

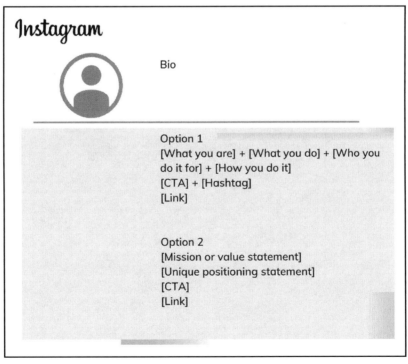

B

Figure 6–8. **A.** *Sample Facebook Bios.* **B.** *Sample Instagram Bios.* continues

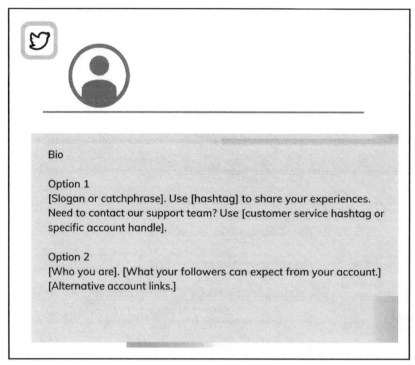

C

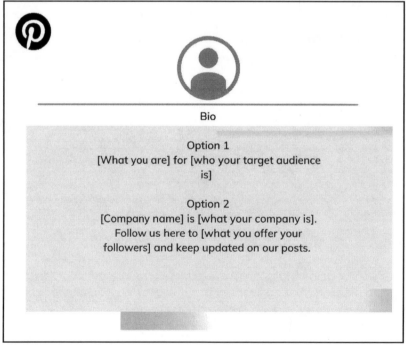

D

Figure 6–8. continued **C.** *Sample Twitter Bios.* **D.** *Sample Pinterest Bios. Adapted from Fontein, D. (2019, April 2).* How to Write Every Kind of Social Media Bio (+25 Free Templates). *Hootsuite.*

In-Person Marketing

In addition to digital marketing, in-person marketing is still a viable option. When considering potential opportunities for in-person marketing, this might include something as simple as hosting a free lecture or seminar about your area of expertise or related to the product you are selling/service you are offering. This could also mean sponsoring a local community event where your niche target market might be in attendance. This type of opportunity will hopefully help you gain more exposure in terms of having your brand be known and seen within your target market. It allows you or a representative from your business to be able to answer questions and provide more information about your product/service in person. This type of marketing often holds great value over simply having your potential clients view digital ads without a human "connected" behind the ad. If you are trying to reach an international audience, perhaps hosting a free or low-cost webinar can attract new leads from global communities.

Networking (External and Internal)

> **❝**
> **Establishing networks of SLP colleagues who are in a similar work setting or specialty, facing the same challenges, is vital to continued growth and happiness in private practice.**
> *Catherine Conlin*
> *Bright Brain Thinking* **❞**

Networking is a very crucial part of your business, regardless of whether you are selling a product, providing therapy services, or serving as a keynote speaker at a seminar. In terms of owning and operating your own business, networking will not only become a vital tool to help you gain clients, but will also help you continue to grow, refine, revise, and enhance your business. The two ways to do this are through both internal networking and external networking. When we describe external networking, we refer to any networking event that you are engaging in to gain more direct leads or client referrals. Examples of this could be joining your local chamber of commerce, joining a business networking group that is specifically designed to help members gain clients, attending LinkedIn-sponsored or Facebook-sponsored networking events, and engaging with local or virtual networking groups that help you broaden your network. You want to make sure that you're expanding your network because you never know when someone outside of your target audience might unexpectedly find value in your services.

When we discuss internal networking, we are referring to the act of engaging in your professional community. In your case, that could be a community of SLPs, SLP Entrepreneurs, or other related private practice owners. The reason for this is not primarily to gain clients but rather to engage in sharing resources and working on creating collaborations with those colleagues. Many of our highlighted SLP Entrepreneurs in Chapter 8 have collaborated with other professionals that may or may not be SLPs. You want to have a network of people who have similar challenges and resources to share and compare so that you can each refine, revise, and enhance your respective businesses.

In terms of a traditional or conventional private practice, if you choose to enroll in becoming a preferred provider/in-network, you will broaden your exposure and network simply by being in the provider directory. You may also find that during a networking event of local private practice or business professionals, you might have the opportunity to do some in-person marketing (e.g., if you were to run into a local ENT physician). You would want to make sure that you had at the very least your business card with your logo and information about your services. You should not only take the opportunity to talk with that physician, but also give them some tangible items to take back to their office, such as a small infographic or flyers. Make sure that you get their contact information, or at least record their name and other pertinent information so you can follow up in case they do not contact you.

> **"**
>
> **Find a mentor. Find someone who has experience doing what you want to do and get to know them.**
>
> *Melissa Jakubowitz*
> *eLiveNow*
>
> **"**

Part of having that executive presence and being confident during networking engagements is making sure that you are prepared with a concise message about what you do and, most importantly, how you can impact others by bringing value to them or their organizations. This is where your "elevator pitch" comes in. It is labeled as an "elevator" pitch because it should be brief enough to provide your intended audience with your message in the time it takes to ride an elevator. This is a concise message that you will share with people who you are just meeting for the

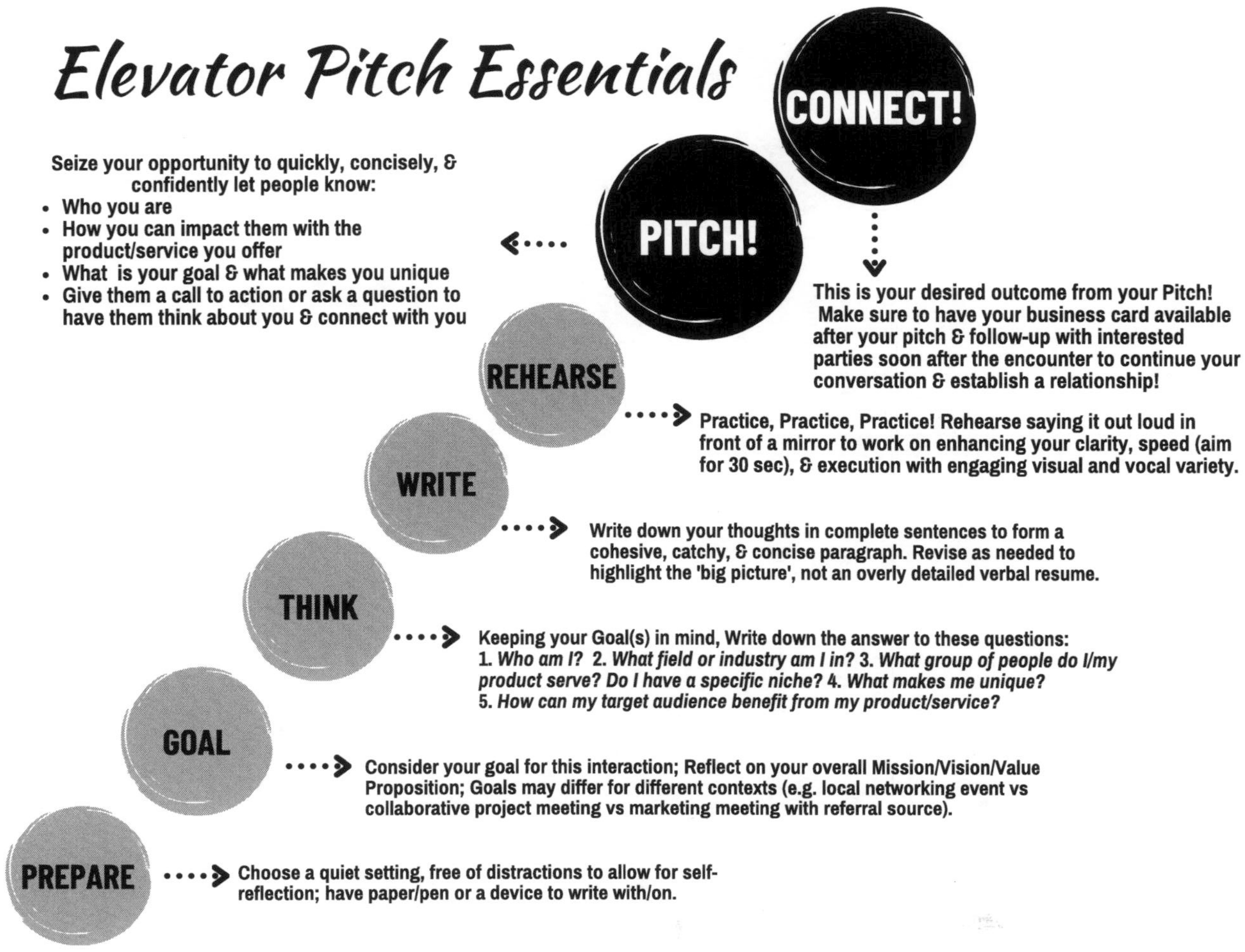

Elevator Pitch Essentials

Seize your opportunity to quickly, concisely, & confidently let people know:

- Who you are
- How you can impact them with the product/service you offer
- What is your goal & what makes you unique
- Give them a call to action or ask a question to have them think about you & connect with you

CONNECT!

PITCH!

REHEARSE

WRITE

THINK

GOAL

PREPARE

This is your desired outcome from your Pitch! Make sure to have your business card available after your pitch & follow-up with interested parties soon after the encounter to continue your conversation & establish a relationship!

Practice, Practice, Practice! Rehearse saying it out loud in front of a mirror to work on enhancing your clarity, speed (aim for 30 sec), & execution with engaging visual and vocal variety.

Write down your thoughts in complete sentences to form a cohesive, catchy, & concise paragraph. Revise as needed to highlight the 'big picture', not an overly detailed verbal resume.

Keeping your Goal(s) in mind, Write down the answer to these questions: 1. Who am I? 2. What field or industry am I in? 3. What group of people do I/my product serve? Do I have a specific niche? 4. What makes me unique? 5. How can my target audience benefit from my product/service?

Consider your goal for this interaction; Reflect on your overall Mission/Vision/Value Proposition; Goals may differ for different contexts (e.g. local networking event vs collaborative project meeting vs marketing meeting with referral source).

Choose a quiet setting, free of distractions to allow for self-reflection; have paper/pen or a device to write with/on.

Figure 6–9. *Elevator Pitch Essentials.*

191

first time. It is an opportunity to identify what you do and how you can help them. This encounter needs to be short and impactful. You never know who you are going to meet who may either find interest in utilizing your product or service themselves, or may know of somebody else that can benefit from your product or service.

To create your elevator pitch, you need to make sure that you state your name, and in functional, yet catchy terms, express how you help individuals and organizations. After your pitch, have your business cards ready (if in-person) and/or provide your social media/email contact links. You may find that you need to prepare slightly revised "elevator pitches" based on where, and in what context, you are sharing this information with your audience. Consider what you wish to gain from that connection. Refer to Figure 6–9 for an elevator pitch script that highlights some strategies for perfecting your elevator pitch.

Marketing Tactics

Once you've set up your marketing channels (e.g., website, email list, and social media), you will have to share content with your audience that provides value and helps you reach your marketing objectives. During this part of your marketing plan, you are going to develop the marketing tactics that you will execute using your marketing channels. According to Smart Insights, your marketing strategy dictates the marketing activity needed to achieve your business goals and vision, whereas tactics answer *how* that will happen. Additionally, tactics should support the overall direction of your business by contributing to your goals. To ensure that your tactics are contributing to your objectives, you can align your tactics with your strategies. We will use the objectives that we set earlier to develop examples of marketing tactics (Chaffey, 2021).

Tactics for Increasing Brand Awareness

- **Write a blog:** In 2021, 92% of content marketers used blog posts as part of their marketing strategy. Additionally, businesses with a blog received 55% more visitors to their website and produced 67% more leads every month than those that didn't (Lin, 2021). Experts suggest that you should aim for 1,500 to 2,000 words for your blog post length. Also, consider that quality is more important than quantity. What kind of value can you offer your target audience? Make your blog posts detailed, and be sure to include keywords that you discovered during your keyword research.

- **Make a video:** In 2021, 86% of businesses used video as a marketing tool, with 93% of marketers saying that it was an important part of their marketing strategy (Wyzowl, 2021). You can use videos to accomplish several of your marketing objectives, including brand awareness, sales, lead generation, and engagement. Additionally, you can post videos across your different marketing channels. For example, you can post your videos on YouTube, link to them in your social media posts, and embed them on your website.

- **Create a podcast:** According to Podcast Insights, there were two million active podcasts in 2021, with more than 48 million episodes (Winn, 2021). Statista estimates that 57% of all consumers in the United States above the age of 12 listen to podcasts (Statista, 2021). A podcast is an audio broadcast, which is easy to listen to while commuting or multi-tasking. Therefore, creating a podcast enables you to reach your target audience in another way and capture those who may not have the time or attention to read a blog.

Tactics for Increasing Sales

- **Use call-to-action buttons on your website:** Whether you are selling products or services, you need to let your potential customers know what you want them to *do* when they visit your site. Do you want them to "Buy" or "Call" or "Schedule?" If you do not ask your site visitors to do anything, the odds are that they will not.

- **Add customer testimonials to your website and social media:** Testimonials provide a way to demonstrate what is referred to as "social proof." Sprout Social found that a whopping 91% of shoppers read online reviews prior to making a buying decision, and that buyers are more likely to buy from businesses recommended by their peers. In fact, Sprout Social found that 40% of consumers find new brands to follow online based on recommendations from friends and family. Even more telling, 82% of Americans ask for recommendations from family and friends before making any type of purchase. So the more social proof, by way of testimonials, ratings, and even number of followers, the more confident potential customers will feel in buying your product or service (West, 2021). You can pay for a program to collect customer testimonials, embed a form on your website, or contact previous customers directly to request that they write a testimonial.

- **Reach out to influencers:** Ask a popular blogger if they will write a review for your product or service in one of their blog posts.

Tactics for Increasing Engagement

- **Build your social media presence:** As we discussed in the Social Media section earlier, it is important to choose the social media channels that your target audience is on. Once you've created your profile, you will be able to engage with your audience by posting, sharing content, and replying to comments. You can also run paid ads on social media. In order to do this, you must determine your primary audiences versus your secondary targeted audiences. For example, think about whether you are marketing to individuals or organizations, local, national, or international audiences. What does your service delivery look like—is it in-person, online, or on-site? What industries are you reaching with your products: are they healthcare-related, education-related, or a little bit of both?

- **Use LinkedIn to network:** If you are marketing B2B, LinkedIn is the place to be. Once your profile is set up, share content, make connections, and join groups. You want to establish yourself as an expert in your niche.

- **Respond to customer reviews:** Whether you are selling a product or service, you should welcome feedback from your customers. If a customer takes the time to write a review, they have likely had a very positive experience or a very negative experience. While we hope that all of your customers will leave a positive review, responding to negative reviews is a great way to demonstrate your professionalism and your extraordinary customer service.

Tactics for Lead Generation

- **Hold a contest:** As mentioned earlier, giveaways are a great way to entice your target audience to give you their email address. You should choose a giveaway of something that is relevant and valuable to your audience.

- **Offer a free download:** We discussed this as another option for growing your email list. Potential customers provide their email address in exchange for a digital download, such as an e-book or guide that you've created.

- **Write an email newsletter:** Newsletters are used by 82% of B2B marketers, and 31% of businesses cite newsletters as their highest-performing tactic for generating leads. When visitors opt in to receive an email newsletter, they are asking to hear from you on a regular basis. Whether your emails are sent weekly or monthly, newsletters are a great way to stay in touch with your audience.

Tactics for Increasing Revenue

- **Host a webinar:** You can present a free webinar with a paid offer at the end. Consumers are used to the sales nature of free webinars. Spending a few extra minutes is a small price to pay for an hour's worth of free content. Be sure that you have a specific call to action during your webinar and that you make it easy for your audience to purchase your product or service. Even if your webinar attendees do not purchase from you during the webinar, you are able to use this as an opportunity for brand awareness and to present yourself as an expert in your niche.

- **Partner with another business**: There are a number of ways to partner with other businesses. The key is to develop mutually beneficial relationships. If you offer complementary products or services, you may bundle these into unique offerings for your target audiences.

- **Post case studies on your website:** A case study is similar to a testimonial, but it is a more detailed story. Ask previous clients and customers to write a case study about how your product or service helped them. You can then use your own words to tie it together. Include these three elements in your case studies: problem, solution, result. You can then use the case studies as social proof to encourage your target audience to make a purchase. You can include these case studies on your website, social media platforms, and in your email marketing campaigns.

In this chapter, we've shared a variety of considerations for your marketing endeavors, networking efforts, and branding. Now use Figure 6–10 (on the next page) to help you brainstorm ideas for your business.

Marketing/Branding/Networking Brainstorming Boxes

DETERMINE YOUR PRIMARY
& SECONDARY TARGET
AUDIENCES &
KEY MESSAGES

WEBSITE HOSTING &
WEBSITE DESIGN

BASIC CONTACT INFO VS
CONTENT CREATION &/OR
PRODUCT/SERVICE PAYMENT
SECTION

DETERMINE YOUR
BRANDING– COLORS, LOGO,
FONT(S), STYLE OF
LANGUAGE/GRAPHICS

IN-PERSON MARKETING
FREE LECTURES, VENDOR
EVENTS,
SEMINAR/CONFERENCES

NETWORKING
[EXTERNAL]
CLIENTELE

NETWORKING
[INTERNAL]
RESOURCES, COMMUNITY,
COLLABORATION

DIGITAL MARKETING
EMAIL LIST
SOCIAL MEDIA PAGES
PODCASTS
VIDEOS

Figure 6–10. *Marketing-Networking-Branding Brainstorming.*

CHAPTER CHECKLIST

☐ Choose your business name

☐ Define your brand elements

☐ Complete the SWOT Analysis Template (Figure 6–2B)

☐ Create your Buyer Personas (Table 6–1)

☐ Determine your marketing expenses (Table 6–2)

☐ Create a marketing action plan

☐ Set your marketing objectives

☐ Choose your marketing channels

☐ Create your website (Figure 6–5)

☐ Create your social media profiles

☐ Select your email program

☐ Sign up to attend networking events (in person or online)

☐ Create your elevator pitch (may need different ones for different contexts/events) (Figure 6–9)

REFERENCES

AllBusiness Contributor Group. (2019, May 25). 10 key steps to building a great small business website. *Forbes*. Retrieved September 12, 2021, from https://www.forbes.com/sites/allbusiness/2019/05/25/small-business-website-tips

American Marketing Association. (n.d.). *Definitions of marketing*. Retrieved July 1, 2021, from https://www.ama.org/the-definition-of-marketing-what-is-marketing/

Barker, S. (2019, February 20). Six brand-building strategies for small businesses and startups. *Forbes*. Retrieved September 22, 2021, from https://www.forbes.com/sites/forbescoaches council/2019/02/20/six-brand-building-strategies-for-small-businesses-and-startups/?sh =533a41666bab

Barnhart, B. (2021, March 9). *Social media demographics to inform your brand's strategy in 2021*. Sprout Social. Retrieved September 12, 2021, from https://sproutsocial.com/insights/new-social-media-demographics/

Chaffey, D. (2021, September 30). *Strategy vs tactics for marketing—why the difference*. Smart Insights. Retrieved September 30, 2021, from https://www.smartinsights.com/marketing-planning/marketing-strategy/marketing-strategy-vs-tactics-difference/

Clement, J. (2021, April 28). *Mobile percentage of website traffic 2021*. Statista. Retrieved September 12, 2021, from https://www.statista.com/statistics/277125/share-of-website-traffic-coming-from-mobile-devices/

Content Marketing Institute. (2020). *11th Annual B2B Content Marketing Benchmarks, Budgets, and Trends: Insights for 2021* [PDF].

Digital.com. (2021, September 29). *Despite pandemic, 1 in 4 small retail businesses still don't have a website*. Digital.com. Retrieved October 1, 2021, from https://digital.com/despite-pandemic-1-in-4-small-retail-businesses-still-dont-have-a-website/

Dodhia, Z. (2021, April 21). 4 branding strategies every startup founder should know about. *Entrepreneur*. Retrieved September 12, 2021, from https://www.entrepreneur.com/article/368944

Doyle, A. (2021, January 27). *When and how to use an elevator pitch*. The Balance Careers. Retrieved October 1, 2021, from https://www.thebalancecareers.com/elevator-speech-examples-and-writing-tips-2061976

Eckstein, M. (2021, April 11). *Social media engagement: Why it matters and how to do it well*. Buffer Library. Retrieved September 22, 2021, from https://buffer.com/library/social-media-engagement/

Fontein, D. (2019, April 2). *How to write every kind of social media bio (+25 free templates)*. Hootsuite. Retrieved September 12, 2021, from https://blog.hootsuite.com/social-media-bio/

FutureLearn. (2020, November 4). *How to create a marketing strategy and measure your results*. FutureLearn. Retrieved September 12, 2021, from https://www.futurelearn.com/info/blog/how-to-create-a-marketing-strategy.

Getman, C. (2021, June 30). *How to write a marketing plan*. Vital Design. Retrieved September 22, 2021, from https://vtldesign.com/digital-marketing/digital-marketing-strategy/how-to-write-marketing-plan-template/

Google. (n.d.). *Keyword Planner*. Google Ads. Retrieved September 22, 2021, from https://ads.google.com/home/tools/keyword-planner/

Henry, S. M. (2021, August 2). How to craft the perfect elevator pitch. *Women's Business Daily*. https://www.womensbusinessdaily.com/career/how-to-craft-the-perfect-elevator-pitch/

Hootsuite. (2021). *Social trends 2021 survey*. https://www.hootsuite.com/webinars/social-trends-2021

Hubspot. (2021). *Not another state of marketing report* [PDF]. https://www.hubspot.com/state-of-marketing

Kenton, W. (2021, September 6). *Brand*. Investopedia. Retrieved September 22, 2021, from https://www.investopedia.com/terms/b/brand.asp

Kirsch, K. (2021, August 13). The ultimate list of email marketing stats for 2021. *HubSpot Blog*. Retrieved September 22, 2021, from https://blog.hubspot.com/marketing/email-marketing-stats

Leone, C. (2020, November 18). How much should you budget for marketing in 2021? *WebStrategies, Inc.* Retrieved September 22, 2021, from https://www.webstrategiesinc.com/blog/how-much-budget-for-online-marketing-in-2014

Lin, Y. (2021, July 5). 10 blogging statistics you need to know in 2021. *Oberlo.* Retrieved September 22, 2021, from https://www.oberlo.com/blog/blogging-statistics

Lin, Y. (2021, July 23). 10 powerful podcast statistics you need to know in 2021. *Oberlo.* Retrieved September 12, 2021, from https://www.oberlo.com/blog/podcast-statistics

Lua, A. (2020, July 24). *Social proof: What it is and 18 ways to use it in your marketing.* Buffer Library. Retrieved September 22, 2021, from https://buffer.com/library/social-proof/

Market Business News. (2021, March 30). *What are marketing tactics? Definition and examples.* Market Business News. Retrieved September 12, 2021, from https://marketbusinessnews.com/financial-glossary/what-are-marketing-tactics-definition-and-examples/

Moz. (n.d.). *Domain authority: What is it & how does it work?* Moz. Retrieved September 30, 2021, from https://moz.com/learn/seo/domain-authority.

Parsons, N. (2021, February 5). How to conduct a market analysis for your business in 4 steps *LivePlan Blog.*. Retrieved September 14, 2021, from https://www.liveplan.com/blog/market-analysis-in-4-steps/

Pew Research Center. (2021, April 5). *Social media use in 2021.* Pew Research Center. Retrieved September 10, 2021, from https://www.pewresearch.org/internet/2021/04/07/social-media-use-in-2021/pi_2021-04-07_social-media_0-01/

Pitre, A. (2021, June 22). 39 simple ways to grow your email list. *HubSpot Blog.* Retrieved September 14, 2021, from https://blog.hubspot.com/blog/tabid/6307/bid/32028/25-clever-ways-to-grow-your-email-marketing-list.aspx

RetailMeNot, Inc. (2018, April 25). *RetailMeNot survey: Deals and promotional offers drive incremental purchases online, especially among millennial buyers.* PR Newswire. Retrieved September 22, 2021, from https://www.prnewswire.com/news-releases/retailmenot-survey-deals-and-promotional-offers-drive-incremental-purchases-online-especially-among-millennial-buyers-300635775.html

Rock Content Writer. (2021, September 5). Social media profile: Here are 6 tips to create a great one. *Rock Content.* Retrieved September 22, 2021, from https://rockcontent.com/blog/social-media-profile/

Schwab, S. (2011, May). Finding your brand voice. *Crackerjack Marketing.* Retrieved September 22, 2021, from https://crackerjackmarketing.com/blog/finding-brand-voice/

Statista. (2021, March 19). *Number of e-mail users worldwide 2025.* Statista. Retrieved September 12, 2021, from https://www.statista.com/statistics/255080/number-of-e-mail-users-worldwide/

Statista. (2021, October 26). *U.S. Podcasting industry—statistics & facts.* Statista. Retrieved November 1, 2021, from https://www.statista.com/topics/3170/podcasting/

U.S. Small Business Administration. (n.d.). *Market research and competitive analysis.* SBA. Retrieved September 22, 2021, from https://www.sba.gov/business-guide/plan-your-business/market-research-competitive-analysis

Valentine, G. (2021, December 10). Council post: Executive presence: What is it, why you need it and how to get it. *Forbes.* Retrieved December 10, 2021, from https://www.forbes.com/sites/forbescoachescouncil/2018/07/31/executive-presence-what-is-it-why-you-need-it-and-how-to-get-it

Vocell, J. (2020, June). A beginner's guide to SSL: What it is & why it makes your website more secure. *HubSpot.* Retrieved September 12, 2021, from https://blog.hubspot.com/marketing/what-is-ssl

West, C. (2021, May 24). *Social proof: How to use psychology in digital marketing.* Sprout Social. Retrieved September 18, 2021, from https://sproutsocial.com/insights/social-proof/

Winn, R. (2021, August 25). *2021 podcast stats & facts (new research from APR 2021).* Podcast Insights. Retrieved September 22, 2021, from https://www.podcastinsights.com/podcast-statistics/

Wyzowl. (2021). *State of video marketing survey 2021.* Wyzowl. Retrieved September 20, 2021, from https://www.wyzowl.com/video-marketing-statistics/

YEC Council. (2021, June 4). Council post: Five tips to grow your email list in 2021. *Forbes*. Retrieved September 22, 2021, from https://www.forbes.com/sites/theyec/2021/06/04/five-tips-to-grow-your-email-list-in-2021/

CHAPTER 7

Sustaining Your Business Practices and Cultivating Long-Term Growth

PROFITABILITY

Accurate bookkeeping is the basis for all financial management. You can either do your own bookkeeping, pay for a bookkeeping program, or hire a bookkeeper for your business. Bookkeeping is what occurs on an ongoing basis and allows you to have the necessary information to create financial reports at given time periods throughout the year. These financial reports are going to help you determine the financial fitness of your business, inform business decisions, and allow you to apply for business funding. When you are just starting your business, you likely established a bookkeeping process and hired a certified public accountant (CPA). This person can help you prepare financial statements for your business on a quarterly and annual basis.

Most types of business financing require an application process that asks for financial statements such as your P&L (Profit and Loss) statement, balance sheet, and cash flow projections. Therefore, as a business owner, you should know your financial statements well enough to be able to discuss them with a lender. For this chapter, we will focus our attention on the P&L statement, also known as an income statement. Even if you are not applying for lending, this statement is going to let you know whether your business is profitable for a given period of time. You can run a P&L statement monthly, quarterly, or on an annual basis. First, let's review the key terms that will appear in the P&L Statement: sales, cost of goods sold, gross profit, operating expenses, and net profit.

- **Sales:** This is the amount that you receive from selling your products and services. Sales can also be referred to as revenue or income.

- **Cost of goods sold:** This is the cost to create your products. For example, if your business sells t-shirts, what is the cost to print each shirt? If you employ other workers, –labor is also included in the cost of goods sold.

- **Gross Profit:** This is the profit that is left after the cost of goods sold is subtracted from your sales. For example, you sell a t-shirt for $25 (sales), and it costs you $10 to make it (cost of goods sold), your gross profit would be $15 (sales – cost of goods sold = gross profit).

- **Operating expenses:** This can also be referred to as overhead costs and includes the expenses associated with running your business. These expenses include items such as your website, insurance, rent, taxes, and so forth. For example, if you offer home visits for your private practice, what are the costs of your materials and transportation to deliver the services?

- **Net Profit:** This is what remains after you've paid your expenses. This is the amount that is used to calculate your tax liability.

The basic formula for a P&L statement is as follows:

Revenue – Cost of Goods Sold = Gross Profit

Gross Profit – Operating Expenses = Net Profit

All quality business accounting software will generate a P&L statement like the one in Figure 7–1. The accuracy of your P&L statement will depend on your input data, such as receipts, invoices, and accounts receivable. This is where having a reliable bookkeeping system becomes extremely important. You should consider printing out your P&L statement regularly to track your business progress, whether that is monthly or quarterly. You can then use your P&L statement as the basis for creating your cash flow projections.

We discussed setting your prices in Chapter 2. Your prices are going to determine how many sales are needed to reach your revenue goals. Keep in mind that your prices should change over time. Oftentimes, SLPs are hesitant to raise their prices for fear that they will tarnish the relationship that they have with their existing customers. However, when you think like an entrepreneur, you will realize that as your expenses increase, your prices will need to increase concurrently. Also, consider that the average cost of inflation is approximately 2% annually. Therefore, if you don't increase your prices, you will in effect be giving yourself a pay *cut* every year. It is generally easier to raise prices on products than services. A product is typically purchased one time; so you pay the price that it was at the time of your purchase. Some stores will have a price match guarantee window, where you can request the price difference if the retailer lowers their price within a one- or two-week period. However, if someone purchased your e-book on Monday for $30 and it is priced at $25 on Friday, they may not ask for a price adjustment.

For services, on the other hand, it is a little more complicated to change your prices. If you are providing ongoing therapy, coaching, or a subscription service, for example, you will have to inform your clients that the prices they are currently paying will be increasing. SCORE suggests five do's and don'ts for raising prices without losing customers (SCORE, 2019, May 19).

1. Do study what your competitors are doing.

2. Do explain your reasons.

3. Do expect to lose some customers (and gain some).

4. Don't be sneaky.

5. Don't apologize.

There are also creative ways to structure your service price increases that will make a smoother transition for your clients. One way to structure your price increase is to create a lesser option for customers who either don't want to or can't pay higher

INCOME STATEMENT (PROFIT & LOSS STATEMENT)		
BUSINESS NAME		
Time Periods		
		End of Year 1
Sales		
Cost of Goods Sold		
GROSS PROFIT		$ -
Operating Expenses		
Salary (Office & Overhead)		
Payroll (taxes, etc.)		
Outside Services		
Supplies		
Repairs & Maintenance		
Advertising		
Car, Delivery, Travel		
Accounting Expenses		
Legal Expenses		
Rent		
Telephone		
Utilities		
Insurance		
Taxes (real estate, etc)		
Interest		
Depreciation		
Other Expenses:		
Miscellaneous		
(other 2)		
(other 3)		
TOTAL OPERATING EXPENSES		$ -
NET PROFIT/LOSS BEFORE TAXES		$ -
Income Taxes		
NET PROFIT/LOSS AFTER TAX		$ -
Owner draw or dividends		
RETAINED EARNINGS		$ -

Figure 7–1. *Sample Profit and Loss Statement. Modified from SCORE. (2011, April 26). 3-year profit and loss projection. SCORE.*

prices. For example, let's say your clients are being seen for one-hour sessions at $100 per hour; instead of increasing the price to $110 for a one-hour session, you can recommend a 45-minute session at the $100 rate. Another option is to raise the prices by adding fees. If you are doing home visits, you may start charging a travel fee. If you provide accent modification training, you may consider charging the fee for your online practice portal or having clients purchase their own course materials. The third option is to consider ways to add value along with the price increase. For example, if you are a consultant, you can offer asynchronous support in addition to weekly live meetings. HubSpot provides a template for a price increase letter (HubSpot, n.d.).

Dear [Insert Contact Name],

We're writing to inform you that due to [Insert reason(s)], the price of [Insert product/service name] will be increasing from [Insert current price] to [Insert new price].

We completely understand that a price increase is never ideal and work to avoid one whenever we can. Please know that as a result of this increase, we will be able to:

1. *[Explain benefit #1 the customer will see as a result of the increase].*
2. *[Explain benefit #2 the customer will see as a result of the increase].*
3. *[Explain benefit #3 the customer will see as a result of the increase].*

Because the increase goes into effect on [Date], all [Orders/Contracts] made before then will be honored at the previously agreed upon rate.

[Insert company name] appreciates your continued support and business. We know you have options for your [Insert product category] and we thank you for partnering with us. Should you have any questions or concerns about this increase, we encourage you to reach out to [Name/Department] at [Insert phone number and/or email address].

Sincerely,
[Your Name]

HIRING EMPLOYEES

If you are ready to hire employees, congratulations! This means that your business has grown to the point where you are no longer able to manage your workload on your own, which is a great problem to have. If you're in private practice you may have hesitated to start a waiting list, or maybe your waiting list already has 10 names on it. When do you need to hire employees to help relieve the burden? Is it now, or when you think you have a caseload to fill a part-time or full-time employee? If you want your practice to grow, you definitely want to consider hiring employees sooner rather than later. You may decide to hire a biller, front desk staff member, or another speech-language pathologist. If you are a content creator, you may choose to hire a copywriter, social media ad manager, or even a sales team. There are several factors to consider before you start the hiring process.

Federal and state laws determine the classification of employees and independent contractors. If you are planning to expand your practice, be sure that you have done your research to ensure that you are complying with all federal and state laws. The major difference between employees and independent contractors is the level of control you have over the worker. An independent contractor determines how he/she will complete the specific task that they have been hired to do. This person is self-employed and can have contracts with multiple people or organizations simultaneously. Additionally, an independent contractor may hire other subcontractors to complete all or portions of the task. On the other hand, an employee is required to complete tasks that are designated by the employer in the manner and time frame specified. You (as the employer) are required to pay a portion of employment taxes for the employee, and the employee must be the one who completes the job for which they are hired. An additional distinction is who pays for the tools and materials to complete the job. An independent contractor is responsible for their own expenses (which are sometimes tax-deductible), whereas an employer often provides materials and tools for their employees. Figure 7–2 shows differences between employees and independent contractors from the United States Department of Labor (n.d.).

Many business owners prefer to hire independent contractors for their autonomy, short-term nature of the job, and reduced tax expenses. However, there are stiff penalties for the intentional misclassification of your workers. These include paying fines, retroactive payroll taxes, and even legal fees. SCORE provides a list of seven warning signs that your independent contractor might be (operating as) an employee:

1. You define the work hours.

2. You provide equipment or supplies.

3. The relationship is indefinite.

4. You don't receive invoices.

DIFFERENCES BETWEEN EMPLOYEES AND INDEPENDENT CONTRACTORS

EMPLOYEE	INDEPENDENT CONTRACTOR
Working for someone else's business	Running their own business
Paid hourly or salary	Paid upon completion of project
Uses employer's materials, tools, and equipment	Provides own materials, tools, and equipment
Typically works for one employer	Works with multiple clients
Continuing relationship with the employer	Temporary relationship until project completed
Employer decides when and how the work will be performed	Decides when and how they will perform the work
Employer assigns the work to be performed	Decides what work they will do

Figure 7–2. Differences Between Employees and Independent Contractors.

5. The worker only works for you.

6. There isn't a contract.

7. The worker performs core business services (SCORE, 2019, April 28).

There is no set number of factors to determine whether a worker is an employee or independent contractor. Instead, the key is to examine the entire relationship. As a business owner, you should be prepared to document the factors used to determine your classification. According to the IRS, facts that provide evidence of the degree of control and independence fall into three categories:

1. **Behavioral:** Does the company control or have the right to control what/how the worker does their job?

2. **Financial:** Are the business aspects of the worker's job controlled by the company?

3. **Type of Relationship:** Are there written contracts or benefits?

If you are unsure how to classify the worker, you may consider filing a Form SS-8 with the IRS for assistance in making the determination. Once you have determined the appropriate classification, it is time to begin the hiring process. If you are hiring an employee, you will follow the eight steps in Figure 7–3.

1. **Write employee policies.** The process of hiring new employees begins with setting expectations for your future employees. What will you expect them to do? What is the dress code? How will you discipline employees? All of these

8 STEP PROCESS FOR HIRING EMPLOYEES

1	Write employee policies.
2	Determine skills, and write job description.
3	Find applicants.
4	Have applicants complete an application.
5	Interview applicants.
6	Onboard new employees.
7	Submit IRS forms.
8	Run payroll.

Figure 7–3. *Eight Steps for Hiring Employees.*

questions need to be answered before you post an open position. BetterTeam. com and Rocket Lawyer provide templates to help assist you in creating an employee handbook. These are both listed in the Resource List at the end of this book.

2. **Determine skills and write the job description.** Think first about the mission and vision of your business. Anyone you hire to work for your business represents you and needs to advance the mission of your business. For example, if most of your clients have childhood apraxia of speech (CAS), then you should look for employees who have a lot of experience working with children with CAS. Use your MVVP to drive your job description. Include the basic requirements, such as licensure, education, and schedule, in addition to soft skills, such as communication and organization. There is a job description template at Indeed.com, which is listed as a resource at the end of this book.

3. **Find applicants.** There are many websites where you can post open positions, such as Indeed, LinkedIn, or Glassdoor. Also consider SLP-specific websites, such as ASHA.org or your state association. Finally, contact local universities if you are interested in hiring clinical fellows or if there is an alumni network that they can post your position in.

4. **Have applicants complete an application.** You can get application templates from SBA.gov. There is basic information that you need to collect, including demographic information, educational background, work history, and professional references.

5. **Interview applicants.** After you've reviewed the applications, you will contact the people you'd like to interview. Be sure that you develop a list of questions that will allow you to assess potential employees' clinical abilities in addition to soft skills. You can view sample questions at Indeed.com, but you will also need to develop additional questions that are specific to your needs. If you decide to move forward with candidates, be sure to contact their references before you make an offer for employment.

6. **Onboard new employees.** Onboarding is the process of acclimating new employees to your business. This process should include completing new hire paperwork and providing appropriate training. You may also choose to set up a mentorship program for new employees. This process ensures that new employees know the expectations of their position and have someone to go to with questions.

7. **Submit IRS forms.** You will need to submit tax forms to the IRS on a quarterly and annual basis. Refer to the IRS Employer Tax Guide for the current year to determine specific requirements and timelines (Internal Revenue Service, 2021).

8. **Run payroll.** You can either purchase a payroll program or hire someone to run payroll for your business. Some popular options include:
   - ADP
   - Gusto
   - Square Payroll

If you determine that hiring an independent contractor is more appropriate for your open position, there are fewer steps to complete in the hiring process:

1. Check credentials and employment history.

2. Create a contract.

3. Have the contractor complete a W-9 form.

4. Integrate the contractor into the company.

5. Pay the contractor.

1. **Check credentials and employment history.** You will still want to vet your contractors to ensure that they are qualified to complete the job. This may include requesting that they complete an application, provide a resume, or even checking their references. A contractor should be highly skilled in the tasks that you are hiring them to do. If they are not, then it is likely that you have misclassified them.

2. **Create a contract.** Either party can provide the contract, but both parties need to agree to the terms. This is often referred to as an independent contractor agreement or a statement of work.

3. **Have the contractor complete a W-9 form.** As of the writing of this book, you are required to report wages paid to any contractors more than $600 in any calendar year to the Internal Revenue Service. If you expect to pay the contractor more than $600, be sure to have them sign a W-9 form as soon as they sign the contract. The W-9 form provides you with the contractor's business information that you will need when it is time to file their 1099 form at the end of the tax year. The W-9 is a very brief form that you will keep on record and only needs to be completed once.

4. **Integrate the contractor into the company.** Even though the contractor is not an employee, they will need to know enough about your business to be able to complete the job that you've hired them to do. This may include an initial meeting or even introducing them to other staff members.

5. **Pay the contractor.** One of the differences between a contractor and an employee is the way they are paid. A contractor should submit an invoice to you for payment of services rendered during a defined period. The payment

terms should be included in the contract. You can pay independent contractors single payments through a payroll program, such as Square Payroll.

After you have successfully hired and onboarded your employees, you will need to ensure that they are doing what you have hired them to do. Whether you are hiring employees or independent contractors, it is important that you set clear expectations from the very beginning. By keeping the lines of communication open, you will be able to identify any potential problems early on so you can be proactive rather than reactive. For employees specifically, you play a key role in their performance by establishing a positive relationship and improving their job satisfaction. You want your staff to be efficient and productive, so it is important to effectively manage them on an ongoing basis. There are resources for further management training at the end of this chapter.

> **66**
> **I wanted to create a working environment that provided a chance for working parents to be both a great therapist and a great parent.**
> Amy Grant
> Turning Wheels Pediatric Therapy
> **99**

CONTRACTING, POLICIES, AND PROCEDURES

When you establish a business, you will want to create systems that you can replicate as your volume grows. You need to continuously determine your business policies for various scenarios, regularly revisit them, and modify them as appropriate. Keep in mind that beyond the impactful products or services you provide, you are operating a business and, therefore, need to enforce your policies and procedures as such. With that in mind, you are the only one who can gauge how much flexibility to offer or leniency to give for special circumstances when a policy or agreement has been violated. This refers to your engagement and interaction with clients—whether business-to-business (B2B) or business-to-consumer (B2C), as well as with employees and independent contractors. Here are some considerations to think about when establishing and revisiting your contracts, documentation, policies, and procedures:

- Client engagement policies need to be fully disclosed, reviewed, and agreed upon with signatures. For example, if you have a practice agreement in place for a corporate client working on accent modification, make sure that you review it during the proposal stages, ensuring you obtain the client's signature, indicating they understand the expectations related to practice/carryover activities. You will then refer to it as needed, if the client is not following through with carryover practice activities once services have ensued. Also make sure that your cancellation policy is clearly defined, and that you have signatures acknowledging understanding of the agreement (for clinical and corporate clients).

- Decide your process policy for communication with clients. Do you accept text or WhatsApp messages? Email only? Phone calls to a secure line? Ensure that you establish this at the initiation of services and continually review and reinforce this policy regularly.

- In terms of payment and invoicing, what payment forms are accepted? Personal checks? Cash? Mobile payment? Keep in mind that applications such as Venmo, Zelle, PayPal, Square, etc., may not all be appropriate for business use and may not be HIPAA compliant. In the case of accepting private insurance reimbursement, what clearinghouse are you using for billing? Your payment policy needs to be included in your contracts, including the cost breakdown (with procedure codes if billing insurance for clinical services), accepted payment methods, and payment schedule so that you are on the same page in terms of the expectations and what the policy is should those expectations not be met.

- You should always have your logo available when creating new letterhead and ensure that you put it on your business documentation, including agreements. Make sure that your documentation includes your contact information, your client's contact information, the services promised (be as detailed as possible with this), the service delivery details (e.g., where services will be delivered, scheduling, what a session entails, etc.), and any privacy policies/non-disclosure agreements that you need to have signed either on your behalf or your client's behalf.

- As we mentioned in previous chapters, it is vital to have documentation of all agreements/policies/procedures, and to ensure that all parties have signed to acknowledge understanding and agreement when working with employees and contractors, and when collaborating on various projects with other professionals. As you start to grow as an entrepreneur and your business ventures expand, make sure that you include clauses in your documentation related to non-compete policies or non-disclosure agreements for employees, contractors, and collaborative partners. Also be sure to include procedures in case of the termination of a role, relationship, or partnership.

Figure 7–4 is a sample email that you might send to a school about establishing an agreement to conduct a bilingual evaluation. This would be your initial communication with the client (B2B) prior to signing an agreement. Figure 7–5 is a sample contract (B2C) that you would provide to an accent modification client. This agreement would be signed after the client has decided to work with you and before your first session.

AGREEMENT FOR SCHOOL ASSESSMENT CONTRACT

To: **Special Education Director @ Super School.edu**

Subject: **Bilingual Polish-English Evaluation**

Hello [Director of Special Education]-

Thank you for your inquiry regarding needing a bilingual Polish-English speech-language evaluation. I would love to set up some time to chat with you to find out more about this student, your needs, & projected timeline for this evaluation. I am currently scheduling out starting just after the first week of October. My typical process includes:

- **speaking with you/the School SLP/Team to gather any background info that is available,**
- **talking with the Parents/Guardians via a phone call prior to the evaluation to gather their case history/perspective,**
- **doing the evaluation including a classroom observation,**
- **giving the School SLP my immediate impressions post evaluation,**
- **calling the Parents/Guardians post evaluation to give my results/recommendations & reiterating that formal recommendations/goals will be discussed during the meeting with School Assessment Team,**
- **& sending the report within 10 days-2 weeks to the School SLP to include in the comprehensive documentation & present at the meeting.**

Our cost for the process I described is $$$. Hope that helps shed some light on our process. Please do not hesitate to reach out with any questions.

Looking forward to connecting with you & your Team & helping this student!

Best,

SuperStarSLP
Founder & Director, SuperStarSLP Clinic
Email | Phone | Fax | Website

Send

Figure 7–4. *Sample Email for a School Contract.*

[YOUR BUSINESS LOGO HERE]

Phone: YOUR BUSINESS PHONE # HERE

Email: YOUR BUSINESS EMAIL HERE

Business Communication & Professional Development Training Program Proposal

Client Name:	SuperStar Client
Phone:	555.555.5555[mobile]
Email:	SuperStarClient@ClientEmail.com
Financial Responsibility (if other than Client):	----
Contact Info:	----
Date of Proposal:	March 3, 2020
Trainer:	SuperStarSpeechCoach, MS, CCC-SLP

Accent Modification/Advanced Pronunciation Training Program Description

- **One-on-one training sessions** with our experts **in person or via tele/web conferencing** for convenience and flexibility

- **Initial Baseline Assessment** of speech sound production/phonetic inventory to assess coaching needs for the individual (do at your own convenience prior to designated session)

- **Advanced Speech Sound Analysis** by specialty certified Accent Modification Trainer/Speech-Language Pathologist utilizing tools incorporating highest industry standards

- **Evidence-based, customized Accent Modification/Advanced Pronunciation Training Program** based on xxxxx®/xxxxxx® and other evidence-based methods (focused on individual needs/goals based on initial assessment/analysis and progress achieved)

    - **auditory distinction**: training to learn to identify differences/similarities in sounds

    - **speech sound production** (isolation/word/phrase/structured sentences/functional contexts)

    - **suprasegmentals of speech/voice projection** (e.g. word/phrase stress, prosody/rhythm/intonation, breath phrasing, etc.)

    - **cultural-linguistic diversity awareness & self-advocacy strategy training**

- **Customized practice activities** relevant to individuals' industry/profession - based on your specific curriculum which you can download and save to do at your own convenience

- **Access to Online Practice Lab** xxxxxxxxxxx®

- **Ongoing feedback** from Coach in response to practice recordings/practice activities in between sessions

Professional Communication & Development Training Program Proposal-SuperStar Client -3.2020-Page 1 of 4

Figure 7–5. *Sample Contract for Accent Modification.* continues

- **Midterm Re-Assessment & Speech Sound Analysis** by certified Accent Modification Trainer/Speech-Language Pathologist with midpoint progress/comparison data

- **Comprehensive Final Assessment & Speech Sound Analysis** with comparison to prior assessments to track progress

- **Introduction to concepts covered in Business Communication and Professional Development Program,** related to leadership communication-executive presence and presentation skills

Business Communication & Professional Development Program Description

- Initial evaluation of current performance level and goals related to communication (including speech and voice mechanics), business presentation skills (including performance/presentation apprehension/anxiety level self-assessment), cross-cultural/intercultural/interpersonal communication competence, leadership communication skills, and executive presence.

- 1:1 Sessions [in person/on-site/online] of Customized Advanced Professional Communication & Development Coaching/Training:
    o Presentation Skills Training for small and large groups/familiar and unfamiliar audiences
    o Cross-Cultural/Intercultural/Interpersonal Communication Coaching
    o Leadership Communication Strategy Coaching
    o Executive Presence Coaching

- Curriculum, Content, and Carryover Practice Activities are customized specific to Client's industry and distinct roles/responsibilities within the workplace/client-specified communication goals. Targeted training will be conducted in preparation for scheduled presentations/meetings/phone conferences, etc. Review of these presentations, etc. will be used to provide feedback and extend Client's learning & development during subsequent sessions.

- Client will receive Lifetime Complimentary Registration/Entry to any external seminars/workshops/conferences hosted by SuperStarSpeechCoachServices

Training Program Cadence

- Each "session" consists of scheduled appointments which are approximately 60 mins in length and will be based on a combination of 1:1 in person and online training, 'on-site' observation/training as feasible/appropriate, and practice activities/feedback/consultation provided via written or phone means in between scheduled appointments.

- Trainer will conduct a mid-point assessment to determine progress, at which point, Trainer & Client may choose to alter activities/shift focus of training program, based on the progress made by the Client, as to be determined by both parties.

Professional Communication & Development Training Program Proposal-SuperStar Client -3.2020-Page **2** of **4**

Figure 7–5. continues

- To ensure progress and achieve desired outcomes, Client is expected to
  - Attend all scheduled sessions
  - Provide at least 24 hours (preferably 48 hours) notice of cancellation/need to re-schedule an appointment
  - Complete all carryover practice assignments in a timely manner (Please refer to Practice Agreement)
  - Practice based on guidance from the Trainer
- Trainer will sign any non-disclosure/confidentiality agreements necessary, if providing on-site communication observation/training which may include any confidential/proprietary content.
- Schedule to be determined by Client and Trainer, with typical schedule to be 1 session/1-2 weeks, however frequency may increase closer to known presentation dates, etc. in order to allow for more intensive presentation-specific coaching/training.

Professional Fee Schedule and Payment Terms

- Baseline Assessment/Initial Evaluations (Accent Modification & Business Communication) $— *Complimentary*
- 8-10* sessions of Customized Accent Modification Training Program $
  - Access to ******-*certified* Instructor, Training & Practice Portal $
  - Customized Carryover Practice Activities   -Included-
  - Access to Trainer in between appointments for feedback/Asynchronous Coaching   -
    Included-
- 6-8* sessions of Customized Professional Communication & Development Training Program $
  - Evidence Based, Customized Training Sessions with   -Included-
    - Presentation Skills, Leadership Communication, Executive Presence, Cross-Cultural Communication
  - Customized Carryover Practice Activities   -Included-
  - Access to Trainer in between appointments for feedback   -Included-
- Access to *****© Application (1-year subscription): $— *Complimentary*
- Lifetime Complimentary Entry to *SuperStarSpeechCoachServices* group seminars/workshops/conferences [in-person & virtual]   *Complimentary*

Total Professional Fees:

*The Trainer will conduct a mid-point evaluation to determine Client's progress. This will help determine whether Accent Modification Training will be 8 sessions vs 10 sessions, and subsequently whether the Professional Communication & Development Training will be 6 sessions vs 8 sessions. Total Training Programs combined is not to exceed 16 sessions. Some sessions may be structured to have a combination of content from both curriculums, and would be considered as ½ session from each training program. This will first be discussed with the Client and the program will be modified upon explicit agreement between Trainer and Client.

Professional Communication & Development Training Program Proposal–SuperStar Client –3.2020–Page **3** of **4**

Figure 7–5. continues

First payment of 50% of total professional fees is due at the beginning of the program, and the balance 50% is due before the 10th session of the 16 session program. Other payment/installment plans may be available upon explicit discussion between Client and Trainer.

Please Make Checks Payable to: SuperStarSpeechCoachServices, LLC xxxx xxxxx xxx, xxxxx, xx, xxxxx | A 3% processing fee will be added to all credit card transcactions

Client: SuperStar Client	Signature:	Date:
Financially Responsible Party: (Please print name below, if other than Client)	Signature:	Date:
For SuperStarSpeechCoachServices/Trainer: SuperStarSpeechCoach	Signature:	Date:

Figure 7–5. continued

GROWING AND SCALING

In Chapter 4, we briefly discussed how one would go about growing and scaling by adding additional locations to a private practice. This is obviously a sign that your business plan and processes are successful enough, indicating that there is a need and market for your growth and expansion. This idea of growing and scaling is relevant for any business venture, not just a private practice. If you have a product, maybe the growing and scaling consists of expanding to a wider audience or expanding your line of products that are available, while maintaining their relevance to your main product. Having your core business fully established is vital before you consider expanding your products, services, or locations. For example, in terms of having a secondary location for a private practice, this means that your primary location is successfully bringing in revenue and serving your target patient population. You want to make sure that your steady income and revenue are secure in that primary location before expanding to another location. If you were to add an additional location, you would want to repeat the same *systems* that you have in place in your primary location, the key factor being having solid systems in place to run your business.

Using automations, as well as having strong foundational systems for both basic and complex elements of your business is vital. For example, having an automated system to respond to email inquiries, having a system for returning phone calls, or having a system to keep track of your potential leads for clients or collaborations, are all vital at the initiation of product and service delivery. Moving forward, you need to have systems when delivering the product or service to the customer or client in the most effective and efficient manner. Finally, you will need a system for obtaining feedback and revising your product or service. Regardless of your type of business, having automation and systems in place will make the process of growing and scaling much easier.

When you are initially establishing your business, your focus is on getting through the tactical, foundational tasks to make your vision turn into a tangible reality. As you grow, expand, and scale your business, something to keep in mind is what you envision will happen with your business once you are nearing retirement. Will you sell your business, including the brick-and-mortar space (if applicable), clients, established vendor relationships, etc., or will you gradually start to scale down, stop taking new work, and eventually refer potential customers elsewhere when it is time to close your doors? While this is not necessarily what you need to think about when you first embark on the journey of entrepreneurship, it is definitely a consideration as you reach your decided age of retirement to ensure that what you spent significant time, money, and energy to build is not left without a legacy or value as you head into the next phase of your life.

LEADERSHIP

As you transform into an SLP Entrepreneur, your core business gains more stability, and you venture on to expand your business, it is important to reflect upon your leadership style and leadership communication. When you initially establish your business, leadership skills are vital because you will need to independently initiate finding answers and solutions that you need to progress forward. We chose to include a section about leadership in this chapter instead of earlier chapters because, as you grow as an entrepreneur and your business ventures expand, it becomes more prevalent within your daily business practices to take inventory of your leadership abilities and areas of needed improvement. This is especially true when you start to build in volume, either by growing and scaling your private practice, establishing additional locations, services, and a higher volume of clients, and/or when you start to hire employees/independent contractors. This is not only related to owning a private practice, but it also holds true for any SLP-related business venture. As you start to network more, take on more advisory roles, and explore opportunities to collaborate and innovate with others from related and unrelated fields, being aware of your typical leadership communication practices and general leadership style is a crucial step for continued success.

Take a moment to reflect on a leader in your professional network whom you find to be a highly effective leader and communicator, and jot down your thoughts in the exercise in Figure 7–6. Write down the qualities that you appreciate about that person's leadership style and communication practices. Now, do the same with someone who you consider to be an *ineffective* leader. What is it about that leader's style of communication and work practices that you did not appreciate? Taking a moment to reflect on these qualities will help guide you and help you determine your individual leadership style within your business. Being a leader does not just start when you hire employees or contractors—it also impacts your business when you branch out and your brand gains more exposure. As you start to network and collaborate more, your leadership style, communication, and as always, your overall executive presence, will all play a factor in (a) your level of fulfillment, (b) how successful you are, and (c) how much growth and advancement you are able to accomplish.

Now that you've reflected upon leaders that you have interacted with, take some time to reflect upon *your* leadership style. As part of the ASHA Leadership Academy, Nourse and Waagen (2017) described different qualities within leaders, different styles of leadership, and differences between leadership and management traits. They asked questions such as: Are you more short-term focused? Are you more internally focused? Do you want to focus on managing and executing tasks that are pressing today, or are you more of the visionary/"dreamer" who focuses more on long-term prospects and opportunities? Both are necessary characteristics of leaders, and many leaders sometimes tend to be more focused on the management of a business versus the visionary leadership of a business. Take some time

Figure 7–6. *Effective Leadership Reflection.*

now to reflect on what type of leader you are. Use Figure 7–7 (Doer vs. Dreamer) to help you gain perspective on some of your leadership tendencies.

In your role as a founder, owner, and operator of a small business, you will need to compromise and be a little bit of both a dreamer *and* doer. You will also need to outsource and delegate to others those aspects of your business that are not your

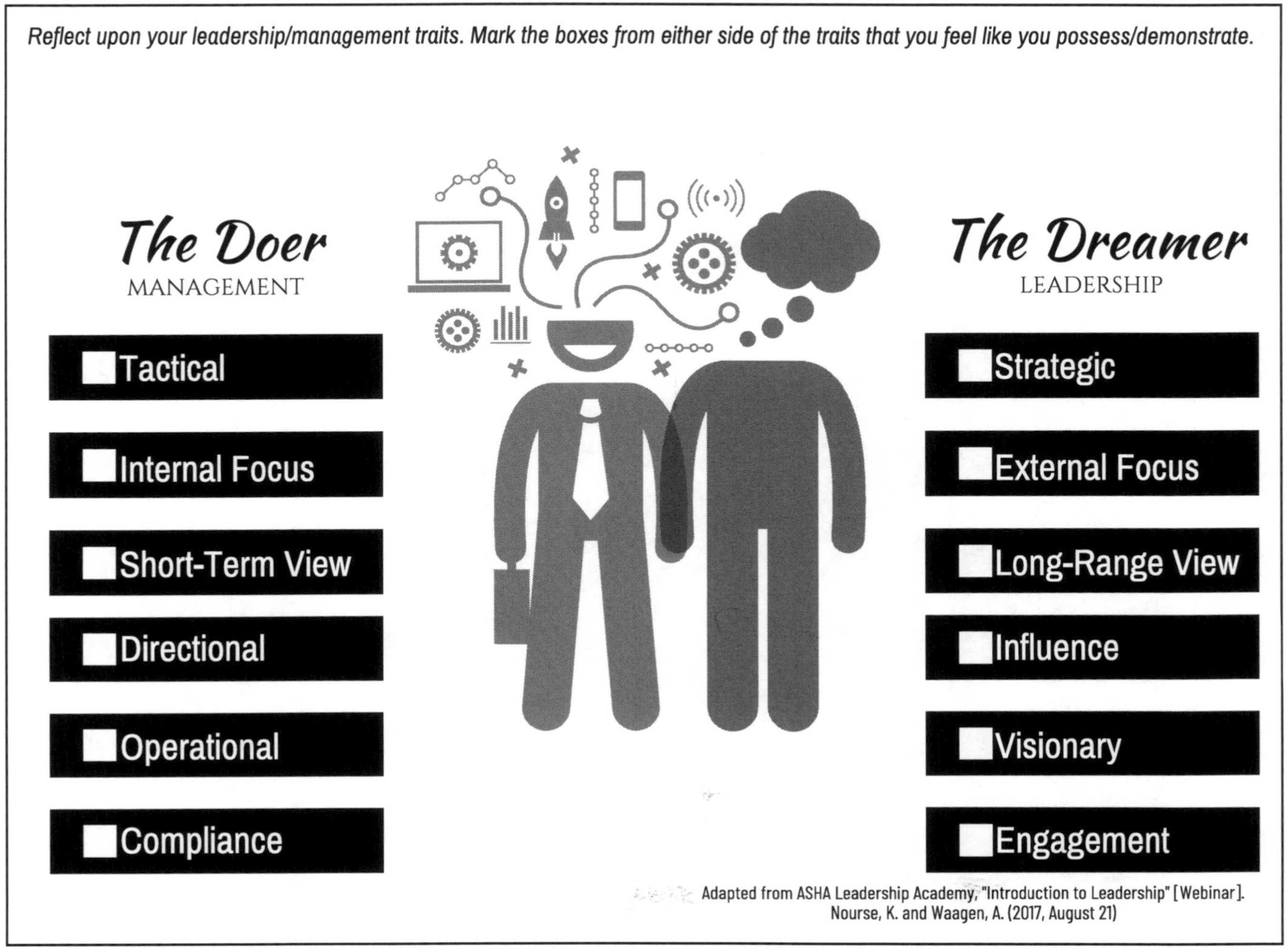

Reflect upon your leadership/management traits. Mark the boxes from either side of the traits that you feel like you possess/demonstrate.

The Doer
MANAGEMENT

- ■ Tactical
- ■ Internal Focus
- ■ Short-Term View
- ■ Directional
- ■ Operational
- ■ Compliance

The Dreamer
LEADERSHIP

- ■ Strategic
- ■ External Focus
- ■ Long-Range View
- ■ Influence
- ■ Visionary
- ■ Engagement

Adapted from ASHA Leadership Academy, "Introduction to Leadership" [Webinar]. Nourse, K. and Waagen, A. (2017, August 21)

Figure 7–7. Doer vs. Dreamer. Adapted from Nourse, K. and Waagen, A. (2017, August 21). "Introduction to Leadership." ASHA Leadership Academy. [Webinar] Retrieved April 21, 2020

strengths and/or the best use of your time, energy, or expertise. As a business owner, you need to step back from the "daily grind" of your business and take a big picture view. How are your time, energy, and talents best utilized in your business? What are you an expert at? Those are the things that you should focus your attention on as much as possible. Then think about what operational tasks you can hire someone else to do. Most businesses will have several essential functions: finance, sales and marketing, customer service, and information technology.

KRISTI ALEXANDER

Founder & CEO, Samech
www.samechonline.com

I help entrepreneurs scale and grow their business by developing processes that will help them maximize their current resources, identify new resources and opportunities, and work to create a cohesive path forward to lessen the pain of getting to that next level.

Important Considerations for Entrepreneurs

While you are doing "all the things" for your business, figure out what part brings you joy. You will have to do it all for a while, but start looking for other virtual helpers that can take on the aspects that you don't love.

Pitfalls to Avoid

Keep your financial house in order. Get an accountant, set up your accounting structure early on, and put away money for taxes.

Advice for Entrepreneurs

You don't have to do this alone! I have found that joining Facebook Groups and signing up for different training sessions has helped me learn and grow and has given me a community that I can reach out to when I'm stuck or have questions. I also encourage you to start talking to people now about partnering so that when you get more work than you can handle, you know who you can go to with the overflow.

Whether you choose a virtual assistant, billing company, or hired employees, examples of the functions that you may want to get help in your business with are:

- Finance: an accountant and/or bookkeeper
- Sales and marketing: social media manager, graphic designer, copywriter
- Customer service: virtual assistant
- Information technology: website developer

Your awareness of your leadership communication and leadership style, along with your overall executive presence, will also be prevalent if you engage in opportunities to serve as an advisor and advocate in a public context. If you are serving as an advisor to different businesses or organizations utilizing your SLP expertise, you will need to be able to have a broad view of that organization or project, and capture the benchmarks that need to be completed, with your focus on their long-term goals and overall mission. You also need to ensure that your communication is aligned with that of a leader, which includes being authentic, transparent, engaging, and having a mission or call to action in mind for your audiences. Having the confidence to bring up difficult conversations if an organization is going down the wrong path is essential. As an advocate, you need to be organized, have data to back what you are advocating for, and have an engaging manner to inspire your audience to follow through with your call to action.

MAINTAINING YOUR ARSENAL OF "EP" × 3— ETHICAL PRACTICE, EXECUTIVE PRESENCE, AND ELEVATOR PITCH

You have evolved and transformed into an entrepreneur. As you continue to seek out and create professional and entrepreneurial opportunities that align with your business's overall mission and life aspirations, keep in mind these three very important "EP" factors. Having EP × 3 at the forefront of your mind will arm you with the tools necessary to persevere through challenges toward success.

> **EP × 3**
>
> Ethical Practice
>
> Executive Presence
>
> Elevator Pitch

- **Ethical Practice.** Staying ethical in the way you conduct yourself, both as a service provider and/or as a business owner, is of utmost importance and cannot be emphasized enough. We have discussed needing the right level of expertise in terms of when to start a private practice or SLP-related business. Although you will most likely venture into a business related to your clinical area of speech-language pathology expertise, the beauty of owning your own private practice or SLP-related business is that you can expand your areas of expertise within our field if you choose. Though you can serve any type of client you would like within your business, you need to invest a significant amount of self-study, continuing education, and seeking out SLP colleagues who are willing to mentor you. You must remain ethical with regard to seeing clients that you are qualified and have the expertise to serve. If you don't yet feel like you have the clinical expertise to see a particular clientele, find others to refer to or seek out mentorship and self-study prior to engaging in providing services to that clientele. In some cases, this may mean that you have to wait before your business can earn revenue for services rendered to that population. Additionally, you must remain ethical when setting prices, receiving reimbursement, maintaining secured documentation, and most certainly during service delivery.

As you venture into new business endeavors or expand your existing ones, conducting business transactions in an ethical manner is equally as crucial. Along with maintaining administrative regulations and keeping professional certifications updated and active, you must conduct all business engagements with integrity. Engaging in any unethical practice with or without legal repercussions could have a detrimental impact on you and your brand's reputation, limiting your marketing and networking opportunities, and stunting your overall growth towards your personal and professional aspirations.

- **Executive Presence.** Another key tool to always arm yourself with throughout your entrepreneurial endeavors is your executive presence. Marketing, networking, branding, or rebranding are constant pursuits of every business owner. You need to consider your executive presence as being crucial to the success of your marketing efforts, networking opportunities, and the building and maintenance of your brand awareness. You want to establish yourself as the go-to expert for your area of expertise or type of products. The way you build your executive presence is discussed more in depth in Chapter 3, but you need to maintain that executive presence throughout all of your interactions and engagements, whether that is with your direct clients, secondary target audiences, or during networking events and opportunities. Having that confidence is key in succeeding at building your brand and expanding your network to lead to the eventual growth and prosperity of your business.

- **Elevator Pitch.** We discussed the purpose and process of preparing an "elevator pitch" in Chapter 6. Being ready with your short, but engaging message of what you do and how you can impact individuals and organizations is a simple and small, but powerful, tool in broadening your potential opportunities for future business endeavors. Being ever ready with your elevator pitch indicates to the people you meet that: you know your business and your value proposition; you are experienced in networking and, therefore, open to opportunities to collaborate and/or bring on new clients; and you possess the confident leadership skills that make you a valued and trusted individual to do business with.

CHAPTER CHECKLIST

☐ Complete your Profit and Loss Statement (Figure 7–1)

☐ Identify ways to establish systems in your business

☐ Determine what can be automated

☐ Decide whether you need to hire employees/contractors or outsource tasks

☐ Identify your leadership style (Figure 7–7)

☐ Update policies and contracts

REFERENCES

Betterteam. (n.d.). *Employee onboarding process*. Betterteam. Retrieved September 30, 2021, from https://www.betterteam.com/employee-onboarding-process

Henry, S. M. (2021, August 2). How to craft the perfect elevator pitch. *Women's Business Daily*. Retrieved September 22, 2021, from https://www.womensbusinessdaily.com/career/how-to-craft-the-perfect-elevator-pitch/

HubSpot. (n.d.). *50 customer service email templates* [Free download]. Retrieved September 22, 2021, from https://offers.hubspot.com/customer-service-email-templates?hubs_post-cta=author

Indeed Editorial Team (Ed.). (2021, April 12). *Steps for hiring a 1099 employee (plus what forms are required)*. Indeed Career Guide. Retrieved September 23, 2021, from https://www.indeed.com/career-advice/career-development/hiring-a-1099-employee

Internal Revenue Service. (2021). *Publication 15 (2021), (circular E), Employer's tax guide*. Retrieved September 22, 2021, from https://www.irs.gov/publications/p15

Maverick, J. B. (2021, October 21). *What's an example of a P&L statement?* Investopedia. Retrieved October 22, 2021, from https://www.investopedia.com/ask/answers/122314/whats-example-pl-statement.asp

Nourse, K., & Waagen, A. (2017, August 21). "Introduction to Leadership." [Webinar]. ASHA Leadership Academy. Retrieved on April 21, 2020, from https://community.asha.org/Go.aspx?MicrositeGroupTypeRouteDesignKey=fdb2f4a1-4a4d-4c6d-bcde-f767260ab16b&NavigationKey=96b4fa97-a7bf-4952-97fa-5a488b982a6c

SCORE. (2011, April 26). *3-year profit and loss projection*. SCORE. Retrieved September 22, 2021, from https://www.score.org/resource/3-year-profit-and-loss-projection-0

SCORE. (2019, April 28). *7 clues your independent contractor is really an employee . . . under the law*. SCORE. Retrieved December 9, 2021, from https://www.score.org/resource/7-clues-your-independent-contractor-really-employee-under-law

SCORE. (2019, May 19). *How to raise prices without losing customers*. SCORE. Retrieved September 22, 2021, from https://www.score.org/resource/how-raise-prices-without-losing-customers

SCORE. (2021, July 29). *Employee or independent contractor? Understanding the classification tests*. SCORE. Retrieved September 22, 2021, from https://www.score.org/resource/employee-or-independent-contractor-understanding-classification-tests

United States Department of Labor. (n.d.). *Misclassification of employees as independent contractors*. Retrieved September 23, 2021, from https://www.dol.gov/agencies/whd/flsa/misclassification

CHAPTER 8

Looking Ahead and Learning From Established SLP Entrepreneurs

Inspirational Stories and Profiles of Successful SLP Entrepreneurs

In This Chapter

This chapter is a curation of profiles of SLPs that have established traditional and non-traditional private practices and other entrepreneurial ventures.

Topics include:

- Background Stories from SLP Entrepreneurs
- Benefits of Being an Entrepreneur
- Challenges of Being an Entrepreneur
- Lessons Learned
- Advice for Aspiring Entrepreneurs

A large, underlying mission of this book is not only to provide you with the foundational framework to embark on your private practice or SLP-related business journey, but also to hopefully inspire you to take risks, take on challenges, think outside the box, and chase after your dreams. While establishing your own business and transforming into an SLP Entrepreneur will have its challenges, we want to provide you with some inspiration from our own community of SLP Entrepreneurs. In this chapter, we highlight some of our SLP colleagues who are already creating some incredible impact in the world with their SLP-related business ventures. We hope that you read through each SLP's journey, insights, and perspectives and that you find a story that resonates with you.

You will find some underlying themes within the stories that these individuals have shared with us about their entrepreneurial journeys. We have tried to represent a variety of SLP Entrepreneurs who are engaged in diverse SLP-related ventures, including growing their clinical private practices, expanding their collaborative projects with others, utilizing their SLP expertise in the corporate sector, innovating SLP-related product development, including training tools and platforms to help strengthen and ease the workloads of our SLP community, and serving in capacities as advisors, advocates, and consultants. Enjoy the perspective of these inspiring SLP Entrepreneur colleagues and envision your future self as you transform from an SLP to an SLP Entrepreneur. We can't wait to see all the amazing things *you* do next as an SLP Entrepreneur!

ALLISON GELLER, MA, CCC-SLP

Founder, Connected Speech Pathology: http://www.connectedspeechpathology.com

Professional Background

I have over 20 years of experience in outpatient, inpatient, and acute settings for the areas of speech-language, cognitive/linguistic, and dysphagia for adults and children. As the clinical coordinator of research in the Aphasia Rehabilitation Research Lab in the Neurological Institute at Columbia University Medical Center in New York, I conducted clinical research focused on identifying ways to improve effective communication in persons with aphasia. I am certified in Compton PESL for accent modification, Lee Silverman Voice Treatment (LSVT), and have undergone specific training for gender-affirming voice modification. My specialized training and experiences give me an eye for selecting the most talented speech pathologists from around the country to join our team.

Reason for Going Down This Path

I became a speech-language pathologist so I could help clients feel confident in their communicative abilities and feel understood. I am passionate about effective, convenient, and accessible online therapy.

Biggest Benefits of Entrepreneurship

We have been able to provide access to the best speech pathologists across the country. Online speech therapy has been especially helpful for clients who are limited by transportation, scheduling conflicts, mobility issues, or geography. It also benefits those who are socially distancing due to COVID-19.

Biggest Challenges of Entrepreneurship

The biggest challenge this company has faced is in building the right team to work together to fill the needs of clients across the country and with a wide range of communication challenges. Our success rates with solving our client's challenges lean heavily on having the right speech therapists to match each client's unique needs. We have been fortunate enough to optimize this to allow great things to happen at Connected Speech Pathology.

Advice for Others Interested in Starting a Business

Think about the big issues that you want to address in your practice. Set goals, and strategies, and know your capabilities. Keep asking the tough questions about where you want to go and whether the path that you are following will take you there. Follow your passion! It will help you get through the tough times.

What Do You Know Now That You Didn't Know Before Starting Your Business?

Reaching out to the outstanding colleagues in our field to bounce off ideas can help you launch your practice. Our connections and support system have made all of the difference.

AMY GRANT, MS, CCC-SLP

Founder, Turning Wheels Pediatric Therapy: http://www.turningwheelstherapy.com

Professional Background

Immediately after finishing graduate school, I began working at Marianjoy Rehabilitation Hospital as a pediatric speech-language pathologist. I worked there for 12.5 years before opening up Turning Wheels Pediatric Therapy in December 2016. In Spring 2020, I opened up a second location in Springfield, IL and in Summer 2021 I opened a third location in St. Charles, IL.

Reason for Going Down This Path

Creating a private practice provided an opportunity to build something that serviced needs that were important to me. As a professional and a mother to young children, I did not feel like there must be a choice between one or the other nor did I think you should have to sacrifice being present for your family to be a professional. I wanted to create a working environment that provided a chance for working parents to be both a great therapist and a great parent. As a parent who had been on the patient side of providers, I wanted to create a place that I and my family would want to visit. An inviting location that makes a child and their family feel comfortable. Having a bright, airy space with fun decorations and a friendly overall design helps set the mood right from the start!

Biggest Benefits of Entrepreneurship

My private practice has generated an immense amount of pride and satisfaction helping therapists build careers that fit with their lives while delivering patient care that helps improve lives. The idea that, as a business, we have been able to impact the communities that we serve is truly meaningful! I love that I have created a place where children don't feel like they are coming to therapy and a place where therapists want to come and work! It has also been very special having my husband and three children be part of the process every step of the way. The business means as much to them as it does to me and that is the best part of all of this.

Biggest Challenges of Entrepreneurship

As a business owner, you cannot underestimate the work that goes into ensuring the business functions. My business is extremely important to me in so many ways beyond the financial aspect; it is like another child! You cannot predict all the challenges and events that will come up as a practice owner, so you need to be prepared to assess and address these events and lead your business. It can be a lot of pressure and can be all-consuming at times.

Advice for Others Interested in Starting a Business

I think everyone has different styles and approaches to business, all of which can be effective and impactful. That being the case, I think it is so important for anyone who is looking to start their own business to be grounded in their purpose for starting their business and really explore that purpose to ensure that it is solid enough to keep them going through the good times and bad. Beyond that, my only other pieces of advice would be to not sweat the small stuff, be ready to learn, and listen!!

What Do You Know Now That You Didn't Know Before Starting Your Business?

Building a business is equally difficult yet incredibly rewarding. As an employee, I never fully had a sense of what it took to operate a business and all the details that go into delivering a service day in and day out. Through this journey, I have gained a deep appreciation for businesses and the building that goes on behind the scenes to make it happen.

ANGELA CHUNG, MSC., SLP
Co-Founder and Clinical Director, Speak Fluent Inc.: https://speakfluent.ca/

Professional Background

I completed my Masters of Speech-Language Pathology (MScSLP) at the University of Alberta. I also hold a Bachelor of Arts from UBC, majoring in Speech Sciences, a combination of linguistics and psychology. Currently, I'm registered to work in BC and Ontario, Canada. I started off working several years in the school system, providing speech therapy to a large variety of students. While I enjoyed making a difference for children, my passion remained with providing services to motivated adults. I started my private practice in August of 2020, and it has been growing ever since!

Reason for Going Down This Path

Accent and discrimination has always been a burning topic in my mind growing up. My family immigrated to Canada in December 1999, and it was apparent that their communication skills impacted their lives in key ways, from experiencing discrimination at work to avoiding calls with phone companies. As I entered the field of speech-language pathology, I found my fulfillment from teaching clients about their speech, and hearing about how their improved skills changed their lives. This often looked like a kindergartener using a sound she never used before and having her teachers and classmates start to understand her. It also looked like a young adult learning how to manage his stuttering behaviors and finding the confidence to speak to new people.

These two passions naturally led me to accent modification, but there weren't a lot of clinics that worked exclusively in this area. I solved that problem with the help of my partner, Michael. Michael, a serial entrepreneur, wanted me to have my own project that I was passionate about. At the height of the pandemic, we started talking about an idea, a project that made perfect sense to me—and that's how I started an adults-only virtual speech clinic. Our arrangement was that he would deal with all the business side of things, and I would manage the clinical side of things. This allowed us both to play to our strengths and do what we love.

Biggest Benefits of Entrepreneurship

One of the biggest benefits of starting my own clinic is that I get to choose what population I work with. Working with adults who can truly express what they're looking for and recognize the changes in their communication skills has been extremely rewarding.

Biggest Challenges of Entrepreneurship

A common challenge that any private practice will have is making sure we have enough clients to have a full caseload for all the SLPs. Oftentimes there will be months in the year when work is slow—either not enough new clients are coming in, or current clients requesting a hold on their sessions. It can be a big struggle managing the costs of acquiring new clients and maintaining subscriptions for programs that we use (like Zoom).

Advice for Others Interested in Starting a Business

Set hard rules for yourself and be a good boss to yourself. Set policies for no-shows, and do your best to solve problems as they come up (e.g., frequent no-shows, late payments). It's hard to separate your business from your identity, so don't be too hard on yourself. Sometimes it's worth hiring a professional to help you out with certain problems if you know you would have to spend too long trying to solve it on your own (e.g., making a website, accounting, ads). You don't have to know everything about everything from the very beginning. It's okay to figure things out along the way. Connect with people and learn from them! There's no need to reinvent the wheel.

What Do You Know Now That You Didn't Know Before Starting Your Business?

Starting a business isn't hard. Making it successful is. I didn't realize how much work went into management until we hired more SLPs to work with us. Making sure their work is up to par and that the way they provide service aligns with our mission and values requires regular check-ins and can be stressful if you care a lot about your company's image. My partner and I have to make a lot of tough decisions around our financials and the direction of our company. Is it worth it to hire a receptionist full-time? How much can we spend on ads? How can we solve the problem of connecting with other companies to provide our services?

ANN M. PANNELL, MA CCC-SLP

Owner and Founder, Clarity Speech Coaching: http://www.clarityspeechcoaching.com

Professional Background

I have worked in Acute Hospitals, Rehabs, and Home Care as a Speech-Language Pathologist. I am the Owner and Founder of Clarity Speech Coaching. I am a Partner at Pathfinder Business Consultants. I am a certified Executive Coach and have training in Teaching English to Speakers of Other Languages (TESOL). I serve as Treasurer for the Corporate Speech Pathology Network (CORSPAN). I am the President of the Cary-Preston Women In Networking (WIN) which is a networking and business group of female business owners.

Reason for Going Down This Path

Linguistic discrimination is a widespread phenomenon: Being misunderstood in healthcare, for example, can be a matter of life and death; it can impact patient rapport building, teamwork, and collaboration. After working in health care for 20 years, I have witnessed many brilliant professionals not receive the respect or recognition they deserved related to their communication style, cultural differences, or speaking English as a Second Language. After years of assisting colleagues in mastering their communication, presentations, and assisting with English pronunciation, I saw a genuine need for my private sector services. In 2018, I pursued my passion, founding Clarity Speech Coaching.

Clarity Speech Coaching stems from my conviction to foster diversity of communication and thought by assisting others to be heard and included, and my dedication to helping others communicate their messages and beliefs with clarity and confidence. I welcome all dialog regarding the role I play in advocating for linguistic diversity and providing the most effective services for my clients since my clients are at the heart of my work.

Biggest Benefits of Entrepreneurship

Owning a business allows you to pursue projects and create based solely on your passion and beliefs. I have been able to meet so many wonderful professionals, whether through collaborative projects or as clients, that my business really doesn't feel like work. My clients are at the heart of everything I do, so my time spent working in my business is very fulfilling.

Biggest Challenges of Entrepreneurship

I am an advocate for diversity in the workplace. In 2020 I partnered with Pathfinder Business Consultants where I am able to provide perspective on cultural, generational, and linguistic diversity. The biggest challenges are the misconceptions about the work I do related to English pronunciation: the last thing I am doing is making my clients "sound alike." I am actually working toward the opposite result. I am not reducing anyone's ethnicity, but providing a solution of speaking clearer English so their unique identity, personality, and expertise shine through. When people gain confidence in their communication skills there is a wonderful cascading effect where increased collaboration, creativity, and leadership qualities are exposed. This in itself leads to a more productive, inclusive, and cutting-edge work environment. My passion is developing clients' confidence and unique personality when they communicate and lead, allowing them to thrive and succeed in their work and personal lives.

Advice for Others Interested in Starting a Business

My advice to anyone interested in Corporate Speech Pathology is to speak with a professional who is currently working in the field, shadow the professional and gain mentorship. The Corporate Speech Pathology Network (CORSPAN) where I serve as Treasurer is an international organization of Speech-Language Pathologists who work in corporate speech pathology. We promote our profession, as well as provide advocacy on behalf of our services.

What Do You Know Now That You Didn't Know Before Starting Your Business?

Being a business owner, a mother and a wife brings new meaning to work-life balance. I am fortunate to be able to work in my home; however, time management and organizational skills are stretched in order to maintain the balance of family and clients, as being a business owner is a 24/7 responsibility. I believe in my work, and I also have a very supportive family—with that anything is possible.

ASHLEY PARKS FROATS, MA, CCC-SLP
Versatile Speech Services: http://www.versatilespeech.com/children

Professional Background

I personally think I had a dream job coming out of graduate school. I spent four years working in a rural community hospital in both the inpatient and outpatient settings with adults and pediatrics. One moment I was in the ICU with a patient weaning from a ventilator and a few minutes later I was on the floor of the pediatric gym with a two-year-old. I also had the opportunity to serve in a management role within our rehabilitation department and help initiate a clinical protocol for head & neck cancer patients in our adjoining cancer center.

Reason for Going Down This Path

One of my favorite aspects of that first job was supervising graduate students. This love of teaching and training, as well as a desire to learn a new culture, led me to Kuala Lumpur, Malaysia where I took a part-time job as a speech therapy supervisor at a university clinic. After my husband and I married, we decided to land permanently in Malaysia. As my husband worked to get a new business off the ground, finding a full-time speech therapy job with a work visa proved difficult.

I began the process of enrolling in a PhD program so I could join the faculty of the university where I supervised and in the interim taught English to kids in China through the company, VIPKid. When we found out we had a son on the way, I decided to put the PhD pursuit on hold. Meanwhile, several fellow American expatriate families in this area of the world reached out to me regarding speech therapy for their kids. It seemed like the market was present for a teletherapy business to provide speech therapy services to American "expats" living in Asia who either had no access to an SLP or preferred an American accented therapist and thus, Versatile Speech Services was born!

Biggest Benefits of Entrepreneurship

The greatest benefit to starting my own business has been returning to the field I love! I am able to coordinate with my clients to set my therapy hours and am still able to be at home with my son, and now daughter as well. By accepting private pay only, I have been able to provide exactly what appears clinically necessary without the confines of insurance limitations.

Biggest Challenges of Entrepreneurship

The biggest challenge has been learning the new skill of teletherapy. I am thankful for the skills I learned during my year of teaching English online as well as the plethora of resources available online to train SLPs in providing quality virtual services! I am also thankful for an international tax accountant who has ensured the tax and legal matters are all up to speed!

Advice for Others Interested in Starting a Business

My advice is to look for a gap in the market. Find a hole and make a plan for how you can fill it! There will likely be little start-up cost beyond some basic tests and supplies so taking the leap to start your own business, particularly if it is a side hustle for a while, is a lot less risky than you might think!

What Do You Know Now That You Didn't Know Before Starting Your Business?

I have realized the American expatriate community is somewhat underserved, as often schools abroad do not have the referral and testing pipelines of the public school system in America, nor do they have the extra resources to offer if services are indicated. It's been a joy to fill a gap in needed therapy services and see progress in these students!

BEATA KLAROWSKA, MS, CCC-SLP
Co-Founder, TheraPlatform: http://www.theraplatform.com,
Virtual Speech Center: http://www.virtualspeechcenter.com

Professional Background

My career started as a speech and language pathologist in a hospital setting. I provided services to patients with speech, language, cognitive, voice disorders, dysphagia, and children with various communicative disorders. I conducted video swallow studies and trained families on AAC devices. In 2011, I co-founded Virtual Speech Center, an app development company, and created over 40 apps for speech, language, and cognition. In 2017, I co-founded TheraPlatform (an EMR/practice management and Telehealth Software).

Reason for Going Down This Path

I was inspired to start my software company by one of my professors who was teaching technology classes at the graduate school. He introduced me to AAC devices and telepractice. After he mentioned that ASHA approved telepractice, I started exploring the very topic and technology around it. In the early stages of telepractice, there was no single platform that provided us, therapists, with built-in video, practice management, and teaching aids in one solution, and my dream was to create one.

In 2011, my husband (a software architect) and I developed a prototype video platform. Still, technology back then was not mature and stable enough. We decided to rest till 2017 when video and other technologies around it were more refined and stable. We expanded our team and developed a comprehensive platform that offers practice management, video, EMR, documentation, billing, e-claim, client portal, apps/games, and more!

Biggest Benefits of Entrepreneurship

SLPs use TheraPlatform to manage, grow their private practice, and reach clients in remote areas where therapy was not possible, which is the most rewarding. The benefits of having my own business are autonomy, flexibility, and challenge. I also enjoy connecting with fellow therapists to help them address their software pain points.

Biggest Challenges of Entrepreneurship

The challenges of having a tech business are a fast-paced environment, consistently changing technology, and working around the clock.

Advice for Others Interested in Starting a Business

Starting your own business can be scary, but you can succeed if you have passion, vision, and plan. My advice to new entrepreneurs is to educate yourself about the business you wish to enter and ask big questions: Is this for me? What will it take? Is this the right time for me? Why do I want this?

Do not get discouraged by others who may have doubts or are afraid for you. I think many of us prefer the known and feel comfortable in our zone, but if you have this solid internal need and drive for taking a risk and starting your business-listen to your calling—not others.

Be prepared for making mistakes and learn from them. Don't try to do it all by yourself- ask for help if you can and consider reaching out to mentors in the field. Hire the right people for the job who will share your passion and vision.

A final word of advice—make sure you take some time to rest and do something not related to your business. When one first starts, one will have a million ideas, a million things to do, and breaking the routine and devoting some time to yourself will help you keep going.

I wish you all the best on your journey!!

What Do You Know Now That You Didn't Know Before Starting Your Business?

What I've learned from running a software business is the development process, how software engineers think, and how to communicate with them as the end-user. This helped me make the right choices in terms of the future of the product and the efficacy of the development process.

CARA BRYAN, MA, CCC/SLP

Owner, Speech Pathologist, Singing and Voice Specialist
Co-Owner, The Confident Clinician Cooperative, LP : http://www.confidentclinician.com
South Tampa Voice Therapy, LLC: http://www.southtampavoicetherapy.com

Professional Background

I am a speech pathologist specializing in the rehabilitation of vocal difficulties. I hold a degree in vocal performance and am vocology certified through the National Center for Voice and Speech. I spent the first 14 years of my career in the acute care and outpatient hospital settings, which prepared me for establishing a medically-based outpatient speech pathology practice. I contract my practice with an ENT office to provide instrumental voice and swallowing assessments. My practice accepts clinical fellows to assist with training young clinicians. Providing continuing education, training the next generation, and abiding by a pay-it-forward philosophy prompted me to establish The Confident Clinician Cooperative with my speech pathology colleagues Kristie Knickerbocker, MS, CCC/SLP and Aaron Ziegler, PhD, CCC/SLP.

Reason for Going Down This Path

I chose to pursue private practice for several reasons: I wanted to specialize in voice and provide accessible, comprehensive care for patients outside of a large institution. I desired upward mobility and more from my career than any institution could provide. I wanted to establish the only stand-alone adult-focused outpatient speech pathology practice in my area.

Biggest Benefits of Entrepreneurship

Having my own private practice has been immensely rewarding in many areas: the care I provide my patients, the work environment I've cultivated for myself and my employees, and the immense satisfaction that the time, energy, and hard work I put into the practice is rewarded, appreciated and valued.

Biggest Challenges of Entrepreneurship

The biggest challenges with starting and running a private practice primarily center around learning how to run a successful business and work-life balance.

Advice for Others Interested in Starting a Business

Dream it—then act on it. Start small and remain focused. Form your mission statement. Expect your vision statement to change as you and your practice grow. Remember that the best teacher is your last mistake. Know that the journey is challenging, but the benefits outweigh this by far.

If you're considering pursuing private practice, start researching. Gather as much information as you can. Reach out to other private practice SLPs for mentoring. Network and foster relationships with all potential referral sources. Invest in a good website, book-keeping software, an accountant, and an attorney. And realize that the sky is the limit.

What Do You Know Now That You Didn't Know Before Starting Your Business?

Business. And I continue to learn the business of private practice.

CATHERINE CONLIN, PHD, CCC-SLP
Bright Brain Thinking: http://www.brightbrainthinking.com

Professional Background

I'm a clinically trained speech pathologist certified by the American Speech, Language, Hearing Association. I've been in private practice for 23 years specializing in written language development. I work with school-age children to adults with language-learning challenges including Specific Learning Disability, ADHD, Reading Comprehension Deficit, and spoken and expressive language disorders.

Reason for Going Down This Path

I have loved to read my whole life, making vivid mental pictures that support my comprehension and enjoyment. When I learned that there are individuals who do not have the skills to enjoy reading the way I do, I knew I wanted to specialize in this area of language development.

Biggest Benefits of Entrepreneurship

Flexible schedule, flexible lifestyle, applying the latest in evidence-based practices without needing approval, the ability to try new approaches and methods that are not as well-known but supported by scientific evidence.

Biggest Challenges of Entrepreneurship

The business side of things—marketing, invoicing, scheduling. And working as a solo-practitioner, not always having other SLPs to bounce clinical concerns off of and help with clinical decision-making—somewhat isolating.

Advice for Others Interested in Starting a Business

Set up your business with a protected structure (LLC for example) and don't feel the need to reinvent the wheel—plenty of forms, policies, and practices are available free of charge by others in the field, just ask, and Go for it! It's been the most rewarding career path with a wonderful quality of life.

What Do You Know Now That You Didn't Know Before Starting Your Business?

That establishing networks of SLP colleagues who are in a similar work setting or specialty, facing the same challenges, is vital to continued growth and happiness in private practice.

GRETCHEN MCGINTY, MA, CCC-SLP
Owner, New Leaf Voice, PLLC: http://www.newleafvoice.com

Professional Background

I am a certified speech-language pathologist who specializes in voice disorders and vocal training (gender affirming voice therapy, acting voice, public speaking). Prior to pursuing my career as an SLP, I was a classically trained actress with professional experience in theatre, TV, and Film. As a performer, I had to learn Standard American English and also how to perform various dialects accurately.

Reason for Going Down This Path

I loved acting, but grew tired of the rat race of being a stage actor in NYC and wanted to return home (to NC) and pursue a career that provided more stability, and also felt personally meaningful. After talking to my cousin's wife (another SLP), I realized the training I received in conservatory (phonetics, dialect training, articulation voice training) would make me a great SLP and I wanted to go back to school. I really loved the work I did with my professors in conservatory and how I was able to transform my own voice and speech to pursue a career in acting. I thought it would be really rewarding to get to do that for others. And I was right!

Biggest Benefits of Entrepreneurship

I really love being able to transform people's lives for the better. When someone is ashamed of their voice, it really becomes this huge obstacle that holds them back in life. It is such a joy to be able to show them how they can gain control over their sound, and improve it. Whether I am dealing with someone struggling with an actual voice disorder, or a gender diverse client who wants to transition their voice to match their gender expression; it is a real thrill to get to guide people to creating the voice they can feel confident about. I also really love the huge umbrella that we practice under. We can work with any age group and such a wide range of disorders/challenges.

Biggest Challenges of Entrepreneurship

When I decided to start my own practice, it was not something I had been planning. The voice clinic where I had been working was taken over by new management, and all of a sudden, it was decided everyone would be required to sign these very strict, non-compete contracts. I knew I couldn't stay, so my biggest challenge was suddenly finding myself on my own, without any clue how to start and run a practice. I think I didn't have a super clear idea of what I wanted my practice to be. I just knew that I wanted to be able to continue helping people with their voice, especially my transgender clients since I was the only gender affirming voice therapist in Charlotte at the time.

After the pandemic, I realized I needed to see everyone via telepractice. I already had a platform for this, but there was still a lot of work I had to do in terms of setting up my forms in digital format, uploading new visuals, etc. I took some online trainings taught by other SLPs who had online practices. Prior to the pandemic, I had a hard time convincing people that online coaching was just as effective. Since then, I think people have realized telepractice is a great benefit and I have found I really love working from home!

Advice for Others Interested in Starting a Business

I think it is a good idea to keep your regular SLP job, and take the time to educate yourself about what you need to know prior to starting your own practice. Many therapists start off seeing people privately as a side hustle (just be sure you are not violating any agreement you have with your main employer). Most of us did not study business in school. You need to learn what you need to get your practice started, where do you want to practice (do you need your own space? want to see people in their homes?), and what you want your focus to be. It is also helpful to know what the needs are in your area, how you will market etc. Take time to learn about what private practices are already serving your area and what niche they are serving. What are you bringing to the table?

I would encourage anyone interested in being an SLP Entrepreneur to start learning about business first. There are small business associations in every town that offer free trainings and webinars to get you started. There are also business courses specifically for SLPs online. Don't let your lack of knowledge hold you back! We already have to work so hard in every setting—I think it is very rewarding to aim that work ethic at building something just for you.

What Do You Know Now That You Didn't Know Before Starting Your Business?

There is still so much I am learning about business and marketing in general. I am always learning new things regarding SEO, social media posts, etc. Truthfully, there are some things I may be able to learn from a book or course, but there are some things I just need to hire a professional to help me tackle. My confidence and growth have really been boosted by working with a business coach to help me clarify my goals and what to tackle first.

JENNIE BJOREM, MA, CCC-SLP

Bjorem Speech Publications: http://www.bjoremspeech.com
Children's Therapy Services: http://www.childrenstherapycts.com

Professional Background

I have been a pediatric speech pathologist for 22 years. After working in the schools for 3 years I opened my private practice 19 years ago, WOW! Children's Therapy Services (CTS) was a home-based therapy company providing therapy for the birth-3 population in the Kansas City Metro Area. Early on, I contracted 25 SLPs, OTs, and early intervention specialists. As therapy models changed, I opened a brick-and-mortar and have grown from one private client a week to over 400 clients per week. Having a clinic I owned allowed me to hone in on apraxia and only take on apraxia clients. I began studying everything there was to know about childhood apraxia and eventually felt comfortable and knowledgeable enough to call myself a specialist. In 2017, I published my first speech therapy product on my own after three speech publishing companies turned me down. The Bjorem Speech Sound Cues were originally stickers on sticks and I would use them to cue kids on sounds, movement, phonemic awareness in therapy. The therapists at the clinic would frequently steal my sticks and they eventually talked me into publishing them. Bjorem Speech Publications was officially born in 2019. We have since grown to over 28 physical speech therapy products! We sell to countries around the world every day. Today I live in Colorado and I have a wonderful clinic director that runs the clinic in Kansas. I run Bjorem Speech from my home, present on apraxia around the country, and have a small caseload of kids with apraxia. It has been a wild ride!

Reason for Going Down This Path

I had my first child and was extremely stressed and unhappy in the schools. I left my job and started CTS out of desperation. It was very scary and I had a short-term plan . . . 1 to 2 years but had no idea where it would lead me. I was NOT an entrepreneur, I told my husband!

Biggest Benefits of Entrepreneurship

FLEXIBILITY! TRAVEL! KIDS! ANSWERING TO ME! I have loved this roller coaster journey in my life. It was hard, very very hard, but it allowed me to be me, a mom, a wife, a daughter, a sister, a friend. This life decision has allowed me to specialize in childhood apraxia of speech, help so many families through my clinic, teach others about apraxia, and partner with other speech-pathologists to create products that this field desperately needs. The benefits outweigh the challenges. I am so glad I had the drive and vision to push through the hard times.

Biggest Challenges of Entrepreneurship

Wow, early on there were not a lot of benefits. It was hard, long work and I didn't stop working ... 7 DAYS A WEEK! Many years I didn't take a paycheck, well most years. I borrowed money to pay my contractors and was in debt over 100K by 2018. Trying and failing was common from summer camps to opening a preschool to experimenting with salaries. I cannot count how many times I failed and had to reinvent my business.

Advice for Others Interested in Starting a Business

Have a plan and hire a mentor or business coach. DON'T BE AFRAID TO FAIL. You will fail. It is okay and this is how you will learn. Believe me there are many things I can say to "I will never do that again." Mistakes make you better. Fear is boring.

What Do You Know Now That You Didn't Know Before Starting Your Business?

EVERYTHING! I knew nothing, I had no idea what I was getting into. This includes hiring/firing, accounting, management of people, printing & publishing, insurance, shipping, website building. I am 100% self-taught.

JENNIFER NONN-MURPHY, MS, CCC-SLP

Owner, Clear and Confident Speech Coaching: http://www.ccspeechcoach.com,
Communication Building Blocks: http://www.cbbtherapy.com

Professional Background

My first job after graduate school was working for a local school district. For about five years, I provided speech-language services for students in Preschool thru High School. After having my second child, I knew that I wanted a position with more flexibility, more predictable hours, and a lower caseload. I left the school district and transitioned to working at a private practice clinic in town that had about a dozen SLPs working with students in a 1:1 setting. I enjoyed working side by side with other speech therapists, in addition to being able to pick up my daughters from school during a break at work!

Reason for Going Down This Path

In a way, I was forced to start my own speech-language pathology practice. The owner of the private practice I was working for decided to retire and close her company. I had a decision to make: go back into the schools, apply at another private practice, or try and run a business on my own! What a scary time that was. Thankfully, another speech pathologist at the same company decided to start her own private practice and asked me if I wanted to join her on the journey. We decided to run separate businesses but help each other along the way. That was eleven years ago—we share clinic space, assessments, materials, and ideas. However, she runs her own business and I run mine. We are both sole proprietors without employees. It is a fantastic "partnership."

Biggest Benefits of Entrepreneurship

The biggest benefit of running my own business is the independence to make my own schedule, adjust my days/hours as needed, and to raise my rates on a yearly schedule. I do not need to check in with a boss to make decisions. I have a close relationship with my clients and their families because I am the one who answers their initial request for services, communicates with them about the assessment and therapy process, provides them with therapy, and discharges them from services when goals have been met.

Biggest Challenges of Entrepreneurship

The biggest challenge in my private practice career, by far, was the learning curve at the beginning of starting my business. It was completely overwhelming. Because I had been an SLP for eleven years prior to starting my own business, I knew how to be an SLP. I knew how to assess a student, create goals, formulate lesson plans, write notes and reports, etc. But I was unfamiliar in how to send invoices with procedure codes and diagnostic codes, how to keep track of expenses efficiently, how to find an office space, how to apply for a Nonpublic, Nonsectarian School/Agency Certification, how to write a contract for a school district, how to apply for liability insurance, etc.

The first time you attempt anything new it can be very challenging. It takes time. But now, I can do these things with ease.

Advice for Others Interested in Starting a Business

My advice for others interested in pursuing the path of starting their own speech pathology business is to ask lots of people lots of questions. I asked my family/friends who were in the insurance business about the type of insurance I needed. I asked my family/friends in the tax world about estimated taxes. I asked my family/friends if they knew of any available office space nearby. Take people to coffee and tell them that you need their advice. You can find many answers to your questions online, but the people in your life will want you to succeed and will help you by providing guidance and support.

What Do You Know Now That You Didn't Know Before Starting Your Business?

Starting my own private speech-language pathology practice was the best decision I've made in my career. It was a lot of work and very nerve-wracking in the beginning because there were so many new skills to learn, but I would not change a thing. I am proud that I took the risk.

JESSICA LADOW, MA, CCC-SLP
Speech On The Spot: http://www.speechbus.com

Professional Background

I have been an SLP since 2014 with the majority of my career being in hospital-based pediatrics. My clinical specialties include feeding/dysphagia and voice.

Reason for Going Down This Path

I started my mobile practice in 2020 to have more freedom as a clinician and with my schedule. I also live in a very rural area where access to care is problematic to many people and the mobile nature of my practice removes that barrier.

Biggest Benefits of Entrepreneurship

Freedom with my time and a better work-life balance.

Biggest Challenges of Entrepreneurship

Dealing with insurance and getting reimbursements. At my old job, I was salaried and my income was steady and guaranteed. Now, I am at the mercy of my patients cancelling and how quickly/if insurance reimburses. The reimbursement rates are also very low sometimes which limits my income.

Advice for Others Interested in Starting a Business

Get reimbursement contract rates BEFORE making the leap. Be prepared to spend as much time on admin work as you do seeing patients. Be prepared to make little or no money for many months while things are getting established.

What Do You Know Now That You Didn't Know Before Starting Your Business?

People are incredibly frustrated with working with large hospital clinics and school-based services. They are so excited about the personal care they get with a private practice. I have really learned how much of an asset I am to my community and my field and I no longer feel like a therapy machine just churning out 10 to 13 visits per day.

People and insurances often undervalue our services as evidenced by low reimbursement rates and raised eyebrows at paying weekly copays or private rates. Know your value and find the patients that know that value too. Having good families and good patients to work with make the days worth all the while!

JONATHAN LOVE, MA, CCC-SLP
Owner, Love Institute: http://www.theloveinstitute.org

Professional Background

I am a person who stutters who benefitted from speech and language services. Arnell Brady, ASHA Fellow, was my speech-language pathologist. He helped me to overcome my disfluency disorder using the same fluency shaping techniques I would learn years later. I decided to go into the Communications Disorders field to help children overcome communication disorders, delays, and barriers so they can become effective speakers. Currently, I have 16 years' experience in school-based therapy and roughly 10 years' experience in private practice.

Reason for Going Down This Path

My experience as a child who stutters who benefitted from speech and language services. I benefitted the most from my private practice experience than I did from school-based therapy experience. I was determined to have a private practice to give specialized attention to my patients.

Biggest Benefits of Entrepreneurship

I cannot really say the biggest benefit. The same benefits I would get as an employee are the same benefits I would get as an entrepreneur. I work harder and longer than when I was an employee. I make more money but I also have to pay more money in taxes, pay for my own health insurance, and other aspects. The biggest benefit, I guess, would be the ability to be creative with my services. This creativity does not always lead to stability and more money, but it satisfies my Maslow's Hierarchy of Needs.

Biggest Challenges of Entrepreneurship

The biggest challenges have been dealing with insurance reimbursements. Insurance companies seem to find various reasons not to reimburse for services rendered. This can make your journey into private practice very unfulfilling. You will spend more time documenting your services than providing services. When it comes to school contracting, the biggest challenge is to keep a contract for multiple years. School districts eagerly seek to directly hire their own speech-language pathologists to save them money.

Advice for Others Interested in Starting a Business

Insurance reimbursement: hire a person whose sole responsibility is to take care of insurance needs. Insurance needs include updating credentialing and contracting, assuring proper reimbursement rates according to the insurance pay schedule, verifying eligibility, recouping co-payments, and accurately sending documentation.

Entrepreneurship is a great way to make a living; however, it is not meant for everyone. Which is great! I have heard so many SLPs who feel discouraged when their business journey has to end. It is not a defeat. Entrepreneurship will test your business savvy, not your speech and language savvy. Being a great SLP doesn't always correlate to being a great business owner. Which is FINE!!!!

What Do You Know Now That You Didn't Know Before Starting Your Business?

Everything! My private practice experience taught me about billing, time management, the value of your time, financial discipline, sales and marketing strategies, how to enjoy the small wins, how to embrace the losses and disappointments, and to always cherish time with friends and family.

LISA KATHMAN, MS, CCC-SLP
SLP Toolkit: http://www.slptoolkit.com, BRIQHT Ideas: http://www.bethebrightest.com

Professional Background

I graduated with an MS in Communication Disorders from Arizona State University in 1997, convinced I'd be working with adults in a medical setting. My first job as a CF was home health and primarily pediatric, which resulted in every job after that being with the pediatric population (home health, preschools, and K–12). I eventually became the lead SLP in the largest school district in Arizona.

Reason for Going Down This Path

In my role as Lead SLP, I was able to view the role of a school-based SLP through a wider lens—having been a practitioner myself and then working in a more administrative role. This is when I connected with Sarah Bevier, my co-founder. We realized the pain points of SLPs were not going to be solved with current district support, and we decided to solve them ourselves!

Biggest Benefits of Entrepreneurship

As an SLP, your growth throughout your career is centered primarily on the therapeutic skills that you gain through experience, changing settings, or changing the age of clients you work with. As a business owner, I was able to grow in ways I never even knew I could or wanted to be—law, accounting, marketing, sales, customer happiness, etc. I thrive on being challenged so this was a huge benefit.

Biggest Challenges of Entrepreneurship

Business owners face many challenges. It's kind of like parenting—you think the hard part is when your kids are very young and it'll be easier when they're older. Issues never go away, they just evolve with the stage you're in. So perseverance, a growth mindset, and a strong support community are essential to push through the challenges.

Advice for Others Interested in Starting a Business

When we first set out to build our software, one of our developers asked us why we were going into business. We started our whole sales pitch of what school-based SLPs need and why, and he stopped us. He said, "I didn't ask what you want your business to do. I asked why you want to go into business." It was a genuine question aimed at getting to the root of whether or not we had thought about the work it takes to start and maintain a business. Some people want to start a business due to the end result of a successful business—the flexibility, income, even a title like CEO. But it is not easy. There will be long days and long nights, time sacrifices with family and friends, financial sacrifices that may result in your electricity getting turned off or maxing out credit cards, so you have to be passionate about your why or you will not have the strength to persevere to get to the point of seeing the benefits.

The biggest thing is to have faith in yourself, and as Nike says—just do it. The hardest part of starting a business is transitioning from idea to action. Form that LLC. Map out your business plan. Do at least one intentional thing each day to nurture its growth. And be sure to have grace with yourself in the process.

What Do You Know Now That You Didn't Know Before Starting Your Business?

There is not room enough to share all I've learned. You learn every day, and should seek knowledge and growth for yourself and business daily.

MARGARET F. MORRIS, MA, MS, CCC-SLP

Owner, Triad Speech Consultants: http://www.triadspeech.com

Professional Background

For over 30 years I worked with children helping them to advance their communication. My love was working with children with multiple disabilities. Advancing communication skills allows our kids/clients to have more opportunities and more fun. In 2016, I realized that adults lacking expected U.S. communication skills were missing out on opportunities and fun. I was ready to move out of the little chairs and ready for a new challenge. So I made a pivot and learned Accent Modification training.

Reason for Going Down This Path

I was fortunate to get connected with my local North Carolina Small Business Center (NCSBC) in the fall of 2016. They offer free courses and mentors to help people to start and grow their small business. All paid by our tax dollars! Serendipitously, my local SBC had just started a small business launch challenge with our structured curriculum and the possibility of winning part of a $50,000 grant! I learned so much about having a small business from how to get registered, to keeping track of finances, to networking, and to giving a good business pitch. I am proud to say that I came in second place and was awarded a $10,000 grant. I used that money to advance my marketing and education in business communication skills.

All states have numerous Small Business Development Centers. Some have adapted the name to Small Business Development and Technology Centers. The SBDC offers similar programs as the NCSBC—they have classes and mentors. Also, many cities offer help to small businesses in the way of courses, grants, and contests for funding.

Biggest Benefits of Entrepreneurship

I have had the privilege of helping many adults be more confident and successful. My job is very flexible so that I can work anywhere as long as I have a strong internet connection. My experience and expertise are reflected in my salary.

Biggest Challenges of Entrepreneurship

The biggest challenge is marketing! As a small business owner, you have to do everything. Marketing is an area that takes continual adjustments and requires many formats—in-person networking, emails, posting on social media, writing, images, videos, etc. The second biggest challenge was building a support system. I need to be around other small business owners to support and educate me. I believe it is critical to success to find groups to meet with regularly to help you during both successful times and times of (painful) learning.

Advice for Others Interested in Starting a Business

#1. Connect with your local small business organizations such as Small Business Development and Technology Centers! We did not learn how to be a small business owner in college! #2. Find a networking group of diverse small business owners that inspire and support you. Go to the meetings and meet with other members. #3. Find a group of SLPS that are doing similar work and meet with them regularly.

As SLPs we have many different skills to offer to adults in the area of communication. Our skills are going to reflect our training and our personalities. It is essential to clarify your niche, clarify your program and stick with that long enough to know if it is going to provide you with a salary and be inspiring. This training is a "luxury" and is not payable by insurance so it's important to know that it will take you 6 months or even years to build up to a full-time salary.

What Do You Know Now That You Didn't Know Before Starting Your Business?

I have learned how to network, market, and manage a business. I have learned how to identify a niche and I am continually learning how to better market to and coach my niche.

MCKELL SMITH, MS, CCC-SLP

Founder + CEO, Salt Lake Speech and Language, TheraV: http://www.theravnetwork.com

Professional Background

As a speech-language pathologist, I have worked in a variety of settings, mostly working with school age in my private practice. From my experience doing teletherapy from early in my career, and seeing a need for a better solution, I created TheraV—an online platform for therapists built by a therapist.

Reason for Going Down This Path

I always knew I wanted to own a private practice, and when the opportunity presented itself I jumped at the chance. In regard to the software company, I kept feeling a push to create something as it appeared no one else was doing it, so I jumped in with both feet.

Biggest Benefits of Entrepreneurship

The biggest benefits have definitely been seeing the impact my work has had on others. I love seeing the growth in individuals, as well as the expansion of reach we allow therapists to have via our online platform.

Biggest Challenges of Entrepreneurship

The biggest challenge has been navigating the startup world and the world of software. It has been a steep learning curve, but I truly enjoy learning and have had fun learning new things.

Advice for Others Interested in Starting a Business

There will never be the "perfect time." You'll never know what you don't know unless you jump in and figure it out along the way. If you feel called to do it, do it! You have the tools within you to figure it out and do it!

I truly believe you are capable to create and do anything you want to do! If you feel a push or a calling, don't let the nerves or "imposter syndrome" get the best of you. You can do it! There is a community of people behind you cheering you on!

What Do You Know Now That You Didn't Know Before Starting Your Business?

How lonely the world of business can be, especially while you are in the learning process. But when we are uncomfortable, that's when we are able to grow the most.

MEGAN SUTTON, MS, CCC-SLP

Co-Founder, Tactus Therapy Solutions Ltd (Tactus Therapy):
http://www.tactustherapy.com

Professional Background

I studied linguistics and cognitive science as an undergraduate, which is how I learned about aphasia. I decided to become a speech pathologist with the intent to help people with aphasia communicate using technology. After grad school, I focused my early career on inpatient and outpatient rehab, gaining as much exposure as I could to aphasia therapy. When the iPad came out in 2010, I saw it as the tool I had been waiting for. I formed a company with a friend who was a programmer, and we started developing apps. We now have around 20 unique titles on iOS and Android with big plans for the future.

Reason for Going Down This Path

I never set out to be a business owner or a software developer, but the need was there. Both my patients and fellow SLPs needed better therapy software. I ran the business as a side project while working my full-time job for about 18 months, but by then the business needed my full attention (and I needed my free time back). It was heartbreaking to leave the rehab job I loved, but I'm able to help so many more people now, and I have no regrets.

Biggest Benefits of Entrepreneurship

My life is completely different now from when I was working clinically. Whereas I used to work in a hospital with patient appointments all day long, I now work from home on the computer most of the day. I love not having a commute and the stress levels are (usually) lower. Being my own boss means I can decide what to focus on, and that is a great responsibility and freedom.

The biggest benefit is the impact I'm able to make. I used to be able to help a dozen or so people a month, but now my therapy programs are being used around the world by thousands of people each month. The Tactus Therapy website has been a powerful platform for sharing information, and tens of thousands of visitors a month read my How-To guides and other articles. I've been invited to speak at conferences, appear on podcasts, and even help write a book, so I have the opportunity to broadcast the messages I feel are most important. I'm a huge advocate of technology, evidence-based practice, and person-centered care, and I use those platforms to amplify those themes.

Biggest Challenges of Entrepreneurship

Learning to run a business has been a steep learning curve. It's one thing to have an idea for an app, and quite another to know how to develop, test, market, and support one. Running a business involves so many legal, financial, and logistical issues that were brand new to me. Now with a few full-time employees, I'm learning more about HR, insurance, and tax incentives. These were never things I wanted to learn!

I'm incredibly fortunate that my business partner has been an amazing support from day one. We've built our company together and continue to make each decision together, so at least I haven't had to do this alone. As we grow, I'm learning to delegate what I can and find good help for the areas of the business that are not my strengths.

There are lots of unique challenges, but that's what keeps it exciting. It's been hard for me as an introvert to put my name and face out there in the public sphere, but the mission helps me overcome my self-doubt. I'm getting better about taking time away from work, which can be a challenge for anyone working from home when the emails pour in at all hours. And I really miss the personal connection I had with my patients, so I have to keep myself involved in clinical and volunteer opportunities to feed that passion when I can.

Advice for Others Interested in Starting a Business

When people come to me with ideas for apps, I always ask if they want the specific thing they have in mind to exist, or if they want to create and run a business. If you can offer the suggestion to someone already in business, that's the fastest way to see your idea come to life. But if you want to be an entrepreneur and take all the risks (and get all the rewards) associated with that, then go for it!

A new business is a lot like a new baby—it requires constant attention and you have no idea if you're doing it right. You will lose sleep and worry constantly at first. But if you're successful with your business, you'll be so proud of what you've created—and it does get easier over time.

What Do You Know Now That You Didn't Know Before Starting Your Business?

So, so much. I had never heard of a marketing funnel. I didn't know what ROI, CTR, QA, or a million other business and programming acronyms were. But all that is learnable. The most important thing I've learned is to trust myself and put myself out there to help more people help more people. I got into this field to help people with aphasia through technology, and I feel so incredibly fortunate that I am actually doing that on a scale I never imagined possible.

I've also recently been learning that I may have a bigger impact on my fellow SLPs than on the stroke survivors directly. As I reflect on what I've been doing, a large part of my time has been spent on promoting best practices, educating SLPs about evidence-based practice, and providing tools and information to bridge the gap between research and practice. I'm beginning to appreciate my unique role in the knowledge translation process as someone who is both free from the constraints of academia and outside of the health care system, but helping to connect these institutions. That's a very exciting and satisfying contribution to make.

MELISSA JAKUBOWITZ, MA, CCC-SLP, BCS-CL, ASHF
CEO/Founder, ELiveNow: http://www.eLiveNow.com

Professional Background

My career began in the schools, working at an elementary and middle school. After a couple of years in the schools, I transitioned to private practice where I specialized in pediatric school with an emphasis on working with children diagnosed with learning disabilities and autism. After 20+ years in private practice, I transitioned to telepractice when I was hired to run the clinical department of a large telepractice company. After 5 years working for someone else, I transitioned to my telepractice company where I am now in the process of building an SLP-specific platform.

Reason for Going Down This Path

Having spent many years as a private practitioner and building my practice, I felt like I had done all I had set out to do. It was time for a transition. After letting my network know I was looking for something new, a friend put me in touch with the founders of a brand new telepractice company. I was hired as the VP of Clinical Practice where I developed all the policies and procedures and training for clinicians. I also had the opportunity to train the sales and marketing staff about what SLPs and other SpEd professionals do. After 5 years, I missed being my own boss and went out on my own again with a focus on telepractice. Telepractice became a passion for me and I wanted to assist SLPs in developing their telepractice skills to provide the highest quality, most effective and ethical practices with this new service delivery model.

Biggest Benefits of Entrepreneurship

I love being my own boss! Setting my own hours, hiring the most highly qualified people to work with me is exhilarating. It allows me flexibility and keeps me stimulated and interested in new developments in our field.

Biggest Challenges of Entrepreneurship

For my current business, where I now need to raise money is quite daunting. I began my brick & mortar practice with little money and was able to expand just by simple marketing practices that were available at that time (the late 1980s to early 1990s).

With my current business, I have had to learn about hiring software engineers, how to work with them and how to find money to support my business until we become profitable.

Advice for Others Interested in Starting a Business

Find a mentor. Find someone who has experience doing what you want to do and get to know them. Most SLPs who have been in private practice are willing to help out newbies. Also, finding a business mentor is important as well. You want someone who can help you with the business aspects of building a practice as this is new to most SLPs

When you make the decision to open a practice, learn as much as you can about how to start a business. SBA and SCORE were a great help to me as they offer free and low-cost classes in finance, writing a business plan, hiring, marketing, etc. You don't necessarily need an MBA but you do need people (CPAs, lawyers, etc.) who are on your side and can assist you in getting off to a good start.

What Do You Know Now That You Didn't Know Before Starting Your Business?

So far I've learned how to market using social media, find angel funding, and how to find good mentors.

MEREDITH P. HAROLD, PhD, CCC-SLP
Founder, The Informed SLP: http://www.theinformedslp.com

Professional Background

Former school-based SLP and university faculty turned business owner.

Reason for Going Down This Path

I didn't. I started blogging about our field's research because I knew it would be helpful to my peers. Then slowly grew and grew until now it's my full-time job, and the job of 50 other people in our field as well.

Biggest Benefits of Entrepreneurship

Getting to be the decision-maker.

Biggest Challenges of Entrepreneurship

Realizing that many people at the top are highly motivated by money and/or power, and will do a lot to grow and protect it, while being very hesitant to talk about it. It makes me uncomfortable, sometimes, moving in these circles.

Advice for Others Interested in Starting a Business

The sunk cost fallacy is your biggest enemy. You have to be honest with yourself about whether or not what you're doing is worthwhile, and valuable. If not, ditch your bad ideas, quickly, without shame or regret, and move on to new ones. And, because none of us are truly capable of objectively analyzing our own ideas and actions, surround yourself with people who will tell you the truth, instead of just telling you what you want to hear.

What Do You Know Now That You Didn't Know Before Starting Your Business?

In business, you mostly get to make your own rules for how everything works. Which is really empowering and exciting. But also a little wild, when you realize that the whole system is made up of individuals doing exactly this—deciding how they want it to work.

MONICA LOWY, MA, CCC-SLP, CHLC, APP

Founder and Director, Bodylink Speech Therapy: http://www.bodylinkspeechtherapy.com

Professional Background

NYS and NJ licensed Speech-Language Pathologist with 25 years of experience. Certified Holistic Life Coach and Integrative Bodywork Practitioner.

Reason for Going Down This Path

I have always had an independent spirit and also saw the need for a more holistic approach to speech therapy including bodywork (craniosacral therapy, Polarity Therapy) as an adjunct to more traditional treatment.

Biggest Benefits of Entrepreneurship

Being able to fulfill my vision and make changes in my practice as I see fit.

Biggest Challenges of Entrepreneurship

The usual—paperwork, keeping up with social media, keeping referral streams going.

Advice for Others Interested in Starting a Business

Do your research, put together a business plan, get very clear on which population(s) you want to serve, and know whether you want to take insurance or private pay (or both). If you don't have the stomach for ups and downs in a practice, rethink it!

In addition to using good business sense, follow your heart! Being happy in private practice takes both common sense and strong intuition about what will work and where you want to go.

What Do You Know Now That You Didn't Know Before Starting Your Business?

A practice is like a living organism. If you feed it and water it consistently it will grow!

A. MONIQUE PORTELLI, MClSc, S-LP(C)

Said Hear: http://www.saidhear.ca

Professional Background

I'm a Canadian Speech-Language Pathologist with over 32 years of experience in the profession. I have worked in the education system (for a School Board) as well as in community health (providing home and school care services) before embarking on private practice. My current practice entails providing direct and virtual care and working as an independent contractor with a company providing virtual care to clients in schools and private settings. I'm also a certified Fitness and Yoga instructor with over 17 years of experience in that industry.

Reason for Going Down This Path

As someone who has lived, studied, and worked in Canada, I have experienced both the benefits and shortcomings of socialized medicine. I believe in affordable and adequate health care for all, but I have seen waitlists increase, restrictions placed on the amount and types of therapy allowed, and people who exploit the system (providers and clients alike). Our taxes help pay for services, and know that rehabilitation medicine is a small part of overall health, and Speech Pathology is an even smaller part of the rehabilitation budget. It's a challenging puzzle and because of those challenges, I was very reluctant to start into private practice. I came to realize that I can provide services privately and maintain my professional integrity. When a former employer offered me the opportunity to switch to being an independent contractor, I weighed the pros and cons and took that path.

Biggest Benefits of Entrepreneurship

I was very fortunate that once my partner and I started our family, I was able to work part-time in a company that allowed me to set and be accountable with my schedule. It afforded me the ability to better balance home and work life. This continued flexibility I have allows me to set my own time and my own caseload.

Biggest Challenges of Entrepreneurship

My partner, a retired Hearing Aid Specialist, often says that people like us are health professionals by choice but "business people by accident." I did not have strong business acumen and while studying at University many of my colleagues expected to be working in funded environments (even to the point where private practice was seen to be, by some, as opportunistic in a negative way). Luckily I began my private practice through my partner's well-established company so I was able to learn more about the business side as we went along.

Advice for Others Interested in Starting a Business

Start by asking LOTS of questions to yourself and to others. Find a lawyer and an accountant with whom you have a good relationship. Speak with others in small business-not just in the health care field. Learn more about all aspects of your potential business-positive and negative. Know that in the beginning, it may be challenging and slow going, but an established business takes time. Make a sound and realistic business plan and keep revising that plan. Most importantly, set your limits. Know where this path may negatively interfere with key factors in your life-like your family and your own personal health. Don't fret if you think your "limit" is too small. We often are told to "dream big"-what I might suggest instead is to "dream ENOUGH." My own plan changed a few years ago and now I work because I WANT to and as long as I cover my expenses and have a little extra, that is all I need.

What Do You Know Now That You Didn't Know Before Starting Your Business?

I've learned to be open to new areas of interest for my practice including discovering accent modification and the entire virtual therapy setting (a positive spin on our current pandemic situation). I've learned that I can find old paths as well. After 25 years of not working specifically with child language, I'm once again working with this population. Above all, I've learned to recognize my own worth, what I can offer to my practice and my clients, and the joy and satisfaction that my work brings.

RENE L. ROBLES, MS, CCC-SLP

CEO, Five Oaks Speech Therapy Services: http://www.Fiveoaksspeech.com

Professional Background

I have worked as a Speech-Language Pathologist for a local school district for 19 years.

I have experience as a supervisor in a private practice while working for the school district.

Reason for Going Down This Path

After working for a school district for a significant amount of time in my career. I decided to broaden my experience and get involved with the community through my own private practice.

Biggest Benefits of Entrepreneurship

The most satisfying benefit is to have the freedom to make decisions that allow me and my company to work with patients on a one-on-one basis. This modality gives us the opportunity to see success much faster than what we experience in educational settings. Further, our company services pediatric to geriatric populations with a wide variety of needs allowing for the professional growth of our therapists.

Biggest Challenges of Entrepreneurship

At first, the biggest challenge was adjusting to being a business owner and understanding regulatory, legal, and financial needs. Next, was finding the right employees that match our company values while trying to grow the company. Finally, understanding insurance, Medicare, and other partnerships to develop them into positive patient experiences.

Advice for Others Interested in Starting a Business

The best advice I give other aspiring business owners is to have a clear understanding and path to your business. Is the goal of your business to work for yourself and only see a few patients a week or to run a company with multiple locations and employees? These two models have very different paths and financial implications that need to be defined upfront.

Surround yourself with positive influences and distance yourself from those that do not support your goals. Have some perspective, not all things that seem bad initially remain that way if you stay positive and keep moving forward. When one door closes, kick it down.

I want to make sure all who decide to have a partner choose the person that you completely trust. Cristina and I became partners having known each other through various modalities. When I started my company I wasn't planning on having a business partner but when Cris asked if I was interested I kept an open mind and decided perhaps we could move forward with a partnership. We had a sit-down dinner and discussed everything from our backgrounds, our culture, our experiences, our beliefs, and our future. We were also of different ages as I am 20 years older than Cris. Funny thing is, I was the SLP at the high school when Cris attended that high school. We also had our husbands meet before we moved forward with the partnership because we needed their support as well. If we weren't on the same page we knew we couldn't move forward with teaming together.

We have a relationship based on trust and full communication. When we have disagreements or something the other person has done has bothered either one of us we make sure to communicate about it. There have been some very difficult conversations but they need to be had in order to grow. We also make sure that our disagreements are not taken personally or with disdain. I completely trust Cris and I know she trusts me. One of our biggest goals is to serve our community. Together we strive to care for our patients and their families all while working together and forming not just a business relationship but a true love and friendship.

What Do You Know Now That You Didn't Know Before Starting Your Business?

We as SLPs know all about how to help our patients, but I didn't learn in college how to run a business. Now, I've learned all about Profit and Loss Statements, changing business tactics in a pandemic, financial reporting, tax preparation, insurance billing, employee benefits, and the list goes on and on. To this day, it's a constant learning environment that requires you to have a great support and networking system to bounce ideas, relieve stress, and problem solve.

SARAH BEVIER, MS, CCC-SLP

Co-founder/CEO, SLP Toolkit: http://www.slptoolkit.com

Professional Background

I graduated with a BS in Speech and Hearing Science in 2005. I then took some time off to raise my family. In 2008 I began working as an SLP-A, started graduate school in 2009 while working as an SLP-A, and received my MS from ASU in 2012. In 2015, I began SLP Toolkit with Lisa Kathman.

Reason for Going Down This Path

We desperately needed solutions for the challenges faced as a School-Based SLP. It isn't easy to manage large caseload sizes with a diversity of needs. We needed a better way to assess communication strengths and needs, develop goals and measure progress.

Biggest Benefits of Entrepreneurship

It is gratifying to know that we have created a solution that SLPs need and love. Nothing brings us more joy than hearing how our software has improved someone's work life, helps them feel confident in their job, and improves student outcomes. It was a difficult decision to leave the school setting to focus on the business, but knowing that we are impacting the lives of so many children makes it worth it!

Biggest Challenges of Entrepreneurship

We knew absolutely nothing about running a business. Creating the software was one thing, but running a business is an entirely different thing. Understanding everything about marketing, sales, customer service, finances, and managing a team has been a steep learning curve.

Advice for Others Interested in Starting a Business

Do it! If you have an idea that you are passionate about, put action behind it. There are plenty of times when I question my ability to create and run a business, but when you push past the discomfort and fear, the rewards are great! For every low point or challenge, there have been ten high points and successes. It's not easy, and you need to prepare for working harder than you have ever worked on anything and the risk of investing money and time into the business, but don't let fear and doubt hold you back! If SLPs are anything, they are resourceful and problem solvers! Knowing what I know now, I can honestly say I think we make the best business owners! You don't need an MBA to run a successful company; you need a helpful idea, passion, perseverance, and a strong work ethic!

This field is relatively new in the grand scheme of things, which means there are many opportunities for innovation and improvement! If an idea comes to you, it wants to come to fruition, and if not you, then who?

What Do You Know Now That You Didn't Know Before Starting Your Business?

One of the best lessons I have learned is the importance of listening to your instincts. I went into business naively, and there is a real advantage to going with your gut. You will get advice from many people. Everyone has an opinion, and it can easily steer you in a different direction if you let it. I have learned to trust myself. That doesn't mean that I don't listen and learn from others, but I have to trust the decisions that I make and be willing to accept the results.

J SCOTT YARUSS, PhD, CCC-SLP, BCS-F, F-ASHA

Professor, Michigan State University;
President, Stuttering Therapy Resources, Inc.:
http://www.StutteringTherapyResources.com;
SLP Seminars, LLC: http://www.SLP-Seminars.com;
Consulting/Private Practice: http://www.Yaruss.com

Professional Background

I received my BA in Linguistics & Psychology from the University of California, Berkeley in 1989; my MS in 1991, and my PhD in 1994, both in Speech-Language Pathology, from Syracuse University. I worked as an Assistant Professor at Northwestern University from 1994 to 1998. I then transitioned to Assistant/Associate Professor at the University of Pittsburgh from 1998 to 2017. During that time, I was also the Associate Director of Audiology and Speech-Language Pathology at the Children's Hospital of Pittsburgh. Since 2017, I've been a Professor at Michigan State University. Regarding my other professional roles, I have been a speech-language pathologist in my private practice since 1992. I've been the President of Stuttering Therapy Resources and Co-Owner of SLP Seminars, LLC since 2011. I've presented more than 700 continuing education/professional development workshops and more than 200 conference papers. I've also been the author/co-author of more than 100 peer-reviewed papers and more than 250 other publications.

Reason for Going Down This Path

As a child, I knew that I wanted to be a scientist, but I had no idea what area of science I wanted to engage in. I have long been interested in the study of language and people, and when I undertook my graduate studies at Berkeley in Linguistics and Psychology, I knew that I had found areas of study that I was passionate about. I did not discover the clinical side of these disciplines until my senior year in college, however, and I was very lucky that I did. Speech-Language Pathology offered a career path where I could pursue those areas of interest, while still helping people and contributing to the scientific literature.

Really, for me, it was serendipity—I heard about the field almost by chance, and within weeks, I was volunteering at a center for autistic children. I chose to study stuttering, again almost on a whim, because I knew that it was an area that intersected many of the aspects of the field that drive me: linguistics, psychology, neurology, social interaction, and cognitive science. I have been very fortunate to be able to incorporate all of these areas, and a few more, in my research, clinical, and professional endeavors, and I feel fortunate every day that I found this field and was given the opportunity to explore my interests while helping others.

More specifically related to entrepreneurship, I have been able to build upon the expertise that I have developed as a stuttering specialist to serve as a consultant and educator for speech-language pathologists all around the world who seek to learn more about stuttering. I have traveled to more than 15 countries giving lectures on stuttering therapy, and I have given hundreds of professional development presentations here in the U.S. Through Stuttering Therapy Resources, a publishing company that I co-founded with Nina Reeves, I have been able to provide practical treatment guides to thousands and thousands of speech-language pathologists, all with the goal of helping clinicians feel more confident in their skills for helping people who stutter. This is what I have wanted to do since the early days of my career—help others directly and indirectly—and I am grateful for the academic and clinical and professional opportunities that my career has offered me.

Biggest Benefits of Entrepreneurship

I have found working in this field to be very rewarding, because I get to support others in their life journeys while, selfishly, pursuing my own scientific/research interests. As an academic, I am afforded an uncommon degree of scheduling flexibility. Though I work all the time, I can choose when and where to do it, and this has allowed me to spend time with my family in ways that I would not have been able to do with a more regularly scheduled job. The clinical aspects of the field have also allowed me to pursue my related interests: I have been in private practice for 30 years now, and that has informed my teaching and research while still allowing me to make an impact on a person-by-person level. My consulting and presenting roles, as well as my most recent endeavor, publishing through Stuttering Therapy Resources, Inc., has allowed me to connect with speech-language pathologists around the world to identify their needs and try to meet those needs by developing practical therapy materials focused on "helping SLPs help people who stutter."

Biggest Challenges of Entrepreneurship

I have been fortunate and privileged in my career path, and I am acutely aware of that every day. The challenges that I have faced have more to do with expanding into new areas rather than hurdles related to my interests or opportunities. For example, when my coauthor/business partner (Nina Reeves) and I decided to start Stuttering Therapy Resources, we knew that we would face hurdles related to learning how to run a publishing business. This involved delving into legal and professional issues related to copyright, as well as practical issues such as printing and warehousing and shipping and advertising. We knew that we could write books that would help speech-language pathologists in their daily practice, but the process of turning those books into physical publications that we could put in an envelope and mail to thousands of SLPs around the world involved some growth and expansion of our skills. It's been enjoyable all the way along, but some of it is far removed from the daily practice of being a speech-language pathologist.

Advice for Others Interested in Starting a Business

It is worth taking risks even if they don't all pan out. Throughout my career, I've tried more than a few ideas that ultimately didn't turn out the way I planned. Sometimes, this has turned into new ideas that worked out even better; sometimes, this has just meant that I need to start over and try something else. Regardless, I have always learned something from these attempts, and I try to do everything I do as practice for the next opportunity.

I have been particularly grateful for the collaborations that I have formed with other people. So many of my collaborators have become dear friends—and so many of my dear friends have become collaborators. Working with others is tremendously rewarding, even in entrepreneurship, so I would encourage people to reach out to others, share ideas, try new partnerships, and don't be afraid to see where new ideas might lead.

What Do You Know Now That You Didn't Know Before Starting Your Business?

Oh my goodness, the list is endless. Much of what I have done in my side-projects has been tangential to the practice of speech-language pathology even if it was ultimately related to publishing SLP-related materials. For example, I've had to learn a lot more about marketing, social media, web design, and back-end website coding than I had expected to learn. Fortunately, I enjoy that stuff, but wow it's a lot of learning.

SERENA MURISON, MS, CCC-SLP

PlaySpark: http://www.play-spark.com

Professional Background

I am a speech-language pathologist who works primarily with Autistic and Neurodivergent populations. I started a business with my long-time work partner, Kylie, who is an occupational therapist. We started our business as a way to provide resources to other therapists. Our business has expanded to apparel that promotes Neurodiversity Acceptance and donates to nonprofits run by Actually Autistic adults. We also run a small pediatric therapy private practice in Asheville, NC.

Reason for Going Down This Path

Kylie and I felt we had a valuable and unique perspective to share with the therapy world. We trusted our instincts and put the time in to develop our brand in a way that represented our mission. We continue to lean into what feels right for us.

Biggest Benefits of Entrepreneurship

The benefits of being self-employed and in charge of my own career are so vast it is hard to properly describe them. I feel capable, confident, and free. I wouldn't change it for the world.

Biggest Challenges of Entrepreneurship

Self-doubt is the biggest challenge to overcome. There is always a voice of doubt that becomes the loudest in the hardest moments. I have found myself doubting if self-employment and business ownership will financially sustain me. I have doubted whether what I had to share with the world was valuable. But with that doubt comes another voice of confidence that is much louder and more powerful.

Advice for Others Interested in Starting a Business

Find your niche. Take the time to invest in yourself and become an expert in whatever it is you want to share with others. Reach out to those in the field that you look up to and would like to emulate.

If you do not feel like you have found your place in the field, keep searching for that place. Stay open to the possibility of change and risk.

What Do You Know Now That You Didn't Know Before Starting Your Business?

I have learned that self-employment is possible as an SLP. I have learned the ins and outs of running a business, paying taxes, learning SEO, and other aspects of entrepreneurship I never imagined myself learning.

SHANNON WERBECKES, MS, CCC-SLP

Founder & CEO, Speechy Musings: http://www.speechymusings.com

Professional Background

I attended the University of Wisconsin-Madison for my undergraduate degree and then Radford University for my master's degree. After graduating, I worked in a variety of pediatric settings including an outpatient clinic and in the public schools working with students in preschool through middle school. I started my business, Speechy Musings, my first semester in graduate school!

Reason for Going Down This Path

Like many business owners I've met over the years, I stumbled into my business! I originally started it to share my grad school experience (including several of my unique, creative therapy ideas). Since then, I've decided to focus primarily on designing and creating easy-to-use resources for pediatric SLPs. I've gotten incredibly lucky to have created a business that combines so many things I love doing including reading research and designing the perfect page layout.

Biggest Benefits of Entrepreneurship

I've loved so many aspects of being an SLP entrepreneur but by far, my favorite part has to be the flexibility and freedom. I love to travel and have arranged my business systems around the ability to work remotely and more flexibly. My husband and I (and our two dogs!) are currently living in an Airstream trailer while working and traveling around the USA! The second biggest benefit to owning my own business is being able to participate in the creative process over and over again. There are few things I love more than brainstorming, coming up with a new concept, reading a ton of research, synthesizing ideas, and then creating something brand new! I'm always coming up with ideas and having an outlet for that (and one that helps so many other SLPs!) has been incredibly fulfilling.

Biggest Challenges of Entrepreneurship

The biggest challenge of running my own business has definitely been boundaries. It can feel overwhelming to be in charge of everything from marketing, finances, product development, and customer service, especially when you're like me and have no business background or experience! I've learned a lot in the past 9 years about setting priorities, keeping to a schedule, saying "no," prioritizing what is most important, and putting up boundaries about when I work (and most importantly, when I WON'T work).

Advice for Others Interested in Starting a Business

The most frequent piece of advice I share is to just start! Oftentimes, I've seen that people wait until they think they are "good enough," feel "ready," or they pass some arbitrary threshold. You learn more and gain skills more quickly when you're actually IN the arena, creating and getting feedback from others. If you're not making mistakes and improving a ton when you start, you started too late! My other piece of advice is to focus on VALUE for the consumer. The two biggest traps in business, in my experience, are perfectionism and over-complication.

What Do You Know Now That You Didn't Know Before Starting Your Business?

Starting and running Speechy Musings has not only taught me a ton about business but also about myself. One specific thing that I've learned is how to accept and hear critical feedback. I spent the majority of my life avoiding activities where I might receive negative or critical feedback, and when I did get some, I took it pretty hard. It's impossible to make the impact I want to, create all of the ideas I have, and put myself out there on the internet without receiving a few critical thoughts from others in return. In the past years, I've grown so much in my ability to hear what people are saying and make improvements without letting it affect how I see myself and my work. Now, I truly appreciate those who reach out with ideas on how I or my products could be better!

TIA BAGAN, MS, CCC-SLP

Co-Founder, theEATBar: http://www.theeatbar.com

Professional Background

I completed my undergraduate training at the University of Iowa and received my Masters in Science at Rush University Medical Center. After I finished my Certificate of Clinical Competency at Cook County Hospital I returned to Rush Medical Center to work as a clinical supervisor. In 2016, I co-founded theEATBar, a crunchy, melt-in-your-mouth meringue that provides easy calories to those with difficulty eating or enjoying food.

Reason for Going Down This Path

After taking some time off to raise my children I decided I wanted to continue helping others and re-define my role as a Speech-Language Pathologist. Like many entrepreneurs, I saw a need that wasn't being met for many of my patients and their families. When I started testing the market with my ideas I was encouraged at the response and after much soul searching decided to co-found a start-up that ultimately became theEATBar.

Biggest Benefits of Entrepreneurship

Helping others on a larger platform. Early on I was surprised at the global reach of our customer base. There are a variety of individuals across the lifespan who suffer from eating-related issues. Their testimonials of how the bars have improved their quality of life continue to be my greatest joy and greatest satisfaction.

Biggest Challenges of Entrepreneurship

There have been many challenges and many days of self-doubt. This is something that many entrepreneurs will warn you about. Personally, I have found that the more time that passes and the more experience I obtain the better equipped I am to deal with the challenges that arise.

Advice for Others Interested in Starting a Business

Dream big and don't let your fears hold you back. In many ways, our profession has ideally prepared us to approach a start-up endeavor. We rely on evidence-based practice, diagnose situations and treat accordingly and we constantly have to pivot when challenges arise.

Use others for a sounding board when starting your own business, but ultimately follow your own intuition. Many times, I would second guess myself because I felt I didn't have the credentials or expertise. But in the end, often making decisions with the mindset of a clinician as well as a mother were the right ones.

What Do You Know Now That You Didn't Know Before Starting Your Business?

Everything, is the most honest answer. I had never taken a business class or a marketing tutorial and was not familiar with most aspects of the business world. I continue to learn new things every day and use this new knowledge as I try and grow the business.

CHAPTER CHECKLIST

☐ Visit the PluralPlus Companion Website to print templates

☐ Connect and share your story with Adrienne and Sonia to continue to strengthen the SLP Entrepreneur community

Glossary of Terms

As you embark on this journey of entrepreneurship, establish your business, and gain volumes of new information in terms of business practices and procedures, you might find that different entities or people may use different terminology relating to business. We want to highlight some of the frequently used terms that you may encounter during networking meetings, business discovery meetings, insurance billing, and other activities related to your business. This is not an exhaustive list by any means, but a highlight of some high-frequency terms. We purposely defined these terms in our own words with the intention of providing you with a more user-friendly resource.

When you are communicating with non-SLP professionals, make sure that you are explaining what you do and what your business offers in a functional way. Unfortunately, you may find that other business owners or people from the corporate world use industry-specific terms when they speak with you. Sometimes this will include acronyms or terminology that you are not familiar with, and it is OK to "smile and nod" and then look it up later, or to simply ask what they are referring to. Often people may not be aware that they are using jargon that is well known to them and their colleagues in their specific industry, however, is unfamiliar to their current conversational partner. This list will hopefully give you a "crash course" in terms that you may hear as you engage in conversations with individuals from all industries.

1099: tax form filed for independent contractors whom you paid more than $600 in a given calendar year

Affiliate marketing: commission received when someone takes an action using your unique affiliate link

Aspirational Canvas: also called a vision board; a visual representation of your goals and benchmarks to attain those goals; can be written, crafted with photos/sayings, etc.

Automation: an action that occurs *automatically* after another action occurs, common in email programs

B2B (business-to-business): a business model where one business sells its products or services to another business, as opposed to selling directly to the consumer

B2C (business-to-consumer): a business model where a business sells its products or services directly to the consumer

BAA (Business Associate Agreement): a contract that establishes specifically what the business associate has been engaged to do, and requires the business associate to comply with HIPAA Rules' requirements to protect the privacy and security of protected health information

Bottom line: your revenue and cost for a transaction

Brand awareness: the process whereby you spread the word about your business, with the goal of getting your brand in front of as many potential customers as possible

Buyer persona: how you define who your ideal customer is

Call to action: a specific action that you want your visitors to take, such as "subscribe" or "download"

CAQH (Council for Affordable Quality Healthcare): where providers complete their profile for insurance companies to review during the enrollment process

CEO: Chief Executive Officer

CFO: Chief Financial Officer

Clearinghouse: a portal in which you can receive electronic funds for services rendered and verify patients' eligibility of benefits within their insurance systems

CMO: Chief Marketing Officer

Conversion rate: the process of converting a lead into a customer

COO: Chief Operating Officer

Cover art: the image that people will see when they search for your product for sale

Covered entity: any health care provider who transmits health information in electronic form in connection with certain transactions (e.g., if you communicate with health insurance companies on a client's behalf, you are a "covered entity")

CPC (cost per click): how much it costs when someone clicks on your ad

CPT (Current Procedural Terminology): offers health care professionals a uniform language for coding medical services; CPT codes are used for insurance claims processing and may also be referred to as procedural codes

Credentialing: the process that insurance companies use to select in-network providers

CRM (customer relationship management): software that manages information and nurtures relationships with current and potential customers

CTO: Chief Technology Officer

CTR (click-through rate): the percentage of people who click on the link after seeing your ad

Customer acquisition cost: how much of your marketing budget is spent to acquire each customer

Deductible: the amount that the client must pay prior to their insurance benefits starting

Distribution channel: how products and services are delivered

Domain hosting: where your website will live on the world wide web

Domain name: your website address

Drip content: allows you to release course content one lesson at a time on a predetermined schedule

E-commerce: the buying and selling of products or services over the internet

EIN (Employee Identification Number): an EIN is to a business as a Social Security Number (SSN) is to an individual; can also be referred to as a Tax Identification Number (TIN)

Elevator pitch: a concise message that you share with people you meet for the first time about what you do and how you can help them

EMR (Electronic Medical Record): a digital version of a chart with patient information

Engagement: a measure of how people are interacting with your brand, including your social media accounts and content (e.g., likes, comments, shares)

EOB (Explanation of Benefits): a statement provided by a health insurance company to both you and your patient that outlines the costs of services rendered, what the insurance paid, and what the patient's financial responsibility is

Executive presence: confidently demonstrating and communicating your ability to manage, lead and deliver value

Growth mindset: being open to the idea of "productive struggle" (i.e., hard work, tenacity, and dedication will allow you to learn new skills)

Habit stacking: the concept of pursuing a new activity or task to form it into a habit, by pairing it with a long-standing habit that you already have in place

HIPAA (Health Insurance Portability and Accountability Act): rules that provide federal protections for patient health information held by Covered Entities and Business Associates

ICD-10 (International Classification of Disease): may also be referred to as diagnostic codes. ICD-11 codes came into effect in January 2022. Be sure to check the most recent ICD codes to ensure that you are billing correctly.

Impression: in digital marketing, the number of times a piece of content is viewed

Independent contractor: an individual you hire to complete certain, specified tasks, but that is not an employee of the company

In-network: health care providers that have contracted with an insurance company to accept certain rates

Keywords: the series of words that users search on a search engine

Lead generation: the process of gathering the names and contact information of potential new customers

Lead magnet: a product or service that is provided in exchange for a person's contact information

LLC (Limited Liability Company): a type of business organization that separates assets/liability from your personal assets

Marketing channels: These are the methods through which you will communicate with your target audience

Marketing mix: consists of product, price, place, and promotion

Marketing/Sales funnel: the steps taken to turn leads (potential customers) into paying customers

Mission: what you set out to accomplish with your business

Mockup: a model of what your final product will look like

NPI (National Provider Identifier): used to identify providers when billing; if you have been working as an SLP in private practice, medical settings, and in some cases, schools, you may already have an individual NPI. This number follows you wherever you go. You will register for a group NPI when you establish a clinical private practice.

NPPES (National Plan and Provider Enumeration System): where you request a free NPI for your group (practice) and for you as an individual

Onboarding: orientation to certain tasks, technologies, and policies within an organization

Organic traffic: free traffic that comes from an online search versus a link from another source (e.g., social media, email campaign, or direct link)

Out-of-network: health care providers that do not have a contract with an insurance company

Payor: who pays for a patient's health care services; this may be the patient, a health care company, or an organization (e.g., school, employer, etc.)

PHI (Protected Health Information): "individually identifiable health information," including demographic data, that relates to an individual's health care (e.g., name, birth date, and medical history or condition)

Pre-authorization: obtaining permission from an insurance plan in advance of billing for a client's assessment or treatment

Primary audience: your main target audience that will be your main market to offer services to, and consequently, target your marketing efforts toward

Profit and Loss (P&L) Statement: also known as an income statement, it is used to calculate the profits or losses of a business in a defined time period

Revenue: income earned through business engagements

ROI (return on investment): typically thought of in terms of financial revenue, calculated by dividing the net profit by your costs

Sales page: a web page created with the intention of generating sales for your product or service

S-Corporation: a business owned and operated by one or more people, but no more than 100

Secondary audience: an extension of your primary audience in terms of adding a different type of client or expanding your customer base

SEO (search engine optimization): ensures that search engines index and rank your site

SMART(ER) goals: a meaningful method to set goals; stands for specific, measurable, attainable, relevant, timely, (evaluated and revised)

Sole proprietor: a business owned and operated by one person, who has personal liability for the business

Sponsorship: compensation received when a company pays you to represent their product, talk about it, and promote it to your readers/followers

SSL (secure sockets layer): intended to keep the connection on a website secure (e.g., indicated by "https" instead of "http")

Stakeholder: anyone who is somehow involved in your service delivery or anyone who has a vested interest in your daily business operations

Superbill: a form to document services, fees, codes, and other information required by health plans.

SWOT analysis (strengths, weaknesses, opportunities, threats): assessing the internal strengths and weaknesses of your business, in addition to the external opportunities and threats posed by your competitors

Value Proposition: what you can offer to your stakeholders

Vision: how you envision offering your product or service to create impact

W-9: form used to gather an independent contractor's business information that you will need in order to file their tax form at the end of the tax year

Resources List

We've compiled a list of resources, some of which have been mentioned in this book. While we may use some of these resources in our own businesses, we do not specifically endorse any of these services nor do we receive compensation if you choose to use them. This list is organized alphabetically by topics, which are indicated by bold type.

Accounting and Invoicing

QuickBooks: http://www.quickbooks.intuit.com

Square: http://www.squareup.com

Taxes: http://www.irsvideos.gov/SmallBusinessTaxpayer/virtualworkshop/Lesson6

Wave Apps: http://www.waveapps.com

Billing

Coding: https://www.asha.org/practice/reimbursement/coding/coding_faqs_slp/

Good Faith Estimate: https://www.cms.gov/nosurprises/policies-and-resources/overview-of-rules-fact-sheets

ICD-10 Codes: https://www.cms.gov/Medicare/Coding/ICD10/ICD-10Resources

ICD-11 codes: https://icd.who.int/ct11/icd11_mms/en/release

Medicare Coding: https://www.asha.org/practice/reimbursement/medicare/slp_coding_rules/

Superbill Template: https://www.asha.org/practice/reimbursement/coding/superbill-templates-for-audiologists-and-speech-language-pathologists/

Business Plans

LivePlan: http://www.liveplan.com

SCORE: http://www.score.org/resource/business-plan-template-startup-business

Communication

efax: http://www.efax.com

Faxage: http://www.faxage.com

GoogleVoice: http://www.voice.google.com

Communication/Project Management Tools for Collaborative Projects

Canva: http://canva.com [graphic design]

Google Drive/Google Docs: http://www.google.com [shared documentation]

Google Forms: http://www.google.com/forms [data/feedback collection]

Todoist: http://www.todoist.com

Trello: http://www.trello.com [project task management]

Design Help

99 Designs: https://99designs.com/blog/tips/branding-colors/

Canva: http://www.Canva.com

Fiverr: http://www.Fiverr.com

Upwork: http://www.Upwork.com

Email Marketing Programs/CRM

Constant Contact: http://www.constantcontact.com/

Mailchimp: http://www.mailchimp.com/

Hubspot: http://www.hubspot.com

EMR Options

ClinicSource: http://www.clinicsource.com

SimplePractice: http://www.simplepractice.com

TheraNest: https://theranest.com

Financial Planning

Blocks of 10: A Financial Road Map for the 10 Year Blocks of Your Life by Anthony Paul [Book]

Money Smart for Small Business: http://www.fdic.gov/resources/consumers/money-smart/money-smart-for-small-business

U.S. Financial Literacy and Education Commission: http://www.mymoney.gov

Habit Stacking

13 Steps for Building a Habit Stacking Routine by S. J. Scott. [Website article] http://www.developgoodhabits.com/building-habit-stacking-routine/

Hiring

Employee and Independent Contractor Descriptions: http://www.irs.gov/businesses/small-businesses-self-employed/independent-contractor-self-employed-or-employee

IRS Employer Tax Guide: http://www.irs.gov

Job descriptions: http://www.indeed.com/career-advice/finding-a-job/job-description-template

Income Resources

Earnings by Occupation and Education: http://www.bls.gov

Glassdoor: http://www.glassdoor.com

Income Statistics: http://www.bls.gov

Insurance Resources

CAQH: http://proview.caqh.org

CAQH Help: http://www.caqh.org/solutions/caqh-proview-faqs

EIN: http://irs.gov

HIPAA: http://www.hhs.gov/hipaa/for-professionals/index.html

HIPAA Security guidance: http://www.hhs.gov/hipaa/for-professionals/security/guidance

HIPAA Security Risk Assessment Tool: http://www.healthit.gov/topic/privacy-security-and-hipaa/security-risk-assessment-tool

NPI: http://nppes.cms.hhs.gov

Professional Liability Insurance: http://www.proliability.com

Google Tools

Google Analytics

Google Keep

Google Keyword

Google My Business

Google Search Console

Management

Employee handbook template: http://www.betterteam.com/employee-handbook

Employee manual template: http://www.rocketlawyer.com/sem/employee-manual

Employee onboarding checklist: http://www.betterteam.com/employee-onboarding-process

LinkedIn Management Training: http://www.linkedin.com/learning/topics/leadership-and-management

Market Analysis Sources

Bureau of Economic Analysis: http://www.bea.gov

Bureau of Labor Statistics: http://www.bls.gov

Census Business Builder: http://cbb.census.gov

Census Data: http://data.census.gov

Consumer Credit Data: http://www.federalreserve.gov/releases/G19

Consumer Price Index: http://www.bls.gov/cpi

Consumer Spending: http://www.bea.gov/data/consumer-spending/main

Employment and Unemployment Statistics: http://stats.bls.gov

Federal Reserve: http://www.federalreserve.gov

Gross Domestic Product (GDP): http://www.bea.gov/resources/learning-center/what-to-know-gdp

SCORE Competitive Analysis Template: http://core.score.org/resources/competitive-analysis-template

SCORE Competitor Analysis Course: http://www.score.org/event/analyzing-your-competition

Statistical Abstract of the United States: https://www.census.gov/library/publications/2011/compendia/statab/131ed.html

Statistics of U.S. Businesses: https://www.census.gov/programs-surveys/susb.html

USA.gov Statistics: http://www.usa.gov

U.S. Census Bureau: http://census.gov

Marketing Plan

Buyer Persona Template: http://www.hootsuite.com/resources/blog/buyer-persona-template

Quickstart Marketing Plan Tool: https://www.score.org/resource/quick-start-marketing-plan-tool

SCORE Business Mentor: http://www.score.org

U.S. Small Business Administration: http://www.sba.gov

Online Course Creation Platforms

Kajabi: http://www.Kajabi.com

Podia: http://www.Podia.com

Teachable: http://www.Teachable.com

Thinkific: http://www.Thinkific.com

Online Stores

Boom Learning: http://www.boomlearning.com

Shopify: http://www.shopify.com

Teachers Pay Teachers: http://www.teacherspayteachers.com

WooCommerce: http://www.woocommerce.com

Payroll Services

ADP: http://www.adp.com

Gusto: http://www.gusto.com

Square: http://www.squareup.com

Professional Development for Corporate Speech Training

CORSPAN: http://www.CORSPAN.org

SLPs in Accent Modification (Facebook Group)

Here's how to do Accent Modification: A Manual for Speech-Language Pathologists by Robert McKinney [Book]

LearnToPresent.com

TheAccentChannel.com

Accent Freedom: https://accentfreedom.com

Institute of Language and Phonology-Compton PESL: https://800-language.com/pesl-course-outline/

LDS & Associates-Lorna Sikorski: https://www.ldsassoc.com/trainers/

Professional Organizations for SLPs in Business

American Academy of Private Practice in Speech Pathology and Audiology: http://www.aappspa.org

CORSPAN: http://www.CORSPAN.org

Social Media Tools

Buffer: http://www.Buffer.com

Hootsuite: http://www.Hootsuite.com

Later: http://www.Later.com

Linktree: http://www.linktr.ee

Social Media Bio Templates: http://blog.hootsuite.com/social-media-bio/

Tailwind: http://www.Tailwind.com

Stock Photos
iStock (Photo): http://www.Istockphoto.com
Pexels: http://www.Pexels.com
Pixabay: http://www.Pixabay.com
Shutterstock: http://www.Shutterstock.com
Unsplash: http://www.Unsplash.com

Survey Options
Doodle Poll: http://www.doodle.com/online-polls
Google Forms: http://www.google.com/forms
SurveyMonkey: http://www.surveymonkey.com

Telepractice Platforms
Theraplatform: http://www.theraplatform.com
TheraV: http://www.theravnetwork.com
Webex: http://www.webex.com
Zoom: https://zoom.us

Trademark
U.S. Patent and Trademark Office: http://www.USPTO.gov

Website Builders
Squarespace: http://www.squarespace.com
Wix: http://www.wix.com
Wordpress: http://www.wordpress.org

Index

Note: Page numbers in **bold** reference non-text material.